THERMAL POWER
FROM
NUCLEAR REACTORS

THERMAL POWER
FROM
NUCLEAR REACTORS

A. Stanley Thompson

Oliver E. Rodgers

NEW YORK · JOHN WILEY & SONS, INC.

LONDON · CHAPMAN & HALL, LIMITED

P R E F A C E

This book arose from an attempt to organize the analysis of engineering problems involved in the development of nuclear reactors for the generation of mechanical or electrical power. Along with many other people we were particularly interested in possible peacetime uses of atomic energy for power purposes. There is increasing evidence that interest in the peacetime uses of atomic energy has widened. Relatively large sums, of both government and private funds, have been allocated to several projects for the development of reactors for electric generating plants. The International Conference on Peaceful Uses of Atomic Energy, sponsored by the United Nations in 1955 (the Geneva Conference), has demonstrated a world-wide desire for a peacetime power business based on atomic energy. We anticipate an increasing impetus for the development of thermal power from nuclear reactors.

Our discussion of thermal power from nuclear reactors is limited to the generation of heat in reactors, the removal of heat from reactors, and the use of heat from reactors in thermal power plants. We have attempted to relate the special engineering-design problems which arise because heat is generated by the process of nuclear fission to those engineering-design problems which are customarily handled by engineers concerned with conventional thermal power plants. On the assumption that the book will be read by persons who are not familiar with all of the various subjects involved, we have begun each discussion at a level that is common to all branches of engineering. We have tried to discuss each subject in a way leading to a useful engineering formulation related as directly as possible to the problem of using power from nuclear reactors.

Many important nuclear theories, for instance those proposing mechanisms for fission, are not even mentioned. We do not consider these theories necessary for an initial understanding of the functioning of a nuclear reactor, which can be described primarily in terms of data from experiments. Since the experimental methods for obtaining these data are described in many publications in the field of nuclear physics, descriptions of these methods are not repeated.

We think that a book on nuclear reactors, for engineers, should emphasize the new concepts and methods of analysis which have been developed for the design of reactors. This thought is our justification for what might otherwise seem a disproportionate amount of space (Chapters 2 and 3) devoted to calculations of neutron distribution, criticality, and reactor kinetics.

It is our hope that this book will supplement existing literature on nuclear power by covering methods of handling design problems that have arisen in recent years and that have not been adequately described. Our primary purpose is to present some new viewpoints which have arisen from the necessity to solve design problems for what has been called the "new generation of reactors" for nuclear power—hence the emphasis on numerical methods and dimensional analysis and on non-linear kinetics of reactor behavior. We have tried to tie together the viewpoints about the various reactor problems considered separately to make a unified picture of a reactor. In so doing, we do not intend to imply a lesser importance for those considerations given less emphasis in our book.

Several problems arise in writing a book in so new a field as nuclear engineering. One of these, which creates semantic difficulties for the unwary reader (or author), stems from the non-uniformity of terminology and nomenclature used by different groups of workers in the atomic energy field. A second, of similar nature, stems from the difference in outlook of workers of differing backgrounds (engineers and physicists). An engineer has a feeling of security because of what he considers to be the directness of his experience in working in a familiar field. When he encounters the field of nuclear processes, he must be willing, at least temporarily, to give up his comfortable feeling of familiarity in his attempts to "understand" a neutron, which is an "entity" whose "invention" is justified only by the need to correlate data from indirect measurements. Another whole class of problems stems from present security regulations, as a result of which entire categories of specific properties of materials important to the field are classified "secret" and hence are unavailable. Moreover, those properties of materials which are assumed at present are subject to revision as knowledge is gained. For these reasons we have included relatively few specific properties of materials; we anticipate that the interested reader will refer to the best sources of such information currently available to him. In shielding, too, much of the experimental work which has been done is generally in connection with classified projects and hence is unavailable otherwise. We have not emphasized certain methods now used in calculations of shielding, because we anticipate that these will be superseded by more adequate and manageable ones as experimental work progresses.

A final problem should be mentioned, due in part to the newness of the field: the fact that the nuclear engineering of power plants is a controversial field, in which not all workers will agree as to which problems are important or what methods should be used for attacking these problems. This controversy will only be settled as nuclear power plants are constructed and operated (and discussed in the open literature). We have sometimes chosen to present ways of handling problems which will be considered unconventional by some workers in the nuclear field, but we have based these on methods which have proved powerful and productive in achieving practical solutions to more conventional engineering problems.

We hope that the material we have included will be helpful to those interested in nuclear engineering and will provide a frame of reference for the additional information which will continue to be developed in this field.

A portion of the book is based on a series of class notes from a course called "Reactor Engineering" given by A. Stanley Thompson to a class of graduates in various branches of science and engineering in 1952, at the Oak Ridge School of Reactor Technology, Oak Ridge National Laboratory, Oak Ridge, Tennessee.

The authors wish to express their appreciation to Mr. Carl Taulbee, of the Studebaker-Packard Corporation, for reading the manuscript and making suggestions.

A. STANLEY THOMPSON
OLIVER E. RODGERS

Detroit, Michigan
October, 1955

CONTENTS

LIST OF SYMBOLS

a	constant	G	mass flow per unit time
A	atomic weight (1,* 2, 3)	h	spacing dimension (2)
	constant (1–4)		enthalpy (2, 3, 7, 8)
	mass of a sphere (1)		heat-transfer coefficient (7)
	area (3, 6, 7)	H	function
b	constant	I	intensity per unit area
B	constant	J	net flow through a unit area
c	constant (3, 4)	k	spacing dimension (2)
	ratio of neutron captures outside of fuel to those in fuel (3)		multiplication factor (2, 3)
			coefficient of thermal conductivity (6)
c_p	specific heat at constant pressure		kinetic energy per unit weight (7, 8)
C	velocity of light (1)	K	constant (2, 3, 8)
	constant (2, 6, 7)		fraction of neutrons scattered by Compton effect (4)
d	density (1)		
	extrapolation distance (2)		magnitude of thermal stress
D	diffusion coefficient (2, 3)		$= \dfrac{E\alpha\,\Delta T}{1 - a\mu}$ (6)
	hydraulic diameter (7)		
e	potential energy per unit weight	l	fractional loss of neutrons (1)
E	neutron energy (1, 2)		fraction of neutrons escaping leakage (2)
	modulus of elasticity (6)		length (6, 7)
	efficiency (8)	L	length (3, 6, 7)
	energy per unit weight (8)		thermal diffusion length (2)
f	thermal utilization factor $= \dfrac{\Sigma_{\text{fuel}}}{\Sigma_a}$ (2, 3)		leakage of neutrons (2)
			leakage ratio (4)
	friction factor (7)	m	number (2, 3)
	friction energy lost per unit weight (3, 8)		hydraulic radius (7)
F	flux (4)	M	mass (1, 2)
	friction force on walls of passage (7)		migration length, $M^2 = L^2 + \tau_{th}$ (2, 3)
	free flow ratio (7)	n	number or constant (1, 6)
	function (2, 6)		average density of neutrons (1)
g	acceleration of gravity		

* Numbers in parentheses refer to chapter numbers.

	average density of neutrons per unit volume and per unit of lethargy (2, 3)
N	density, particles per unit volume
N_0	Avogadro's number
N_{th}	average number of collisions required to bring a neutron from fission energy to thermal energy
Nu	Nusselt number
p	probability (1)
.	resonance escape probability: fraction of fission neutrons slowed down to thermal energy without being captured (2, 3)
	pressure (3, 7, 8)
	power per unit volume (3)
P	power (1, 3)
	function (2)
	pressure (7)
Pr	Prandtl number
q	slowing-down density (2)
	heat added per unit weight (3, 6, 7, 8)
Q	heat flow per unit time
r	radius (1, 4, 6)
	fractional increase of fissionable material (1)
	Roentgen unit of dosage (4)
	constant (4)
R	gas constant (7)
	radius (2, 4)
Re	Reynolds number
s	entropy per unit weight
$s(u)$	fission spectrum
S	designates a line (2)
	function of space coordinates (2)
	strength of a source (4, 6)
	wetted perimeter (7)
	entropy (8)
	constant (3)
St	Stanton number
t	time
	thickness (4, 6)
T	temperature (6, 7, 8)
	function of age (2)

u	lethargy (1, 2, 3)
	deformation in x direction (6)
	internal energy per unit weight (8)
	constant (8)
U	total number of atoms of fissionable uranium
v	velocity
	constant (8)
V	velocity after collision (1)
	volume (2)
w	work done per unit weight (3, 7, 8)
	average velocity (7)
W	work done
x, y, z	length
α	maximum fractional energy loss per collision (2)
	linear coefficient of thermal expansion (6)
	constant (2–4)
	dimensionless variable (2, 3)
	function (7)
$\alpha_{1, 2, 3}$	rate of increase of activity with temperature, density, pressure (3)
β	fraction of delayed neutrons (3)
	dimensionless variable (2, 6)
	end-effect factor on pressure loss (7)
	constant (2)
γ	energy released as gamma rays (1)
	density (3, 6–8)
	dimensionless source (6)
	shear strain (6)
	constant (2)
δ	average power density (1, 7)
	excess multiplication factor (3)
	error or increment (2, 3)
δ_1, δ_2	sum of discontinuous changes due to isothermal process in work done, heat added (8)
ϵ	fast fission factor (2, 3)
	strain (6)
	pumping efficiency (7)

η number of neutrons produced per absorption in fissionable material (1–3)

dimensionless time (3)

average pumping power per unit volume (7)

θ angle (1, 2, 4)

characteristic time (3)

κ constant (2)

κ^2 average diffusion operator (3)

λ neutron mean free path (1, 2)

neutron life cycle frequency (3)

proportionality constant for radioactive decay (1, 3)

function relating St and friction factor (7)

μ average cosine of the scattering angle (1, 2)

coefficient of absorption (4)

Poisson's ratio (6)

viscosity (7)

mechanical efficiency (8)

ν average number of neutrons produced per fission

ξ logarithmic neutron energy decrement per collision (1, 2, 5)

dimensionless length (3, 6, 7)

ρ mass density (3, 4, 7)

dimensionless power density (3)

radius (4)

Σ macroscopic cross section: probability of occurrence in 1 cm of travel of particle

$\Sigma_f, \Sigma_a, \Sigma_s$ macroscopic cross section for fission, absorption, scattering

σ microscopic cross section: probability of interaction between two particles (1, 3, 4)

radiation source density (4)

stress (6)

$\sigma_f, \sigma_a, \sigma_s$ microscopic cross section for fission, absorption, scattering

τ Fermi age, $d\tau = \dfrac{du}{3\xi\Sigma_s\Sigma_t}$ (2)

transit time $= \dfrac{L}{v}$ (3)

volume (4)

shear stress (6)

ratio of absolute temperatures (8)

φ neutron flux $= nv$ (1–3)

angle (1, 4)

function (2)

ψ function $= rq$ (2)

function (8)

INTRODUCTION

This book contains a discussion, from a mechanical engineer's viewpoint, of the application of nuclear reactors to the production of thermal power, and a large portion of the book is devoted to a description and an engineering analysis of nuclear reactors. This description requires the use of terms and concepts unfamiliar to persons not directly concerned with the field of nuclear energy. In this introductory section of the book the nuclear reactor is described and the terms and concepts now used in nuclear analysis are introduced, but without a precise mathematical definition of each term. This description is simplified intentionally to focus attention on those concepts necessary for the understanding of nuclear reactors. It is hoped that the reader will gain from the description an overall concept of the functioning of a nuclear reactor so that the following chapters can be more readily grasped.

The nuclear reactor can be regarded as a source of heat which substitutes for the combustion process in the conventional steam or gas turbine power plant. As with any more traditional source of heat, a fuel is required, in this case uranium or plutonium. In the reactor the process analogous to combustion becomes nuclear fission. As with the combustion furnace there is an ash- or waste-disposal problem. A working fluid is required to carry the heat from the reactor to the power-producing components of the plant.

In contrast to the *chemical* reactions, which produce heat in the usual combustion processes, *nuclear* reactions produce heat in a reactor. It is well known that *atoms* consist of relatively heavy *nuclei* surrounded by relatively light negatively charged *electrons*, which define the chemical properties of the atom. Each nucleus consists primarily of *protons* having a positive charge and *neutrons* which are electrically neutral. The number of protons in the nucleus is equal to the number of electrons in an electrically neutral atom. The neutrons present in the nucleus make up the remainder of the nuclear weight. The relative number of neutrons varies from one chemical element to

1

the next, being approximately equal to the number of protons in light elements and about one and a half times as many in heavy elements. A given chemical element always has the same number of protons; however, the number of neutrons in a given element may vary. These variations of the same element are called *isotopes*. It is customary to describe a particular isotope by two numbers, along with the chemical symbol, the lower being the number of electrons and the upper being the sum of the number of protons and neutrons in the nucleus. For instance, $_{92}U^{235}$ represents the isotope of uranium having 235 protons and neutrons in its nucleus. All uranium atoms have 92 electrons.

The nuclei of many atoms can be split or *fissioned* when they are bombarded by atomic particles. The key reaction of a nuclear reactor is a nuclear fission of a heavy atom, such as uranium, isotope-235, by a moving neutron. The products of this reaction, or fission, are two or more relatively heavy particles (new atoms of different chemical elements), an assortment of particles such as *beta particles, gamma rays*, and *neutrinos*, energy of fission which is primarily kinetic energy in the heavy particles, and, last and most important, more neutrons. The generation of more neutrons permits a continuing, or *chain*, reaction, if from each nuclear fission one new neutron is available to cause another fission. A major problem in the design of nuclear reactors is the conservation and control of neutrons in order to maintain this chain reaction. This subject will be discussed more thoroughly later.

The useful output of the reactor is primarily the kinetic energy in the heavy particles which can be transmitted to a working fluid, through the mechanism of heat transfer. The assortment of other particles produced by nuclear fission causes a serious problem. Beta particles are electrons and travel relatively short distances before being absorbed in the reactor or surrounding structure. However, neutrons and gamma rays travel long distances since they are not readily absorbed, and can cause serious damage to living tissue. Neutrinos have no known effects on tissues. The *radiation dosage* required to cause damage is minute compared to the quantities emitted by a reactor. Consequently *shielding* must be provided around reactors to protect operating personnel. Shields consist of thick layers of bulk materials like concrete and iron, or lead, to *absorb* the gamma rays, with *moderators* like water to *slow down* fast neutrons, and with strong neutron *absorbers* like cadmium or boron to *capture* the slow neutrons. Because of the thickness of the shielding it is necessary to perform all operations on reactors by remote-control mechanisms.

The ash from the nuclear fission process consists of the new atoms formed by the fission process. Most of these are highly *radioactive*, giving off gamma rays, and some of these strongly absorb neutrons and thus interfere with the chain reaction process. Materials which absorb neutrons non-usefully are called *poisons*. These fission products must be removed from nuclear reactors and replaced with new fissionable material for continuous operation. The radioactive fission products constitute a serious waste-disposal problem.

The production and conservation of neutrons in the reactor will now be discussed in a preliminary way. For a uniform rate of power generation, the rate of fission must be constant, requiring that one neutron from each fission produce a new fission. The losses of neutrons, which must be controlled to produce this condition, may be escape from the reactor, or non-useful capture in reactor structure, in fission products, or in fissionable material.

It is found that the probability that a neutron will cause fission when it strikes an atom of fissionable material is dependent upon the kinetic energy of the neutron. This probability, expressed as a *cross section* for fission, increases as the kinetic energy decreases. The neutrons emitted from a fission process have a high kinetic energy averaging about two *million electron volts* (2 Mev), in the units in which such energies are expressed. In collisions with various light, stationary atoms, such as hydrogen or deuterium, for example, this kinetic energy of the neutrons is diminished until finally it approaches the energy of *thermal equilibrium* with its surroundings. At room temperature the average kinetic energy of neutrons in thermal equilibrium with their surroundings is about one-fortieth *electron volt* ($\frac{1}{40}$ ev).

Reactors are sometimes classified in terms of the neutron velocity at which it is planned to cause fission. Reactors in which fission is caused primarily by neutrons having kinetic energies close to the thermal level are called *thermal reactors*. For these, *moderators* must be inserted in the reactor to slow the neutrons down quickly and without excessive loss to thermal energy. These moderators are preferably light atoms. The maximum possible transfer of energy from a neutron to a stationary atom occurs if the nucleus of the atom is of the same size as the neutron, as is approximately true for the lightest atom, hydrogen, and becomes less as the nucleus of the struck atom increases in size. This might be compared to the problem of the moving billiard ball, which can, in a head-on collision, transfer all of its energy to a stationary ball of the same size, but bounces back from the wall of the massive table with practically undiminished energy. Reactors which do not slow down the neutrons appreciably are called *fast reactors*. Reactors using primarily neutrons in the region between fission and thermal energies are called *intermediate reactors*.

In the interior of a thermal reactor, large numbers of neutrons created by fission are moving about, colliding with moderator atoms, and being absorbed by fission and various non-useful types of captures. In this process there is an overall movement of neutrons from regions of high neutron density to lower density regions. This movement can be thought of as a *flux* and the process as a *diffusion*. In this process of diffusion, leakage of neutrons from the reactor occurs at the boundaries. Since the amount of leakage depends on the amount of surface of the reactor, whereas the production of neutrons by fission depends on the volume of the reactor, there is a minimum ratio of the volume to surface at which the chain reaction is self-sustaining, or at which the reactor is *critical*. Because the ratio of volume to surface is proportional to some linear dimension of the reactor there is then some size of the reactor at which it is just critical, below which the chain reaction cannot maintain itself because of excess leakage of neutrons, and above which the neutron density, and hence the power, increases indefinitely. This is the *critical size* of the reactor. To minimize the leakage of neutrons, *reflectors* are applied to the outside of the reactor. For thermal reactors the reflectors are required to perform essentially the same function as moderators, and, therefore, are also materials composed of light atoms. For fast reactors, where moderators are not used, the reflectors are composed of heavy atoms, to reflect the neutrons without slowing them down.

Removal of power from reactors requires coolants and structural materials. If these are strong absorbers of neutrons they must be used sparingly, to avoid wasting neutrons. Also, some coolants become radioactive as a result of the absorption of neutrons. If they are pumped outside the active core of the reactor, measures must be taken to protect personnel from the radioactivity of the coolants.

Only one material, as it occurs in nature, is fissionable to an appreciable extent. It is uranium isotope-235 ($_{92}U^{235}$), which constitutes about 0.7 percent of natural uranium. There are a few materials which are not fissionable under normal circumstances, but can be made so by the absorption of a neutron. These materials are sometimes called *fertile*. For instance, uranium isotope-238 ($_{92}U^{238}$), which constitutes the bulk of natural uranium, is not fissionable by thermal neutrons, but on absorption of a neutron becomes uranium isotope ($_{92}U^{239}$), which *decays* by the emission of beta particles (*electrons*) to *plutonium* isotope-239 ($_{94}Pu^{239}$), which is fissionable. If excess neutrons are available from fissions, above those necessary to maintain the chain reaction and those absorbed in parasitic captures in structure and coolant, some of these neutrons can be used for *converting* unfissionable materials to their fissionable counterparts, thus increasing the total supply of fissionable material available. If the supply of fissionable material made by conversion is greater than that used up in fissions, it is said that *breeding* has been achieved. Since the supply of materials which can be made fissionable by conversion is far larger than the supply of naturally occurring fissionable materials, the achievement of breeding may well be the principal key to the peacetime future of atomic energy. The usefulness of natural uranium for many purposes is enhanced by enriching, which is accomplished by removing part of the non-fissionable U-238.

For various reasons it is not possible to design a reactor so that it will be exactly critical. In the first place, all the accumulated tolerances in the design and construction of the reactor preclude the possibility of an exact solution of the criticality problem. In the next place, as the reactor operates it uses up fissionable material, which tends to make it subcritical (unless it is simultaneously breeding new fissionable material within the reactor) and creates among its fission products some materials like xenon isotope-135, which are strong absorbers of neutrons. To prevent the reactor from becoming subcritical, and shutting itself down, or supercritical, and destroying itself, due to variations of *reactivity* with time, and to allow for tolerances, a control mechanism is needed. A new reactor is deliberately designed with an excess of reactivity (more fissionable material than is needed for criticality) sufficient to provide for all subsequent losses, and a means is then provided for dissipating the excess neutrons produced so that the new reactor will not become supercritical. Neutrons can be dissipated by the insertion of retractable *control rods* into the reactor, the control rods being made of material which is a strong neutron absorber, or by backing part of a reflector away to a point where it is less effective so that leakage of neutrons is increased. In certain reactors the supply of neutrons can also be controlled by adding or removing fissionable material. It is on the basis of the foregoing overall considerations of the nature of a nuclear reactor that it is to be studied in its relationship to the other, more usual, engineering components of a power plant with which it must be designed to give an integrated, functioning unit.

Several present and planned reactors have been declassified. Information on these reactors is available to the public, and descriptions and pictures can be found in the books referred to at the end of this Introduction, as well as in current technical periodicals in this field. A common characteristic of those reactors, concerning which a significant amount of information has been released, is that they were designed for purposes other than the production of appreciable quantities of electrical or shaft power. Specific details on those power reactors which are now planned or in operation are generally classified or otherwise unavailable.

In the absence of better and more specific information let us make up, in outline, a rather generalized power reactor, and discuss some of its likely physical characteristics. Figure i-1 shows this hypothetical reactor and some of the necessary auxiliary equipment which accompanies it. The main components of the power system shown in Fig-

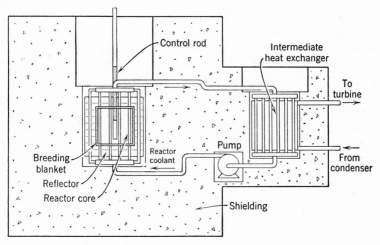

FIG. i-1. Generalized diagram of a reactor.

ure i-1 are indicated by arrows. Some general discussion of the reactor shown here is appropriate.

As shown in Figure i-1, the reactor is used to heat a *primary fluid* which circulates through the heat exchanger (boiler) to heat the working medium used in the turbine. The boiler in this case acts as an intermediate heat exchanger. Generally, because of the radioactivity of the fluid passing through the reactor, the boiler as well as the reactor must be shielded to protect personnel from radiation effects. Alternatives are possible here. For instance, the working medium for the turbine might be passed directly through the reactor, eliminating the intermediate heat exchanger. In this case, the whole turbine and condenser would generally require shielding to protect operating personnel. A second alternative is to move the intermediate heat exchanger inside the main reactor shielding.

Various alternatives are possible for the fluid in the primary reactor cooling circuit. For instance, a moderator (light or heavy water) might be used as a solvent for some soluble salt of fissionable uranium.

This mixture of moderator and nuclear fuel could be circulated through the reactor, where the reactor was maintained critical and, therefore, heat was generated. Such a reactor, having a uniform mixture of moderator and nuclear fuel, is called *homogeneous*. The heat generated in this critical, homogeneous reactor would be dissipated by circulation through the heat exchanger. Fissionable material in some solid form in a critical assembly in the core might be used to heat one of a variety of fluids. If the neutrons in the reactor were primarily at thermal energy, this reactor cooling fluid might be light or heavy water, which are good moderators as well as coolants. With a solid moderator, such as beryllium, beryllium oxide, or graphite in a thermal reactor, several coolants are possible. Some liquid metal with a low absorption cross section for the thermal neutrons, such as bismuth or lead (or a eutectic mixture of these), might be used. Heavy water, or light water or sodium (if a configuration for the reactor core can be found in which the parasitic absorption of neutrons in light water or sodium is not too large), is also a possibility. A eutectic solution of uranium in some liquid metal or a stable suspension of some uranium compound in a liquid might be used as a circulating fuel with a solid moderator. In a fast reactor, where parasitic absorption due to the structural materials and coolants is not so serious, liquid sodium or potassium (or a eutectic mixture of these) might be used as a reactor coolant. These reactors, in which the fuel and moderator are not uniformly mixed, are called *heterogeneous* reactors.

Let us now discuss briefly some of the possible characteristics of the reactor core under various circumstances. The reactor core can be made small by either one of two alternatives. In a thermal reactor the core can be made small by the use of a good moderator (of the order of 1 foot diameter for light water or 3 feet for heavy water, or beryllium, or beryllium oxide). A major disadvantage of water-moderated reactors for power purposes is that the high temperature needed for power purposes generally requires very large pressures in the reactor shell to maintain the density of the water high enough for it to function effectively as a moderator. In those reactors which use good moderators to achieve a small core size, any high-temperature structural materials, which are required to remove the heat generated, tend to absorb a disproportionately large quantity of neutrons. A thermal reactor using graphite as a moderator will tend to be large (perhaps 20 feet across the reactor core). Thermal reactors using heavy water or graphite as moderator have the inherent advantage of being able to use natural, or slightly enriched, uranium as the nuclear fuel. Fast reactors are made relatively small by a different expedient

—loading them with relatively large quantities of highly enriched uranium (or plutonium). In these cores the relatively large investment of enriched uranium in so small a core (of the order of one foot in diameter) necessitates an increased emphasis on heat transfer in order to attain large enough amounts of power from the large and expensive inventory of fissionable material.

If it is intended to convert fertile materials to fissionable materials, the core will contain fertile materials, U-238 or Th-232, either mixed more or less uniformly with the fissionable material in the core, or wrapped around the core in a breeding blanket, or both. The core will generally be surrounded by a reflector to conserve the supply of neutrons.

The whole assembly will be surrounded by some 8 to 10 feet of shielding material, generally of concrete and steel, to protect personnel. All parts of the assembly which are subjected to large amounts of particle bombardment from the reactor must be cooled to prevent damage due to the high temperatures which would otherwise be generated.

Since the reactor continues to generate some heat after it is shut down, owing to radioactive decay of elements made unstable in the reactor, cooling after shutdown is needed. If the reactor can be so arranged that natural convection of the cooling medium, due to variations of temperature in the cooling system, provides adequate cooling, it is a desirable safety feature.

Reactors are considered, in this book, in only one context, as part of a simple four-component system, which can be visualized schematically as shown in Figure i-2. Part 1 is a reactor, and its associated auxiliary equipment, operating at some limiting top temperature T_m, taking in a quantity W per unit time of some working fluid at temperature T_1 and discharging it at temperature T_2. Part 2 is a pump or compressor, providing a pressure rise Δp sufficient to overcome the pressure losses in all other components of the system. Part 3 is a turbine for driving the pump and for providing external power. Part 4 is a heat exchanger which reduces the temperature to a value appropriate to the requirements of the pump.

In this context, as part of a system, reactors are of interest from two aspects: (1) how the operating characteristics of the reactor, or at least some of them, depend on the internal design of the reactor, and (2) what the design specifications for the system demand for the operating characteristics of the reactor. So far as internal design of the reactor is concerned, the distribution of neutrons and the requirements for criticality determine the distribution of power in the reactor as a function of space and time. The thermal output of the reactor depends on temperatures, pressures, and velocities of the cooling medium, and characteristics of the materials in the reactor. Limitations on power output exist due to top temperatures allowed by materials in the reactor and in the power system generally, to temperature differences allowed by considerations of thermal stress, and to pressure losses as they affect power plant efficiency.

The handling of thermal energy without neutron considerations is a fairly commonplace engineering problem, and a considerable amount

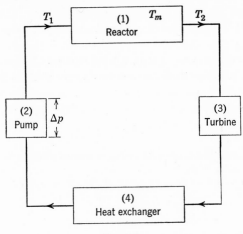

FIG. i-2.

of engineering development has been expended in determining the application of thermal energy to many engineering problems. The handling of neutrons, however, is not yet a commonplace engineering problem, and the distribution of thermal energy in a reactor cannot be considered as a problem independent from neutron considerations. The distribution of thermal energy in the reactor, or even its existence, is entirely dependent on the distribution of neutrons. Materials requirements for neutron purposes seem often to be diametrically opposite to the requirements for materials for the utilization of thermal energy.

The first large reactors which were built, for instance those at Hanford, had as their only purpose the utilization of neutrons for the production of plutonium from uranium fissions. The economy of neutrons determined largely the reactor configuration, whereas the problem in handling the thermal energy was to minimize its nuisance value. A considerable plant, as well as a large amount of electric power from Grand Coulee, is needed to dissipate the energy of fission into Columbia River water. In mobile power plants using nuclear energy, like the naval and aircraft applications, the conversion of thermal energy to mechanical energy is the central problem. The neutron problem, due to the availability of enriched fissionable material, is important only in its bearing on achieving criticality with a reasonable amount of fissionable material and a reasonable size of reactor. Reactors in the future may have to combine the emphases of these two types. If nuclear energy is to compete economically as an extension of world sources of power, it is probably necessary to use fissionable materials economically, including both considerations of power plant efficiency in the usual sense and the maximum use of neutrons in making new fissionable material. It is necessary for the designer of the nuclear power plant to understand the interrelationships between nuclear considerations and the more usual engineering problems of power plant design.

GENERAL BIBLIOGRAPHY

Atomic Energy Commission, *Annual and Semiannual Reports*, U. S. Government Printing Office, from 1946.

Glasstone, S., *Sourcebook on Atomic Energy*, D. Van Nostrand Co., New York, 1950.

Glasstone, S., and M. C. Edlund, *The Elements of Nuclear Reactor Theory*, D. Van Nostrand Co., New York, 1952.

Goodman, C., Editor, *The Science and Engineering of Nuclear Power*, Addison-Wesley Press, Cambridge, Mass., 1947.

Nucleonics, McGraw-Hill Publishing Co., New York.

Smyth, H. D., *Atomic Energy for Military Purposes*, U. S. Government Printing Office, 1945.

Stephenson, R., *Introduction to Nuclear Engineering*, McGraw-Hill Book Co., New York, 1954.

CHAPTER 1

NUCLEAR CONSIDERATIONS

Some characteristics of physical particles considered directly pertinent to the use of the fission process for the production of power are discussed in this chapter. For this purpose certain processes involving the reaction of neutrons with the nuclei of atoms, and the immediate results of these processes, are particularly important, primarily (1) scattering, (2) capture of neutrons by nuclei, and (3) fission of nuclei by neutrons. As a preliminary to the discussion of the interactions of neutrons with nuclei the structure of atoms will be considered. This discussion will be limited to the physical characteristics of atoms and their nuclei which have a bearing on the engineering design of nuclear reactors. No attempt will be made to give a complete description of atoms and nuclei from a physicist's point of view.

Some word seems appropriate at this point about the indirectness of experience involved in the aspects of *nuclear engineering* which touch *nuclear physics*. An engineer is accustomed to say that he measures an area when, in actuality, what he does is to measure linear dimensions and to calculate an area. When an engineer says that he measures a stress, or a strain, or a pressure, etc., what he really does is still more indirect. None the less, the feeling of familiarity that has come from repetition of the processes gives him a comforting, though misleading, feeling of directness about his operations.

A nuclear physicist becomes accustomed to making very indirect measurements, on properties of objects which he cannot see or touch, in an engineering sense. When a physicist describes the properties of a nucleus he does not, in an engineering sense, make a map of the nucleus. Instead, he postulates certain concepts which he labels electron, neutron, proton, neutrino, etc., and whose properties he can correlate with his measurements. The engineer would do well to avoid the trap involved in thinking of these concepts with the same definiteness with which he regards the macroscopic properties of a billiard ball.

11

Description of Atoms

1-1. Atoms—Nuclei and Electrons

An atom is the smallest subdivision of a chemical element which displays the chemical properties of the element. The atom is conceived of as a positively charged nucleus about which are arranged negatively charged electrons, normally sufficient in number to balance the charge of the nucleus, leaving the whole atom electrically neutral.

The number of electrons in the neutral atom is called the atomic number, which almost completely determines the chemical properties of an element. The chemical elements are numbered according to the atomic number, the system of natural elements going from the hydrogen atom with one electron to uranium with 92 electrons. Some elements having more than 92 electrons have been produced artificially, among them plutonium with 94 electrons.

1-2. Nuclei—Neutrons and Protons

The nucleus of the atom is composed of protons, which are responsible for the positive charge of the nucleus, and neutrons which are electrically neutral. The general term, nucleon, is used for both neutrons and protons. The charge on the proton is equal in magnitude and opposite in sign to that of the electron, and, hence, there are the same number of protons as electrons in the neutral atom. The masses of the protons and neutrons make up most of the total mass of the atoms, the electrons being comparatively light. A given chemical element, as determined by the number of electrons in a neutral atom (or protons), can exist in nature with differing numbers of neutrons in its nucleus. These variations of the same chemical element are called *isotopes*. Although two isotopes of the same element are found to have almost identically the same chemical behavior in most respects, the masses of their nuclei are different, and their nuclear behavior is often radically different. The sum of the numbers of neutrons and protons in the nucleus is called the atomic mass number.

1-3. Chemical Designation

The chemical elements are often designated by a system using a letter symbol for the element, for instance, O for oxygen, and numbers designating the numbers of protons and neutrons in the nucleus, for instance, $_8O^{16}$. The subscript number (8) signifies that there are 8 protons in the nucleus of an oxygen atom, and the superscript number (16) signifies that the total number of nucleons (protons plus neu-

trons) is 16. There are, hence, 8 (16 minus 8) neutrons in the oxygen
—16 nucleus. The subscript number is sometimes omitted as super-
fluous, since, to the chemist, the letter symbol O designates oxygen,
which must always have 8 protons, though it can have a different number of neutrons. Oxygen also occurs with 9 and 10 neutrons, these
isotopes being designated, $_8O^{17}$, $_8O^{18}$. In any given, naturally occurring, stable element the fractional quantities of the various isotopes
are always approximately the same. Thus there are always about
99.76 percent of O^{16} in naturally occurring oxygen.

1-4. Atomic Mass Units

The masses of particles are expressed in atomic mass units (amu).
By definition, the atomic mass unit is one-sixteenth the mass of the
most abundant oxygen isotope, which, as indicated above, has 8 protons and 8 neutrons. On this scale the masses of the three fundamental particles are found experimentally to be:

TABLE 1-4-1

Proton	1.00758 amu
Neutron	1.00897 amu
Electron	0.00055 amu

It is pertinent to the field of nuclear energy to note that the masses
of the particles which compose $_8O^{16}$ do not add up to 16.0000, which
is the mass of oxygen—16 on our scale. Rather the mass of 8 protons
plus 8 neutrons plus 8 electrons is seen to be 16.1364, a discrepancy of
0.85 percent. In the combination of the separate elements which
compose this isotope of oxygen, 0.1364 unit of mass have disappeared.
According to Einstein's statement of the equivalence of mass and energy an amount of energy should have been given off, in the process of
making oxygen from its components, equivalent to

$$\Delta E = C^2 \, \Delta M$$

where C is the velocity of light. The energy given off is called the
binding energy of the nucleus, which is generally expressed in Mev
(million electron volt) units. One amu is equivalent to 931 Mev.
Therefore, the binding energy of $_8O^{16}$ is 127 Mev, or almost 8 Mev per
nucleon.

The atomic weight of an atom (or nucleus) is by definition its weight
in atomic mass units. A useful concept for calculation purposes is
the gram-atom. The gram-atom of a substance having an atomic

weight, A, contains, by definition, A grams of the substance. The gram-atom of any substance has been found experimentally to have the same number of atoms, namely, about 0.602×10^{24}. This is called *Avogadro's number.* Hence there are 16 grams of $_8O^{16}$ in a gram-atom, and the atomic mass unit can be expressed in grams, as follows:

$$1 \text{ amu} = \frac{16}{16 \times 0.602 \times 10^{+24}} = 1.66 \times 10^{-24} \text{ gram}$$

Stable and Unstable Elements

1-5. Stable Elements

Atoms experience interactions with particles, or other atoms, on two levels, a superficial level involving only the electrons external to the nucleus, and a more fundamental level involving the nucleus itself. The interactions with the external electrons of atoms control their combination in chemical reactions. The interactions of particles with the nuclei of atoms cause fundamental changes of structure of the nucleus in which the atom often completely loses its original identity. The forces required to disrupt a stable nucleus are very large compared with those required to cause a chemical reaction between atoms. This book is concerned primarily with the results of reactions in the nucleus, since they largely determine the aspects of a nuclear reactor which are new to engineering.

1-6. Unstable Elements

In this section some elements are discussed which are naturally unstable, in the sense that they do not maintain their chemical identity, but rather, owing to internal rearrangements of their nuclei, achieve stability by breaking up into new chemical elements. Since, in the process, particles are ejected, or radiated, and energy is released from the nuclei, these elements are said to be radioactive.

A few elements of the heavy end of the series of chemical elements, those heavier than lead, are naturally radioactive. Particles are radiated from the nucleus of the radioactive material in a process by which the chemical nature of the element is changed, or transmuted, through several adjacent steps in the chemical series, finally ending in some stable isotope of lead. The radiations from the process of radioactive decay, or radioactive disintegration, are of several types. They have been designated for historical reasons as alpha and beta particles and gamma rays.

RADIOACTIVE EMANATIONS

The alpha particles from the disintegration process have been found to be identical with the nucleus of the helium atom, composed of two protons and two neutrons ($_2$He^4). The beta particles are electrons which are supposed to be emitted as a result of a conversion of a neutron to a proton within the nucleus. The designations alpha and beta are left-over terms from the period when it had been determined that there were radioactive emanations, but their chemical identity had not yet been discovered.

The gamma rays are penetrating electromagnetic radiations (like x-rays of high energy) which undergo a considerable interaction with the material through which they pass, causing them to be of engineering consequence. Because of the deleterious effects of gamma rays on biological tissue it is necessary to protect persons from exposure to them. When gamma rays are produced in large quantities, as in a reactor, even structural materials are subject to damage by bombardment with them.

To preserve the concept of the conservation of energy for the process of emission of beta particles, a new particle has been postulated, called the neutrino, which has no electric charge and a small mass compared even with the electron, but which carries some of the energy of disintegration of the nucleus, partly in the form of spin. Because of its lack of electric charge and its low mass, the neutrino has a negligible interaction with matter. It is therefore hard to detect and has no known engineering consequence.

Experiments have shown that in general a single radioactive element does not emit both alpha and beta particles. Gamma rays, however, can be emitted with either of the two.

RADIOACTIVE FAMILIES

There are three natural radioactive series or families. One of these families, the uranium series, starts with uranium, $_{92}$U^{238}, and ends with lead, $_{82}$Pb^{206}, having given off 8 alpha particles and 6 beta particles in 14 steps of disintegration, as well as energy in the form of gamma rays and neutrinos. In the actinium series, uranium, $_{92}$U^{235}, degenerates to lead, $_{82}$Pb^{207}, in 11 steps. In the thorium series, thorium, $_{90}$Th^{232}, degenerates to lead, $_{82}$Pb^{208}, in 10 steps. A fourth family, which has not been found in nature, has been created artificially. It is the neptunium series, named for its longest-lived member, in which artificially formed plutonium, $_{92}$Pu^{241}, degenerates to bismuth, $_{83}$Bi^{209}.

RATE OF DECAY

The rate at which the steps of disintegration of the radioactive material progress is found to be proportional to the amount of disintegrating material present. This is expressed as

$$\frac{1}{N(t)} \frac{dN(t)}{dt} = -\lambda \tag{1-6-1}$$

where N is the concentration of disintegrating material, t is the time, and λ is the proportionality constant for the process, called the decay constant. Integrating this expression gives the concentration of the original material

$$\frac{N(t)}{N(t_0)} = e^{-\lambda(t-t_0)} \tag{1-6-2}$$

where $N(t_0)$ is the concentration at the initial time, t_0. The time for the quantity of disintegrating material to be reduced by a factor of two, called the half-life, is given by

$$T_{\frac{1}{2}} = \frac{\ln 2}{\lambda} \tag{1-6-3}$$

As examples, the half-life of $_{92}U^{238}$ is 4.5×10^9 years, of $_{92}U^{235}$ is 7.1×10^8 years, and of $_{90}Th^{232}$ is 1.4×10^{10} years. For a radioactive series, as one product is disintegrating according to the formulae above, the product next lower in the series is being built up as a direct consequence, but is also generally decaying at its own rate of disintegration. The half-lives of most of these intermediate products is much shorter than the figures given above, some of these being measured in seconds. Thus, for the mth element in a series of radioactive elements,

$$\frac{dN_m}{dt} = -\lambda_m N_m + \lambda_{m-1} N_{m-1} \tag{1-6-4}$$

A set of n such equations must be solved simultaneously, for a series of n radioactive members, to determine the proportions of the constituents at a given time. These equations are typical of all radioactive decay processes.

ARTIFICIAL RADIOACTIVE MATERIALS

It has been found that naturally stable elements are rendered unstable, or radioactive, by the bombardment of their nuclei by particles. In a nuclear reactor many stable elements are made unstable, or radioactive, by bombardment with neutrons. The references at the end of the chapter describe these radioactive decay processes in detail. The radioactive decay of materials artificially made unstable during the operation of a reactor is important for two special reasons. First, because of the damaging effects of radiation on personnel, radioactive materials cannot be allowed to escape at random from the reactor into the atmosphere or into watersheds. All radiations, particularly those from the reactor itself, must be shielded with material to stop the more penetrating emanations. Second, some of the materials which accumulate in the reactor are strong absorbers of neutrons (poisons). To prescribe the continued performance of the reactor, it is important to know the rates of their accumulation and disintegration under various conditions of operation.

Bombardment of the Nuclei of Atoms by Particles

1-7. Reaction of Neutrons and Nuclei

When a moving particle comes sufficiently close to the nucleus of an atom, it is normally deflected from its path of motion by the interaction of the force fields surrounding both the particle and the stationary nucleus. It has been found experimentally that moving particles under certain conditions are capable of entering the nuclei of atoms. In general, the result of the penetration of a particle into a nucleus is to destroy its structural stability, requiring some rearrangement to re-establish stability. (There are exceptional cases in which the new product formed by the bombardment of the nucleus is stable.)

Charged particles, to enter a nucleus, must generally have large kinetic energy (high velocity) to overcome the electrical force fields encountered around the nucleus. The neutron, having no electric charge, has a special ability to enter, and hence, to disrupt nuclei, even with relatively low kinetic energy.

When the nuclei of stationary atoms are bombarded by moving particles, various interactions between the nuclei and the particle are possible. Which of these reactions will occur, and in what amounts, depends on such factors as the magnitudes and types of the force fields surrounding the particle and the nucleus and on the velocity (or kinetic energy) of the incident particle. In the design of a reactor it is necessary to express quantitatively the amounts of these reactions to be expected. Since the experimental measurements of these reactions have been made by nuclear physicists, it has become customary to express quantities in physicists' terms. The fundamental units of measurements are, therefore, the centimeter, the gram, and the second.

1-8. Cross Sections

MICROSCOPIC CROSS SECTIONS

The probability that a particular interaction between a nucleus and a moving particle will occur is called the cross section for that reaction. The microscopic cross section of a nucleus for a given reaction is the effective area, expressed in square centimeters, presented by the stationary nucleus to a moving particle approaching it. A more convenient unit for the microscopic cross section, the barn, equal to 10^{-24} cm^2, has been defined, supposedly because on a nuclear scale of magnitudes (nuclei have radii of the order of 10^{-12} cm) this area is as "big as a barn." The microscopic cross section is usually designated by the symbol σ, with an appropriate subscript to designate the types of process. For instance, σ_f is the microscopic cross section for fission, σ_a for absorption, and σ_s for scattering. These values are a function of the velocity of the neutron as well as of properties of the materials in the reactor.

Microscopic cross section data for the elements are often plotted as functions of the logarithm of energy since the neutrons which react with nuclei in a reactor are distributed over such a wide range of energy. A declassified compilation of information on cross sections is presented in the so-called *Brookhaven Report.**

MACROSCOPIC CROSS SECTIONS

The macroscopic cross section is the probability that the process under consideration will occur in one centimeter of travel of the particle through the reacting medium. The macroscopic cross section, designated by the symbol Σ, is given by

$$\Sigma = N\sigma \qquad \text{(1-8-1)}$$

where N is the number of particles of the reacting medium per cubic centimeter. The macroscopic cross section has the dimensions of a reciprocal length:

$$\frac{particles}{cm^3} \times \frac{cm^2}{particle} = \frac{1}{cm} \qquad \text{(1-8-2)}$$

This length, $\lambda = 1/\Sigma$, is called the mean free path of the particle.

* *Neutron Cross Sections*, Neutron Cross Sections Advisory Group, AEC, May 15, 1952, AECU-2040, O.T.S.

The number of particles per cubic centimeter, N, of reacting medium is given by

$$N = \frac{N_0 d}{A} \qquad (1\text{-}8\text{-}3)$$

where N_0 is Avogadro's number, or the number of particles per gram-atom, A is the atomic weight, or grams per gram-atom, and d is the density of the reacting medium in space in grams per cubic centimeter. Hence, if the microscopic cross section is expressed in barns, the macroscopic cross section is expressed in inverse centimeters,

$$\Sigma = \frac{0.602 d\sigma}{A} \qquad (1\text{-}8\text{-}4)$$

These values vary with neutron velocity or energy for a given material. Macroscopic cross sections are additive. Hence, for a mixture of two materials having macroscopic cross sections Σ_1 and Σ_2 determined by their proportionate densities in space the total cross section is

$$\Sigma = \Sigma_1 + \Sigma_2 \qquad (1\text{-}8\text{-}5)$$

1-9. Process Rates

If the number of moving particles per unit volume is designated by n and their average velocity by v, the product, nv, which gives the number of particles crossing unit area in unit time is called the flux of particles. It is generally designated by the symbol φ. The total number of interactions between particles and nuclei per unit time, per unit volume of reacting nuclei, that is, the volume rate of process, is given by the product of the macroscopic cross section for the process and the particle flux, or $\varphi\Sigma$.

In the nuclear reactor several particle interactions occur which are of interest to a reactor design engineer. Most of these interactions involve neutrons, and they can be separated into two main categories. In the first category are elastic scattering collisions, in which the particles struck by the neutron retain their identity. In the second category of neutron processes are various inelastic interactions in which the neutron actually enters the nucleus, generally destroying its equilibrium and creating a new isotope.

Neutron Processes—Elastic Scattering

In the elastic scattering of neutrons an incident neutron comes close enough to a target nucleus to be repelled by its force field but not close enough to be absorbed by the nucleus. The neutron does not enter the nucleus and, hence, does not disrupt the stability of the nucleus.

Elastic scattering collisions with nuclei result in changes in both the energies and the directions of the incident neutrons. As the term elastic implies, analysis of the elastic scattering collision is based on the requirement that both kinetic energy and momentum for the system of incident particle and target nucleus be conserved. This is analogous to the elastic collisions of billiard balls.

1-10. Lethargy

The change in kinetic energy of the high-velocity neutrons in an elastic collision process is inherently negative. In order to provide an inherently positive variable for use in describing the slowing-down process a new term is defined called the lethargy, designated by

$$u = \ln \frac{E_0}{E} \qquad (1\text{-}10\text{-}1)$$

where E_0 is an arbitrary reference level for the neutron energy. Hence changes in lethargy are related to changes in energy by

$$du = -\frac{dE}{E} \qquad (1\text{-}10\text{-}2)$$

Since, for an elastic collision, dE is negative, the change in lethargy is positive.

1-11. Logarithmic Energy Decrement

DERIVATION OF THE LOGARITHMIC ENERGY DECREMENT

The loss in kinetic energy, or the increase in lethargy, of the neutron in elastic collision is generally expressed by the average logarithmic energy decrement per collision, designated by ξ. By definition

$$\xi = \ln E_1 - \ln E_2 = \ln \frac{E_1}{E_2} \qquad (1\text{-}11\text{-}1)$$

where E_1 is the energy of the average neutron before collision and E_2 after. We will now derive an expression for ξ from the elastic collision theory, in terms of the atomic weight of the *target nucleus*. First, the energy decrement for a single collision will be determined with defined angles of collision. Next a probability equation will be developed to determine the probability for a given angle of collision. These expressions, combined, will give a value for ξ.

In elastic collision theory, neutrons are treated as symmetrical spheres which collide elastically with nuclei, which are also considered to be symmetrical spheres. It is assumed, as has been previously stated, that both momentum and energy are conserved for the system including both the neutron and the nucleus. The results of these assumptions are interpreted in terms of the loss in the average logarithm of the energy of the neutron per collision, which, as stated in Equation 1-11-1, is the logarithmic energy decrement.

Figure 1-11-1 shows a sphere of unit mass at the moment of collision with a sphere of mass A. The velocity of the sphere of unit mass before collision is v_1, and after collision is v_2. The sphere of mass A is

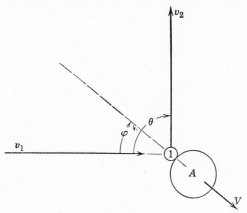

FIG. 1-11-1.

stationary before collision and has velocity V after collision. The angle between v_2 and v_1 is θ. The angle between the line of the centers of the spheres and v_1 is φ.

Conservation of energy for the system requires

$$v_1{}^2 = v_2{}^2 + A V^2 \qquad (1\text{-}11\text{-}2)$$

Conservation of momentum in the direction normal to v_1 requires

$$v_2 \sin \theta - A V \sin \varphi = 0 \qquad (1\text{-}11\text{-}3)$$

Conservation of momentum in the direction of v_1 requires

$$v_1 - v_2 \cos \theta + A V \cos \varphi = 0 \qquad (1\text{-}11\text{-}4)$$

Solving Equation 1-11-3 for $\sin \theta$ and Equation 1-11-4 for $\cos \theta$, squaring both equations, and adding to eliminate θ, gives

$$v_2{}^2 = A^2 V^2 + 2A V v_1 \cos \varphi + v_1{}^2 \qquad (1\text{-}11\text{-}5)$$

Combining Equations 1-11-2 and 1-11-5 to eliminate V gives

$$v_2^2 = A(v_1^2 - v_2^2) + 2Av_1\sqrt{(v_1^2 - v_2^2)/A} \cos \varphi + v_1^2 \quad (1\text{-}11\text{-}6)$$

Solving Equation 1-11-6 for the ratio of the kinetic energy of the sphere of unit mass after collision to its energy before collision gives

$$\frac{E_2}{E_1} = \frac{v_2^2}{v_1^2} = 1 - \frac{4A}{(A+1)^2}\cos^2 \varphi \quad (1\text{-}11\text{-}7)$$

The maximum possible loss which can occur in one collision is given by a head-on collision, when $\cos \varphi = 1$. The energy ratio is then

$$\frac{E_2}{E_1}\,\text{max} = \left(\frac{A-1}{A+1}\right)^2 \quad (1\text{-}11\text{-}8)$$

If the position of the colliding sphere is considered to be completely random, the probability that it will strike within a given area is pro-

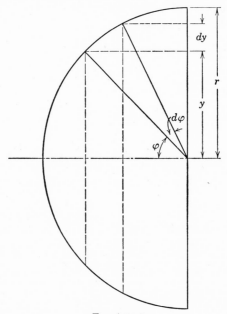

Fig. 1-11-2.

portional to that area. Let us calculate the probability that the sphere of unit mass will contact the sphere of mass A at some angle between φ and $\varphi + d\varphi$.

The probability, $p\,d\varphi$, that those spheres which collide at all will collide at an angle between φ and $\varphi + d\varphi$ is given by the ratio of the area included within the angle $d\varphi$ to the area of the sphere, both projected onto a plane normal to the direction of neutron travel. With reference to Figure 1-11-2,

$$p\,d\varphi = \frac{2\pi y\,dy}{\pi r^2} \qquad (1\text{-}11\text{-}9)$$

Since the distance $y = r \sin \varphi$, then $dy = r \cos \varphi\,d\varphi$, or $y\,dy = -r^2 d(\cos^2 \varphi)$. Therefore,

$$p\,d\varphi = -d(\cos^2 \varphi) \qquad (1\text{-}11\text{-}10)$$

The logarithmic decrement of energy in scattering, ξ, was defined as the average of the ratio $\ln \dfrac{E_1}{E_2}$ over all collisions weighted according to the probability p. Then

$$\xi = \int_{\varphi=0}^{\varphi=\pi/2} \left(\ln \frac{E_1}{E_2} \right) p\,d\varphi = -\int_{\varphi=0}^{\varphi=\pi/2} \left(\ln \frac{E_2}{E_1} \right) p\,d\varphi \qquad (1\text{-}11\text{-}11)$$

Substituting Equations 1-11-7 and 1-11-10 into Equation 1-11-11, we obtain

$$\xi = -\int_{\varphi=0}^{\pi/2} \ln \left[1 - \frac{4A}{(A + 1)^2} \cos^2 \varphi \right] [-d(\cos^2 \varphi)] \qquad (1\text{-}11\text{-}12)$$

This can be rewritten for integration

$$\xi = \frac{(A + 1)^2}{4A} \int_{u=\left(\frac{A-1}{A+1}\right)^2}^{u=1} \ln u\,du \qquad (1\text{-}11\text{-}13)$$

where $u = 1 - \dfrac{4A}{(A + 1)^2} \cos^2 \varphi$, and $du = -d(\cos^2 \varphi)$. The limits of u for $\varphi = 0$, and $\varphi = \pi/2$ are, respectively, $\left(\dfrac{A - 1}{A + 1}\right)^2$ and 1. Performing the integration, we obtain

$$\xi = -\frac{(A + 1)^2}{4A} \left[u(\log u - 1) \right]_{\left(\frac{A-1}{A+1}\right)^2}^{1} \qquad (1\text{-}11\text{-}14)$$

And, simplifying, we have

$$\xi = +1 - \frac{(A - 1)^2}{2A} \ln \frac{A + 1}{A - 1} \qquad (1\text{-}11\text{-}15)$$

Equation 1-11-15 is the log decrement for the slowing-down process for neutrons. Considering that it is based on a very simple analysis of elastic spheres colliding in three-dimensional space, it is probably remarkable that it actually works acceptably well. For all the scattering collisions which occur between neutrons (of essentially atomic mass of unity) and a moderator of atomic mass A, the factor ξ gives a good measure of the average logarithm of the ratio of the energy of the neutron before collision to the energy of the neutron after collision, or the average increase in lethargy per collision.

It is seen that ξ has the value unity for hydrogen, for which $A = 1$, and decreases as the atomic weight increases.

The number of collisions required to bring the average neutron from an initial energy E_0 to a final energy E is given by

$$N = \frac{\ln E_0/E}{\xi} \tag{1-11-16}$$

In terms of lethargy and the logarithmic energy decrement, the number of neutron collisions between the reference energy level E_0 and the energy E is expressed by

$$N = u/\xi \tag{1-11-17}$$

The unit of energy is the electron volt which is defined as the energy required to raise the electronic charge through a potential difference of one volt.   It is abbreviated ev, whereas one million electron volts is abbreviated Mev. Lethargy, being a dimensionless ratio, has no units.

The average neutron energy at fission of uranium is about 2 Mev. The average energy of neutrons in thermal equilibrium with a material at room temperature is about $\frac{1}{40}$ ev. Neutrons in this latter state are called thermal neutrons. The average number of collisions required to slow neutrons from the fission limit to thermal energy is then

$$N_{th} = \frac{\ln (2 \times 10^6 \times 40)}{\xi}$$

The values of ξ for a few elements and the number of collisions necessary to thermalize fission neutrons are:

	A	ξ	N_{th}
Hydrogen	1	1.000	18
Deuterium	2	0.725	25
Beryllium	9	0.209	87
Carbon	12	0.158	114
Oxygen	16	0.120	152

As can be seen, the greatest energy loss per neutron collision occurs with the light elements. Light materials which are good for slowing neutrons and do not absorb many neutrons in the process are called moderators.

AVERAGE COSINE OF THE SCATTERING ANGLE

In the most simplified scattering calculations it is customary to assume that the neutrons are scattered symmetrically about the scattering nucleus. However, owing to the finiteness of the scattering mass, the neutrons are scattered predominately forward. This forward scattering is often expressed in terms of the average cosine of the scattering angle μ, or

$$\mu = \cos \theta_{av} = \int_{\varphi=0}^{\varphi=\pi/2} \cos \theta p \, d\varphi \qquad (1\text{-}11\text{-}18)$$

where θ is the angle at which the neutron is scattered and p, as before, is the probability for collision at an angle between φ and $\varphi + d\varphi$. Substituting for $p \, d\varphi$ its value from Equation 1-11-10 gives

$$\mu = -\int_{\varphi=0}^{\varphi=\pi/2} \cos \theta d(\cos^2 \varphi) \qquad (1\text{-}11\text{-}19)$$

If Equations 1-11-2, 1-11-3, and 1-11-4 are solved for $\cos \theta$ by eliminating all the velocity terms, the result is found to be

$$\cos \theta = \frac{1 - \dfrac{2A}{A+1} \cos^2 \varphi}{\left(1 - \dfrac{4A}{(A+1)^2} \cos^2 \varphi\right)^{1/2}} \qquad (1\text{-}11\text{-}20)$$

Substituting the value of $\cos \theta$ from Equation 1-11-20 into Equation 1-11-19, and performing the integration results in the value of the average cosine of the scattering angle in terms of the atomic mass number of the scattering nucleus,

$$\mu = \frac{2}{3A} \qquad (1\text{-}11\text{-}21)$$

It is seen that, as the mass number A of the scattering nucleus becomes larger, μ approaches zero, or the average scattering angle approaches 90°. For small masses, the average scattering angle is forward.

The average cosine as shown in Equation 1-11-21 will be used in Chapter 2 in connection with the calculations of the diffusion of neutrons through a reactor.

Inelastic Neutron Processes

In an inelastic neutron process, as the term implies, the kinetic energy of the system of target nucleus and incident neutron is not conserved. The neutron actually enters the nucleus of the atom, disrupting its stability. The energy balance in this case depends on the internal readjustment which the new nucleus formed by the entry of the neutron makes to regain stability. Equilibrium can be re-established in a number of ways, which are customarily grouped in three categories: (1) fission, (2) inelastic scattering, and (3) absorption.

1-12. Fission

The fission of nuclei by neutrons is the key reaction on which the operation of nuclear reactors depends. The fissionable elements in combination with incident neutrons produce nuclei which achieve stability by splitting into two or more fragments of comparable size. Thus, in the fission process, two or more atoms of chemical elements near the middle of the chemical series, plus some extra neutrons, are produced from the original fissionable element. The extra neutrons are necessary to the operation of a reactor since they are needed to cause the new fissions which produce a continuous reaction. It is found that the sum of the weights of all the products of fission is less than the sum of atomic weights of the original fissionable elements plus the incident neutron. In the process of fission, then, kinetic energy of the fission fragments has been gained while the weight of the constituents of the original nucleus has decreased. It is found experimentally that the kinetic energy gained is related to the mass lost in fission by the expression from Einstein's theory of relativity,

$$\Delta E = C^2 \, \Delta M$$

where C is the velocity of light.

FISSION PRODUCT SPECTRUM AND DISTRIBUTION OF FISSION ENERGY

The chemical elements into which the fissionable element splits are not always the same, but are distributed about the middle of the chemical series. This distribution spectrum is shown roughly in Figure 1-12-1 for U-235.

Nuclear reactions are often written in the form of nuclear equations, which are convenient for keeping a balance of neutrons and protons taking part in the reaction. The fission reactions represented by Figure 1-12-1 can be shown in this manner. For instance, one possible reaction for the fission of $_{92}U^{235}$ can be expressed so:

$$_{92}U^{235} + _{0}n^{1} \rightarrow _{54}Xe^{141} + _{38}Sr^{92} + 3_{0}n^{1} + Q \qquad (1\text{-}12\text{-}1)$$

where the symbol Q represents the energy released in the fission process, part of this energy being in the form of kinetic energy of the fission fragments and part in the form of gamma rays. The symbols Xe and

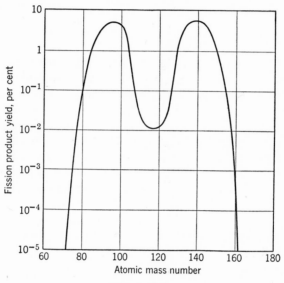

FIG. 1-12-1.

Sr designate, respectively, xenon and strontium. The symbol $_{0}n^{1}$ represents the neutron. Both the subscripts, designating protons, and the superscripts, designating nucleons, must balance on the two sides of the equation.

The amount of heat produced from fission, as well as the number of neutrons released, varies with the reaction. The average energy released per fission of $_{92}U^{235}$ is about 200 Mev. On the average, fission of $_{92}U^{235}$ results in the production of about 2.5 neutrons per fission. These neutrons are emitted from the fission process with an average energy of about 2 Mev per neutron. The energy of fission of U-235 is distributed among the various particles about as shown in Table 1-12-1. The fission fragments are charged particles which are large on the nuclear scale, and do not travel far. Their energy is dissipated, close to the point of fission, in disruption of the atomic structure surrounding the point of fission and in ionizing the surrounding atoms.

TABLE 1-12-1

	Mev
Kinetic energy of fission fragments	165
β-rays (delayed)	7
Kinetic energy of neutrons	5
γ-rays $\begin{cases} \text{prompt} \\ \text{delayed} \end{cases}$	6
	5
Energy from neutron captures	12
	200
Neutrinos	10

Beta rays have longer ranges than the fission fragments, since they are smaller, but are still stopped in the material immediately surrounding the point of fission. Beta rays are charged particles also, and dissipate their energies largely by ionizing the atoms with which they collide. Neutrons are uncharged particles, and, therefore, capable of penetrating great thicknesses of materials before being absorbed. However, for most reactors, neutron economy will dictate that a large fraction of them must be kept within the reactor. Those which do escape from the reactor must be absorbed in shielding to protect personnel from injury. Gamma rays have been found to be very penetrating, energetic emanations (like x-rays with very high energy). They can be absorbed only by large masses of material. A large number of these will escape from the reactor, and for protection of personnel must be caught in shielding. The energy from neutron captures is produced when fission neutrons are captured in surrounding material, most of this energy being in the form of gamma rays. Neutrinos have such long ranges that, for engineering purposes, they can be completely ignored. Of the 200 Mev per fission to be accounted for, it seems that roughly 5 to 10 percent, depending on the reactor configuration, will be absorbed in the shielding around the reactor. For specific cases a detailed accounting must be made. Most of the energy is generated and most of the neutrons are emitted within times after fission too short to be measured. About 0.7 percent of the neutrons and 6 percent of the energy, due to the decay of fission fragments, are delayed for measurable period after fission. The delayed energy amounts to some 12 Mev, 7 Mev being due to beta rays and 5 Mev due to gamma rays. This means that, immediately after a shutdown following a prolonged period of operation, the reactor is operating at 6 percent of its total power. This power then decays approximately according to the empirical formula

$$P = 0.065 P_0 t^{-\frac{1}{5}} \left[1 - \left(\frac{t}{t + t_1} \right)^{\frac{1}{5}} \right] \qquad (1\text{-}12\text{-}2)$$

for periods of 10 seconds $< t <$ 100 days, where t is the time in seconds after shutdown and t_1 is the time of pile operation at power P_0 in seconds. This energy of decay of the fission fragments must be taken into account in the design of the heat-transfer system for a high-powered reactor so that sufficient heat-transfer capacity is available after shutdown to prevent damage to the reactor.

An analysis of the distribution of energy shows that, of the 200 Mev released per fission of U-235, 86 percent is absorbed at the point of fission, and 14 percent somewhere within the reactor, its reflector, and the shield. Some 94 percent, for engineering purposes, is created immediately at the time of fission, whereas 6 percent is delayed, and gradually decays after shutdown. The delayed power decreases by a factor of 2 for each factor of 32 in the time after shutdown. The power which is not absorbed directly at the point of fission is only about 14 percent of the steady-state power, but is about 40 percent of the delayed power, since, of the 12 Mev of delayed energy, 5 Mev are due to penetrating gamma rays.

RATE OF ENERGY RELEASE

The function of a nuclear reactor is to cause the fission of some fissionable material by neutrons. It is apparent that the amount of fissioning which occurs must depend both on the amount of fissionable material in the reactor and on the quantity of neutrons moving about through the fissionable material. We have defined a neutron flux, φ, as the number of neutrons crossing a unit area in a unit time:

$$\varphi = nv \qquad (1\text{-}12\text{-}3)$$

The microscopic cross section presented for fission by a fissionable nucleus, or the probability that it will be fissioned by a neutron of a given lethargy, is signified by σ_f. If the density of fissionable material, in atoms per unit volume, is given by N_f, then the probability for fission per unit of distance, designated by Σ_f, for each neutron is given by the product

$$\Sigma_f = N_f \sigma_f \qquad (1\text{-}12\text{-}4)$$

Σ_f is called the macroscopic cross section for fission. The number of fissions occurring in a reactor, per unit time and per unit volume, is given by the product of the neutron flux φ and the macroscopic cross section for fission Σ_f, this product being integrated over all energies at which fissions are caused. For simplicity, consider for the moment a thermal reactor in which all fissions are caused by thermal neutrons. Then the number of fissions per unit volume per unit time is given by

$$N_f \sigma_f \varphi_{th} \qquad (1\text{-}12\text{-}5)$$

where all quantities are to be measured at thermal energy. The number of fissionable atoms per unit volume is expressed by

$$N_f = \frac{N_0 d_f}{A} \qquad (1\text{-}12\text{-}6)$$

where d_f is the density of fissionable material in space, N_0 is Avogadro's number (0.602×10^{24}), and A is the atomic weight of the fissionable material. The average energy released per fission of the atom of $_{92}U^{235}$ is about 200 Mev. Since 1 ev $= 1.6 \times 10^{-19}$ joule (watt second), one watt of power requires

$$\frac{1 \times 10^{-6}}{200 \times 1.6 \times 10^{-19}} = 3.1 \times 10^{10} \text{ fissions per second}$$

The power generated per unit volume is then given by the product of the number of fissions per unit time, per unit volume, and the number of watts per fission. The microscopic cross section for fission for $_{92}U^{235}$ by a thermal neutron is about 545 barns. The power density δ is then

$$\delta = \frac{(0.602 \times 10^{24}) \times 545 \times 10^{-24}}{235 \times 3.1 \times 10^{10}} x\, d_f \varphi_{th} \qquad (1\text{-}12\text{-}7)$$

or $0.45 \times 10^{-10} d_f \varphi_{th}$ watt per cubic centimeter. For example, a reactor in which there are 100 kg of $_{92}U^{235}$ more or less uniformly distributed, and an average thermal flux of about 10^{13} neutrons per square centimeter per second, would have an operating power of

$$\frac{0.45 \times 10^{-10} \times 1.0 \times 10^5 \times 10^{13}}{10^6} = 45 \text{ megawatts} \qquad (1\text{-}12\text{-}8)$$

FISSIONABLE ELEMENTS

There are several elements which are capable of fission. In nature only U-235 is susceptible to fission by thermal neutrons on an appreciable scale. Other isotopes of natural uranium, particularly U-238, and some natural isotopes of thorium, particularly Th-232, are somewhat susceptible to fission by fast neutrons. Two artificially created elements are readily susceptible to fission by thermal neutrons. These are U-233 and Pu (Plutonium)-239. These elements are made by bombardment with neutrons by a process which will be discussed under "Breeding," Section 1-15. The naturally fissionable isotope U-235 occurs in nature combined with non-fissionable U-238, in the ratio of one part of U-235 to about 140 parts of U-238. For many reactor purposes it is desired to obtain mixtures enriched in the U-235 isotope, since there are many limitations imposed on reactors which must use natural uranium. Since U-235 and U-238 are isotopes of the same chemical element, the methods of their separation must depend on the difference between their atomic weights. There are several methods which have been applied experimentally to the separation process. The production method of prime importance, called the gaseous diffusion process, depends on the greater rate of diffusion of a lighter gas through a porous barrier. The gas, in this case, is the chemical compound, uranium hexafluoride, UF_6. The separation per stage is small, and many stages are therefore required, because of the relatively small difference in masses between the two isotopes.

In summary there are three main sources of fissionable material: natural uranium containing U-235 and U-238; material enriched in U-235 by separation; and U-233 and Pu-239 from conversion of fertile materials in breeder (or converter) reactors.

1-13. Inelastic Scattering

To achieve stability, after it has absorbed a neutron, the nucleus can give back one or more neutrons at an energy lower than that of the incident neutron. This process is designated (n, n) or $(n, 2n)$, etc. The energy of the incident neutron must be relatively high to produce these reactions, about 0.1 Mev for (n, n), about 10 Mev for $(n, 2n)$, and about 20 Mev for $(n, 3n)$ reactions. This process is called inelastic scattering when, for each neutron lost, one new neutron is gained. The process is particularly important for fast reactors, in which its effect is considered harmful since the energy of the emitted neutrons is below the energy at which it is desired to cause fissions.

1-14. Absorption

In the third of the inelastic processes, the neutron is absorbed by the nucleus which re-establishes its equilibrium by a release of energy and particles. The nucleus may give off energy in the form of gamma rays, this process being designated by the symbol (n, γ), leaving the newly formed isotopes stable. The nucleus may give off alpha (α)

particles or protons, the processes being designated (n, α) or (n, p), with or without gamma rays or beta particles, resulting eventually in some new stable nucleus. These four processes are called absorptions, since the main result for reactors is the loss of a neutron by absorption into the nucleus.

Artificially radioactive isotopes of most of the chemical elements have been made by bombarding the elements with particles (in cyclotrons or reactors). The stability of the nucleus depends both on the total number of particles in the nucleus and on the ratio of neutrons to protons. By bombardment with energetic particles a stable nucleus of an element can be changed by adding or subtracting neutrons or protons into a different isotope of the same element or into an entirely different element. If the new isotope formed is unstable it will disintegrate by the emission of particles and possibly with the radiation of gamma rays to some stable isotope, at a rate which can be characterized by the half-life for the process.

Inspection of plots of experimental data on capture cross sections for the elements shows that many elements exhibit a phenomenon called *resonance*, in which the capture cross section at certain values of lethargy is higher by large factors than at other lethargies in the immediate vicinity. For some cases this local increase in cross section may amount to a factor of 1000 or higher. A theory is postulated that the probability for capture of a neutron depends on the length of time the neutron spends in the vicinity of the capturing nucleus. Assuming that the capturing nucleus is in a continuous state of vibratory motion, it is conceivable that, for certain neutron speeds, or energies, the neutron and the nucleus might travel parallel for part of the vibration cycle of the nucleus. Under these circumstances, then, the probability for capture would be high; hence the term *resonance capture*. The probability for escape from such a resonance capture is called the *resonance escape probability*.

1-15. Breeding

BREEDING CONVERSION

One type of process involving the absorption of neutrons is of particular interest for the future development of reactors. This process has the net result of using neutrons to convert certain unfissionable materials to fissionable materials. The two predominant materials for which the possibility is significant are uranium-238 and thorium-232. These materials are called fertile. This process is shown below in the form of nuclear equations for the uranium conversion. The first part of the process consists in the bombardment of uranium nucleus by a neutron

$$_{92}U^{238} + _{0}n^{1} \rightarrow _{92}U^{239} + \gamma \qquad (1\text{-}15\text{-}1)$$

where the symbol γ signifies the release of energy in the form of gamma rays. The sums of both subscripts and superscripts must be the same on both sides of the equation. Uranium-239 is unstable, with a half-life of 23 minutes, and it readjusts its proportion of neutrons and protons in two steps.

The first step is

$$_{92}U^{239} \rightarrow _{93}Np^{239} + _{-1}\beta^{0} \qquad (1\text{-}15\text{-}2)$$

where the symbol Np designates neptunium and the β designates the beta particle, or electron, which has been ejected. Neptunium-239 is unstable, with a half-life of 2.3 days. The next step in the disintegration procedure is

$$_{93}Np^{239} \rightarrow _{94}Pu^{239} + _{-1}\beta^{0} \qquad (1\text{-}15\text{-}3)$$

where the symbol Pu represents the element plutonium. Plutonium is also unstable, but with a very long half-life (about 24,000 years), emitting alpha particles and yielding $_{92}U^{235}$, to connect with the beginning of a radioactive family, the actinium series, which was previously discussed in Section 6 of this chapter:

$$_{94}Pu^{239} \rightarrow _{92}U^{235} + _{2}He^{4} \qquad (1\text{-}15\text{-}4)$$

Here the symbol He designates the helium nucleus (an alpha particle).

The particular example discussed above is a conversion reaction, in which $_{92}U^{238}$, the predominant non-fissionable isotope of natural uranium, is eventually converted, by the absorption of a neutron and the emission of two beta particles, to a fissionable isotope of plutonium, $_{94}Pu^{239}$. This is the fundamental process by which fissionable material for use in atom bombs has been made in the Hanford reactors. By a similar process fertile Th-232 is converted to fissionable U-233.

The process of replacing the fissionable material consumed in fission by new fissionable material is called conversion, since non-fissionable material is converted to fissionable material. The term breeding is also used in connection with the process. A breeder reactor is generally considered to be one which has as one of its primary aims the accomplishment of breeding gain. Breeders and converters are also sometimes differentiated as to whether the material produced is the same as or different from the material consumed in the chain reaction.

BREEDING GAIN

An interesting subject in the field of nuclear energy is the possibility of using nuclear energy as a substantial means of extending our natural resources for the production of power. To discuss this subject we would like to know how much fissionable material is economically available. One determining factor here involves the question whether only materials which are fissionable in the natural state, like $_{92}U^{235}$, are available, or whether it is feasible to convert other materials which are not fissionable in the natural state to fissionable materials in significant quantities. The importance of this question depends on the facts that $_{92}U^{238}$, which is not sufficiently fissionable for use as a nuclear fuel, is 140 times as plentiful as fissionable $_{92}U^{235}$, and that large quantities of $_{90}Th^{232}$ are available. It is common knowledge that the Hanford reactors, and others, do make fissionable $_{94}Pu^{239}$ from non-fissionable $_{92}U^{238}$, at the expense of fissionable $_{92}U^{235}$, and that $_{90}Th^{232}$, which is also not sufficiently fissionable, can be converted to fissionable $_{92}U^{233}$ by neutron bombardment. The question is whether, in the consumption of the relatively small quantity of $_{92}U^{235}$, a significant quantity of non-fissionable materials will be made fissionable. The least we should ask of a system for this purpose would be that for each atom of fissionable material used, a new fissionable atom would be produced, including all losses in chemical processing, etc. Then, supposedly, this new material could be placed in another reactor and the process continued until all the material capable of conversion to fissionable material had been converted and burned up. If, in addition to this, it is desired to add to the currently available stockpile of fissionable material it is necessary to produce more than one new atom of fissionable material for each atom used. The limiting possibilities for this process will be explored.

The ratio of atoms produced to those used can be expressed as

$$\frac{\Sigma_p}{\Sigma_u} \tag{1-15-5}$$

where Σ_p is the production cross section of the fertile material (for instance, $_{92}U^{238}$) and Σ_u is the absorption cross section of the fissionable material (for instance, $_{92}U^{235}$). The fractional increase of fissionable material is then

$$r = \frac{\Sigma_p}{\Sigma_u} - 1 - l \tag{1-15-6}$$

where l represents the fractional loss of fissionable atoms in chemical processing, due to leakage of neutrons, etc. For instance, if 110 atoms of plutonium are produced when 100 atoms of fissionable uranium are destroyed, and if 1 percent of the current supply is lost in processing, etc., the gain in the system is

$$r = \frac{110 - 100 - 1}{100} = 0.09$$

An upper limit can be established for the ratio, Σ_p/Σ_u. This limit is set by the limits of criticality for the reactor in which leakage of neutrons from the reactor is negligible. Let it be assumed that Σ_a, the macroscopic cross section for all absorptions, is composed of three parts; absorptions in fissionable material Σ_u, absorptions involved in producing new fissionable material Σ_p, and non-useful absorptions Σ_c (structure, moderator, and neutron poisons of various kinds). Then the ratio of absorptions in uranium to all absorptions is

$$\frac{\Sigma_u}{\Sigma_a} = \frac{\Sigma_u}{\Sigma_u + \Sigma_p + \Sigma_c} \qquad (1\text{-}15\text{-}7)$$

If there are η neutrons produced for every absorption in fissionable material, the ratio of neutrons produced to those used is $\eta\Sigma_u/\Sigma_a$. If the reactor is to be critical, and if there are no other competing processes which use neutrons, the ratio of neutrons produced to those used must be equal to unity, or

$$\eta \frac{\Sigma_u}{\Sigma_u + \Sigma_p + \Sigma_c} = 1 \qquad (1\text{-}15\text{-}8)$$

Solving Equation 1-15-8 for the ratio Σ_p/Σ_u, we have

$$\frac{\Sigma_p}{\Sigma_u} = \eta - 1 - \frac{\Sigma_c}{\Sigma_u} \qquad (1\text{-}15\text{-}9)$$

Substituting Equation 1-15-9 into Equation 1-15-6 gives the gain in the quantity of fissionable material,

$$r = \eta - 2 - \frac{\Sigma_c}{\Sigma_u} - l \qquad (1\text{-}15\text{-}10)$$

For a perfect reactor there would be no losses in the form of non-useful capture, leakage, or chemical processing. All captures would take place in fissionable or production material. For such an idealized reactor the upper limit on the gain in fissionable material is

$$r = \eta - 2 \qquad (1\text{-}15\text{-}11)$$

The analysis above has been done using cross sections averaged over all regions of the reactor and over all neutron energies. An actual reactor design requires a detailed analysis of the neutron history for the reactor.

For a system consuming $_{92}U^{235}$ the average number of neutrons produced per fission, designated by ν, is $\nu = 2.5$. Not all the neutrons absorbed in the uranium result in fission; the ratio of total absorptions to fissions in $_{92}U^{235}$ for capture of thermal neutrons is found by experience to be 645/545. This means that, from a total of 645 thermal neutrons absorbed in $_{92}U^{235}$, roughly 100 are lost in non-useful absorptions in $_{92}U^{235}$, in which fissionable $_{92}U^{235}$ is converted to non-fissionable $_{92}U^{236}$. Hence the value for η for thermal fissions is less than the value for ν, or

$$\eta = 2.5 \times \tfrac{545}{645} = 2.11$$

If it were possible to use all the 100 neutrons lost in the non-productive captures in $_{92}U^{235}$ by some means such as a non-thermal reactor, the number of neutrons per absorption in uranium would be the same as the number of neutrons per fission, or $\eta = \nu = 2.5$. The maximum possible gain in the system then is bounded by $0.11 < r < 0.5$. Actually, of course, the upper limit cannot be attained because of the various losses in any real system. Incidental losses of neutrons due to leakage and non-useful captures in structural materials and coolants reduce the value of r.

It might be thought that it is not necessary to achieve a positive value for the breeding gain, that something worth while in stretching out the total quantity of fissionable material might be accomplished with the negative values. For considering this possibility, imagine that all the natural uranium in the world has been separated into two neat piles, one of $_{92}U^{235}$, and the other of $_{92}U^{238}$, and that these are at our disposal. All the fissionable material available and a portion of U^{238} will be used in a series of processes. The problem is to calculate the minimum breeding gain which will enable us to use the last of the U^{238} at exactly the time when we run out of U^{235}. In the process, let the gain in fissionable material be designated by r. In this problem, r has negative values. If there is at the beginning one unit of fissionable material, U^{235}, the amount of material produced in the first process is

$$(1 + r)$$

The second process will use this amount, $(1 + r)$, and will alter it by the same ratio, $(1 + r)$, giving

$$(1 + r)^2$$

The third process will use $(1 + r)^2$ units of fissionable material to produce

$$(1 + r)^3$$

This can be carried on until all the fissionable material available is used. Since we wish, in this example, to use up all the material, both U^{235} and U^{238}, the sum of all the processes must account for all the material used. Since there are 140 times as much U^{238} as there is U^{235}, the requirement is that

$$1 + (1 + r) + (1 + r)^2 + (1 + r)^3 + \cdots + (1 + r)^n \cdots = 140$$

$$(1\text{-}15\text{-}12)$$

If the series is infinite, corresponding to an infinite number of processes, this is equivalent to

$$\frac{1}{1 - (1 + r)} = 140$$

Or, solving for r,

$$r = -\tfrac{1}{140}$$

This is a small number, and would be even smaller if it were necessary to use up the thorium supply also. Since r is negative for the problem that was set, this implies a dwindling economy, in which the number of operable reactors available at the start, determined by the original supply of fissionable U^{235}, steadily decreases until finally the last lonely reactor grows cold just as the last of the supply of fissionable uranium is used.

Even for this extreme case, breeding must be almost achieved (r is very close to a positive value). Therefore the difference between achieving an expanding supply of fissionable material and merely using the existing U^{238} is so slight that we should probably put our efforts into making r positive.

It is generally assumed that the nuclear economy should be an expanding one, in which the available supply of fissionable material is used to make as much new fissionable material available as soon as possible. A useful concept is the doubling time, the time required to double the original supply of fissionable material invested in the process.

Considering again a series of n repetitive processes, each with a gain, r, in which the n_{th} process is defined to be operating with twice the original amount of fissionable material

$$(1 + r)^n = 2$$

or

$$n = \frac{\ln 2}{\ln (1 + r)} \qquad (1\text{-}15\text{-}13)$$

For example, if $r = 0.01$, the number of processes required for doubling the supply of fissionable material is

$$n = \frac{0.693}{0.01} = 69$$

It is apparent from the above considerations that the breeding gain, r, should be as large as possible.

The time for completing one process is given by the ratio of the original amount of fissionable material invested to the rate of consumption of the original material. The rate of consumption of the original material is

$$M_u \sigma_u \varphi$$

where σ_u is the microscopic cross section for absorption in fissionable material, φ is the neutron flux, and M_u is the invested mass of fissionable material. Hence, the doubling time is given by

$$t = \frac{n}{\sigma_u \varphi} \qquad (1\text{-}15\text{-}14)$$

It is desirable to bring the operating power of the reactor into the expression for doubling time. Since it takes 3.1×10^{16} fissions per second to make one megawatt of power, the power in megawatts is given by

$$P = \frac{N_0 M_u \sigma_u \varphi}{3.1 \times 10^{16} A_u} \qquad (1\text{-}15\text{-}15)$$

where N_0 is Avogadro's number (0.602×10^{24}) and A_u is the atomic weight of the fissionable material. Combining Equations 1-15-14 and 1-15-15 to eliminate $\sigma_u \varphi$ gives for the doubling time, in days,

$$t = n \frac{M_u}{P} \frac{0.602 \times 10^{24}}{24 \times 3.6 \times 10^3 \times 3.1 \times 10^{16} \times 235}$$

or, approximately,

$$t = n \frac{M_u}{P} \qquad (1\text{-}15\text{-}16)$$

The ratio of P/M_u measures the reactor power in megawatts produced per gram of fissionable material in the reactor. The larger this quantity, the shorter is the doubling time.

It should be noted that the numbers used will vary somewhat, depending on the fissionable materials, both those used and those produced.

How much fissionable material is used up in the process of breeding? To make one megawatt day of energy requires

$$3.1 \times 10^{10} \times 3.6 \times 10^3 \times 24 \times 10^6 = 2.68 \times 10^{21} \text{ fissions}$$

The mass of U^{235} used in an ideal reactor where $\eta = \nu$ is

$$\frac{2.68 \times 10^{21} \times 235}{0.602 \times 10^{24}} = 1 \text{ gram per megawatt day}$$

In the process, plutonium is produced at approximately the rate of $(1 + r)$ grams per megawatt day (neglecting the difference in atomic weights of uranium and plutonium). The gain in fissionable material is r grams per megawatt day, approximately.

If there is a limited supply of fissionable material available, and it is desired to make as much new fissionable material available as rapidly as possible, it is necessary to burn the supply on hand as rapidly as possible, assuming that the gain is positive, and, incidentally, assuming also that some competitive use can be found for the thermal energy created.

Calculating the gain, r, for any specific reactor requires a detailed accounting for the distribution of neutrons and fissionable material. The balance is close, which determines whether breeding can be successful.

REFERENCES

Bethe, H. A., *Elementary Nuclear Theory*, John Wiley and Sons, New York, 1947.

Cork, J. M., *Radioactivity and Nuclear Physics*, Edward Brothers, Ann Arbor, Mich., 1946.

Glasstone, Samuel, *Sourcebook on Atomic Energy*, D. Van Nostrand Co., New York, 1950.

Glasstone, Samuel, and Milton C. Edlund, *The Element of Nuclear Reactor Theory*, D. Van Nostrand Co., New York, 1952.

Halliday, D., *Introductory Nuclear Physics*, John Wiley and Sons, New York, 1950.

Neutron Cross Sections, Neutron Cross Sections Advisory Group, AEC, May 15, 1952, AECU-2040, O.T.S.

Pollard, Ernest, and William L. Davidson, Jr., *Applied Nuclear Physics*, John Wiley and Sons, New York, 1945.

Sullivan, William H., *Trilinear Chart of Nuclear Species*, John Wiley and Sons, New York, 1949.

CHAPTER 2

REACTOR EQUATIONS AND CRITICAL MASS

We have said that the functioning of a nuclear reactor depends on the maintenance of the key process, fission of some fissionable material by neutrons. The reactor which maintains a steady rate of fissions over some measurable period of time is said to be critical. If the fission rate is increasing, the reactor is said to be supercritical. As long as the reactor is in the supercritical condition, the power developed is increasing, since the power generated by the reactor is proportional to the rate of fissions. If the fission rate is decreasing, the reactor is said to be subcritical. The power in this case is decreasing, and the reactor eventually will cease completely to generate power.

The purpose of this chapter is to present formulae for the calculation of the conditions under which a reactor will be critical, and to account for the distribution of neutrons in the reactor for this situation. The formulae presented are in the form of differential equations, which are based on a simplified model for the motion of neutrons called diffusion theory. Although some attempt is made to justify these equations, where justification is relatively easy, the only ultimate criterion for their acceptance or rejection is whether by suitable adjustment of empirically determined coefficients the equations can be made to work well enough for engineering purposes. For the actual design of reactors, theoretical corrections to the coefficients used in diffusion theory can be made by local approximations to the more exact theory. A more exact theory for neutron distribution is variously called *the theory of the random walk*, or *the Boltzmann equation*, or *the transport theory*. This theory takes into account the fact that neutrons are not scattered symmetrically about the scattering nucleus. In general the transport equations are too detailed and tedious of solution for purposes of reactor design. Therefore, the incentive for making the diffusion equations work is high, since they are more susceptible to engineering calculations. Improvements in the knowledge of coefficients appropriate to the diffusion equation would be of much more value in reactor design than development of more exact equations.

Some methods of solution to the diffusion equations are presented. The emphasis is on the numerical solution of these equations, since they provide a more general tool for the solution to engineering problems in reactor design.

2-1. The Neutron Cycle

The criticality of reactors can be discussed in general terms by considering the life cycle of an average neutron from its birth in one generation of fissions until its death in an absorption in causing a new fission. This cycle starts with the fission of a fissionable atom by the absorption of a neutron. In the process of fission, several new neutrons are given off at high energy. These new neutrons then move through the reactor until they disappear owing to any one of the competing processes by which neutrons are lost. As the neutrons move about they are scattered by atoms of the materials in the reactor and lose energy. If there are sufficient light atoms in the reactor (moderators) the neutrons will be slowed down to thermal energy, at which point they are in thermal equilibrium with the materials of the reactor. At any lethargy during the slowing-down process, or after the neutrons have become thermal owing to slowing down, some of the neutrons may be absorbed either in non-useful capture or in causing fissions, or may leak from the reactor. Those neutrons which cause new fissions again result in the formation of a new generation of fast neutrons, starting the cycle over again.

The cross sections for the various processes competing for neutrons are very much dependent on the energy of the neutrons. Neutrons are formed at an average energy of about 2 Mev and are in thermal equilibrium at room temperature at about $\frac{1}{40}$ ev. Because this energy spread is so wide, and because the change in the logarithm of energy for an average collision is nearly constant through the slowing-down range, it is customary to plot cross sections as a function of the logarithm of neutron energy, or lethargy, and to use this as an independent variable in slowing down calculations for neutrons. Lethargy, u, was defined in Chapter 1 as

$$u = \ln \frac{E_0}{E} \tag{2-1-1}$$

where E_0 is the energy of reference at which lethargy is zero, and E is the neutron energy for which the lethargy is u. It is desired to pick the reference energy E_0 so that u is always a positive quantity. E_0 is usually taken as 10 Mev to include most of the fission neutrons having energies above 2 Mev. On this scale the lethargy of thermal neutrons is

$$u_{th} = \ln (40 \times 10^8) = 19.8$$

The lethargy of the average fission neutron is

$$u_f = \ln \left(\frac{10^7}{2 \times 10^6} \right) = 1.65$$

As an example of the neutron cycle let us consider a simple thermal reactor. Fissions will be accomplished primarily by thermal neutrons, a few being caused by neutrons at fission energy. Neutrons will be absorbed during the slowing-down process and at thermal energy. The average density of thermal neutrons at time t is represented by n, the average neutron velocity by v, and the average macroscopic cross section for fission is Σ_f. The average number of fissions per unit time, at time t, per unit volume due to thermal neutrons is hence

$$nv\Sigma_f$$

If the average number of new neutrons having an average lethargy, u_f, which are formed per fission is represented by ν, the number of new neutrons formed per unit time at time t, per unit volume, due to thermal neutrons is given by

$$\nu nv\Sigma_f$$

Some of these new fast neutrons cause more fissions before being slowed down from fission energies. Let the quantity of neutrons be increased owing to "fast fission" by the factor ϵ. Now the number of new neutrons formed per unit time, at time t, per unit volume, is given by

$$\epsilon \nu nv\Sigma_f$$

In the thermal reactor most of the fissions occur after the neutrons have been slowed down to thermal energy. Let Δt_1 represent the average time for neutrons to slow down to thermal energy, and p represent the fraction of the fission neutrons which are slowed down to thermal energy without being captured. During the slowing-down process some of the neutrons will travel to the edge of the reactor and will leak out. Let the fraction of neutrons escaping leakage during slowing down be l_1. Then the number of neutrons which become thermal, per unit volume, per unit time, at time $t + \Delta t_1$ is given by

$$\epsilon p \nu nv\Sigma_f l_1$$

The neutrons, after reaching thermal lethargy, are subject to three processes which cause them to disappear. They can be captured in non-useful processes, they can cause new fissions, or they can leak from the reactor. Let the average macroscopic cross section for all absorptions, fission and non-fission, be represented by Σ_a, and the fraction of thermal neutrons escaping leakage be l_2. The fraction of thermal neutrons available for causing new fissions is given by Σ_f/Σ_a. If the average time the neutrons remain thermal is Δt_2, the number of new fissions per original fission, per unit time and per unit volume, at time $t + \Delta t_1 + \Delta t_2$, or one neutron generation time after the first fission, is given by

$$\frac{\epsilon p v n v \Sigma_f l_1 l_2}{n v \Sigma_f} \frac{\Sigma_f}{\Sigma_a} = \epsilon p v \frac{\Sigma_f}{\Sigma_a} l_1 l_2$$

Generally this combination of terms is called the effective multiplication factor, and is represented by k_{eff}. Then

$$k_{eff} = \epsilon p v \frac{\Sigma_f}{\Sigma_a} l_1 l_2 \tag{2-1-2}$$

For the reactor to be critical it is necessary that $k_{eff} = 1$, so that the number of neutrons in succeeding generations will remain constant. If the reactor is very large, the leakage may become so small as to be almost negligible, making l_1 and l_2 approximately unity. For a very large reactor then, the multiplication factor, generally represented by k, approaches

$$k = \epsilon p v \frac{\Sigma_f}{\Sigma_a} \tag{2-1-3}$$

It is convenient to introduce the cross section for absorption in fuel, including both fission and non-useful captures, Σ_{fuel}. Then the multiplication factor can be written

$$k = \epsilon p v \frac{\Sigma_f}{\Sigma_{\text{fuel}}} \frac{\Sigma_{\text{fuel}}}{\Sigma_a} \tag{2-1-4}$$

Or, with the substitution,

$$\eta = v \frac{\Sigma_f}{\Sigma_{\text{fuel}}} \tag{2-1-5}$$

and

$$f = \frac{\Sigma_{\text{fuel}}}{\Sigma_a} \tag{2-1-6}$$

The multiplication factor is

$$k = \epsilon p \eta f \tag{2-1-7}$$

This equation is sometimes called the *four-factor formula*. The factor

ϵ is called the *fast-fission effect*. The factor p is often called the *resonance escape probability* (since many captures during slowing down in a thermal reactor are resonance captures). The factor η represents the number of neutrons which result from the capture of one neutron in fuel material. Note that η differs from ν, the number of neutrons per fission, by the ratio of fission captures to the sum of fission plus non-useful captures in the fuel. The factor f is called the *thermal utilization factor*. It represents the ratio of absorptions of neutrons in fuel to the total absorptions in fuel, structure, coolant, etc.

The picture of the neutron cycle presented above has some validity for thermal reactors, if all materials are distributed more or less uniformly through the reactor, since for this case the average terms in the four-factor are fairly easily approximated. For our present purposes the main value of the picture is in the easy visualization made possible by its oversimplification. Many reactors of engineering importance are, however, not thermal, and not uniform. Therefore a more general method of attack is needed to provide for the detailed bookkeeping for the account of neutrons. The next section will derive differential equations for the analysis of neutron distribution in reactors where the distribution is not uniform.

2-2. Conservation of Neutrons

The nuclear design of reactors is based primarily on an analysis of the conservation of neutrons. Because scattering, absorption, and fission characteristics vary with the energy, or lethargy, of the neutrons, as well as with the position in many reactors, it is necessary to take as an elementary unit for analysis a small unit volume and a small unit band of energies, or lethargies, of neutrons within the unit volume. The equation for the conservation of neutrons within this elementary unit must include the following items:

1. Leakage of neutrons of the lethargy interval being considered from the elementary volume. This item gives the measure of the net effect of neutrons moving into and out of the unit volume.

2. Absorption of neutrons of the lethargy interval being considered, due to all causes.

3. Slowing down of neutrons within the elementary unit of volume. This item measures the net effect of neutrons slowing down to enter the elementary energy band of interest and those slowing down still further so that they are no longer in the energy band.

4. Production of new neutrons due to fission.

5. Time rate of change of the number of neutrons within the given

element of volume and the band of energy. This item must equal the sum of the previous four items.

Each of the above items will now be discussed to derive mathematical expressions in a form which can be used for a solution of the problem of the conservation of neutrons in a reactor.

2-3. Leakage

Because of the motions of neutrons in a reactor, there is a flow into and out of any given volume of the reactor. If the flow into the volume is less than the flow out, we say that there is a net leakage of neutrons from the volume. Let us consider the amount of this leakage, based on a model called *diffusion theory*. The movement of neutrons is considered to be completely random, and a statistical approach is taken for the accounting of the neutrons. The net flow of neutrons in the reactor can be analyzed in a manner similar to that used for the analysis of gas flows. Let us first consider the net flow of neutrons through a surface in the reactor. After this flow is determined, the flows into and out of all sides of an elementary volume will be summed up to give an expression for the net leakage.

Let a line S be drawn so that the maximum variation of neutron density, at a given time, occurs along this line, and let this variation of density locally be linear with distance along S. This situation is represented schematically in Figure 2-3-1 for neutrons of a given

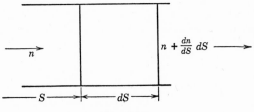

FIG. 2-3-1.

lethargy. Here n is the density of neutrons per unit volume and per unit of lethargy. According to diffusion theory for a system of small particles, the net flow, J, of neutrons in the interval dS, through a surface normal to the direction S, can be defined in the form

$$J = -D \frac{dn}{dS} \qquad (2\text{-}3\text{-}1)$$

where D is called the diffusion coefficient. This will be discussed later.

The ratio $\dfrac{dn}{ds}$, called the gradient of the neutron density, measures the maximum local rate of change of density of neutrons in space and the direction of that variation. It is therefore a vector quantity. The gradient of n is generalized for systems of coordinates which are orthogonal (mutually perpendicular coordinate lines) by the vector notation

$$\frac{dn}{dS} = \nabla n \qquad (2\text{-}3\text{-}2)$$

For instance, in a rectangular coordinate system, ∇n is expressed in vector notation as

$$\nabla n = i\frac{\partial n}{\partial x} + j\frac{\partial n}{\partial y} + k\frac{\partial n}{\partial z} \qquad (2\text{-}3\text{-}3)$$

where i, j, and k are unit vectors in the x, y, and z directions. A discussion of gradients and vector notation can be found in many reference books.*

Although the value for the diffusion coefficient which is appropriate to a given reactor, or even for a given position and lethargy in a given reactor, must eventually be empirically justified, analytical approximations can be made. The simplest of these approximations is taken from diffusion theory. Let us find, according to this approximation, the net flow through a surface normal to the direction S, due to a gradient $\dfrac{dn}{ds}$ in the neutron density. This will require an analysis of the scattering of neutrons in terms of an average neutron velocity and the mean free path of neutrons between collisions.

The average neutron arriving at a given point can be considered to have come in a random direction from an average distance equal to the mean free path, λ_s, that is, from a point on the surface of a sphere of which the point of arrival is the center and of which the radius is λ_s. This situation is represented pictorially in Figure 2-3-2. The contribution to flow through dA from a unit ring on the surface of the sphere defined by $d\theta$ is the product of the neutron density, the area of the ring, and the normal projection of dA. The density of neutrons at a given point on the surface of the sphere from which neutrons are scattered to the center is

$$n + \lambda_s \cos\theta \frac{dn}{dS} \qquad (2\text{-}3\text{-}4)$$

* H. Margenau and G. M. Murphy, *The Mathematics of Physics and Chemistry*, D. Van Nostrand Co., New York, 1943.

The surface area, at angle θ, from which neutrons are scattered, is

$$2\pi\lambda_s \sin\theta\lambda_s \, d\theta \qquad (2\text{-}3\text{-}5)$$

Since all neutrons are assumed to be in random motion at a common velocity, v, the flow of neutrons through this surface is given by the

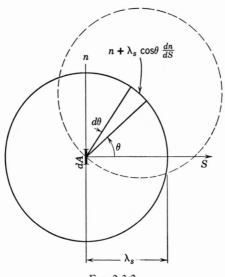

FIG. 2-3-2.

product of the two terms of Equations 2-3-4 and 2-3-5 by the average velocity of the neutrons, or

$$\left(n + \lambda_s \cos\theta \, \frac{dn}{dS}\right)(2\pi\lambda_s \sin\theta\lambda_s \, d\theta)v \qquad (2\text{-}3\text{-}6)$$

The fraction of these neutrons reaching the surface dA is given by the ratio of the projection of dA on a sphere shown in dashed lines in Figure 2-3-2, with its center at the scattering point to the whole surface area of the sphere, or

$$\frac{dA \cos\theta}{4\pi\lambda_s^2} \qquad (2\text{-}3\text{-}7)$$

The number of neutrons crossing the surface dA per unit time originating from the surface area included within the angle $d\theta$ is hence

$$-\left(n + \lambda_s \cos\theta \, \frac{dn}{dS}\right)(2\pi\lambda_s \sin\theta\lambda_s \, d\theta)\frac{v \, dA \cos\theta}{4\pi\lambda_s^2} \qquad (2\text{-}3\text{-}8)$$

Or, for a unit area,

$$- \left(n + \lambda_s \cos \theta \, \frac{dn}{dS} \right) \frac{v \cos \theta \sin \theta \, d\theta}{2} \qquad (2\text{-}3\text{-}9)$$

where the negative sign indicates that the flow of neutrons from left to right is considered positive.

The total flow, or current, of neutrons through a unit area normal to the direction S, per unit time, is given by the integral of the neutron flow over the whole sphere, or

$$J = - \frac{nv}{2} \int_0^{\pi} \cos \theta \sin \theta \, d\theta - \frac{\lambda_s}{2} \frac{dn}{dS} v \int_0^{\pi} \cos^2 \theta \sin \theta \, d\theta \qquad (2\text{-}3\text{-}10)$$

Performing the integrations, we see that the first term is zero. The second has the value

$$J = - \frac{\lambda_s v}{3} \frac{dn}{dS} \qquad (2\text{-}3\text{-}11)$$

Comparing Equations 2-3-11 and 2-3-1, we see that for this approximation the value of the diffusion coefficient is

$$D = \frac{\lambda_s v}{3} \qquad (2\text{-}3\text{-}12)$$

This is the equation for the diffusion coefficient from simple diffusion theory. The mean free path λ_s is the inverse of the macroscopic cross section, Σ_s. In terms of the macroscopic scattering cross section

$$D = \frac{v}{3\Sigma_s} \qquad (2\text{-}3\text{-}13)$$

This is called Fick's law.

The diffusion theory is based on the assumption that neutrons are symmetrically scattered, that is, that there is an equal probability that the neutron will recoil from an elastic scattering collision in any given direction. Since most collisions occur with atoms of finite size and finite mass, the scattering is, in fact, not symmetrical. This was discussed in Chapter 1, and an expression for the average cosine of the scattering angle was developed. A more accurate analytical approximation to the diffusion coefficient is made by correcting by using a solution to what is called the Boltzmann equation, or transport theory,* which takes into account non-uniform scattering. An ap-

---

* R. E. Marshak, "Theory of the Slowing Down of Neutrons by Elastic Collision with Atomic Nuclei," *Reviews of Modern Physics*, Vol. 19, No. 3, July, 1947.

proximate calculation based on transport theory gives a better value for D.

$$D = \frac{v}{3(1 - \mu)\left\{\Sigma_s + \Sigma_a\left(\frac{1}{5} + \frac{\mu}{1 - \mu}\right)\right\}} \tag{2-3-14}$$

Here μ, the average cosine of the scattering angle, is a measure of the departure from symmetrical scattering, and is given by Equation 1-11-21 of Chapter 1:

$$\mu = \frac{2}{3A}$$

where A is the atomic weight of the scattering nucleus. If we choose to retain the simple form of the diffusion coefficient shown in Equation 2-3-13, we can define a new cross section, Σ_t, as

$$\Sigma_t = (1 - \mu)\left\{\Sigma_s + \Sigma_a\left(\frac{1}{5} + \frac{\mu}{1 - \mu}\right)\right\} \tag{2-3-15}$$

The term Σ_t is known as the macroscopic transport cross section. It is a corrected cross section to take account of the forward scattering of neutrons. A transport mean free path is defined by λ_t, where

$$\lambda_t = \frac{1}{\Sigma_t} \tag{2-3-16}$$

In terms of the macroscopic transport cross section, the diffusion coefficient becomes

$$D = \frac{v}{3\Sigma_t} \tag{2-3-17}$$

It should be noted that the dimensions of D are in units of length squared per unit time.

With this revised diffusion coefficient, the diffusion theory becomes adequate except near boundaries or large disturbances in neutron flux. Many engineering problems involving indeterminate or awkward boundary conditions are handled by a principle due to Saint Venant. This principle states that the detailed distribution of a boundary constraint over a portion of a body is important only within distances from the boundary comparable to some characteristic dimension of the body, provided that the overall constraint on the body is correct. For the problem of the bending of a clamped beam of circular cross section, for instance, such a characteristic dimension might be the diameter, D, of the beam, and the details of the clamping would be important only within a distance from the boundary less than D. In the reactor one such characteristic dimension is the mean free path between scattering collisions of neutrons, λ_t, and the details of the neutron distribution at the boundary are important only within the distance of one or two mean free paths from the boundary. In this case the overall constraint is made correct by a device called the extrapolation distance. The neutron flux near the boundary is treated as if it went to zero, not at the boundary, but at some extrapolation distance, d, past the boundary. A calculation by the more exact transport theory * demands that this extrapolation distance be 0.71 times the transport mean free path, $\lambda_t = 1/\Sigma_t$, or

$$d = 0.71/\Sigma_t \tag{2-3-18}$$

Wherever there is a very sudden change in the scattering properties, such as at the junction between regions, one containing a good scattering material and the other having poor scattering, it is necessary to remember that the detailed neutron distribution at the junction cannot be found from diffusion theory.

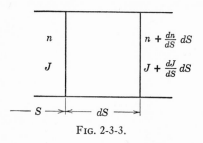

FIG. 2-3-3.

We are now ready to sum up the net neutron flow over all sides of the unit volume and determine an expression for the leakage. It has been stated above, in Equation 2-3-1, that the net flow of neutrons through a surface in the reactor is given by $J = -D \dfrac{dn}{dS}$, or $-D \nabla n$. The difference between the net flow out of a volume element of the reactor and the net flow in represents a leakage of neutrons. Consider again the element of volume contained between S and $S + dS$, with cross section dA, as shown in Figure 2-3-3. The net flow per unit area, per unit time, and per unit lethargy interval into the element in the direction S is given by Equation 2-3-1 as

$$J = -D \frac{dn}{dS} \tag{2-3-19}$$

* S. Glasstone and M. C. Edlund, *Nuclear Reactor Theory*, D. Van Nostrand Co., New York, 1952, p. 105.

The flow out in the same direction through the opposite surface is

$$J + \frac{dJ}{dS} dS = -D \frac{dn}{dS} - \frac{d}{dS}\left(D \frac{dn}{dS}\right) dS \qquad (2\text{-}3\text{-}20)$$

The difference in flow is the leakage from the element. For an element of cross section dA, the leakage of neutrons having lethargy between u and $u + du$, between the times t and $t + dt$, is given by

$$dL = \left\{ -D \frac{dn}{dS} - \frac{d}{dS}\left(D \frac{dn}{dS}\right) ds + D \frac{dn}{dS}\right\} dA\, du\, dt \quad (2\text{-}3\text{-}21)$$

or

$$dL = -\frac{d}{dS}\left(D \frac{dn}{dS}\right) dV\, du\, dt \qquad (2\text{-}3\text{-}22)$$

where dV is the element of volume. This is generalized for orthogonal coordinate systems, as before, by a vector notation:

$$dL = -\nabla \cdot (D\, \nabla n)\, dV\, du\, dt \qquad (2\text{-}3\text{-}23)$$

Equation 2-3-23 is a scalar equation, since the dot product of two vectors is a scalar. The vector notation here becomes merely a convenient shorthand to express the various coordinate forms for the leakage term. It becomes for the rectangular coordinate system

$$dL = -\left[\frac{\partial}{\partial x}\left(D \frac{\partial n}{\partial x}\right) + \frac{\partial}{\partial y}\left(D \frac{\partial n}{\partial y}\right) + \frac{\partial}{\partial z}\left(D \frac{\partial n}{\partial z}\right)\right] dV\, du\, dt \quad (2\text{-}3\text{-}24)$$

Similar expressions exist for other orthogonal coordinate systems. It is instructive to consider the dimension of Equation 2-3-23. First ∇ has the dimensions of an inverse length. The diffusion coefficient, D, has the dimensions of length-squared over time. The neutron density, n, has the dimensions of a number (of neutrons) divided by length-cubed and lethargy. Volume has the dimensions of length-cubed. Then the dimension of dL is neutrons, or dL measures, as it should, the total number of neutrons in the energy group under discussion to be accounted for by leakage from the volume element during the time interval dt.

2-4. Absorptions

Neutrons are lost in the reactor owing to absorptions in various materials, including the fuel, structures, coolants, control devices, and various incidental materials. If the total macroscopic cross section for absorptions is designated by Σ_a, the total number of neutrons of lethargy between u and $u + du$ absorbed from the differential volume during time dt is given by

$$dA = \Sigma_a nv \, dV \, du \, dt \qquad (2\text{-}4\text{-}1)$$

2-5. Slowing Down

The next term accounting for the loss of neutrons from the element is due to slowing down, by which neutrons are taken out of the lethargy increment du. The slowing down of neutrons is conveniently discussed in terms of the rate at which neutrons pass the lethargy u. This is called the slowing-down density, and is customarily designated by q. q is defined as the number of neutrons per second per cubic centimeter which are slowed down past the lethargy u. The number of neutrons lost from the element $dV \, du \, dt$ is then the difference between the number crossing lethargy u and those crossing lethargy $u + du$, or

$$dS = \frac{\partial q}{\partial u} dV \, du \, dt \qquad (2\text{-}5\text{-}1)$$

It is desirable, for consistency, to express q in terms of the neutron density n. This is to be done now. The number of neutrons in the differential element $dV \, du \, dt$ is given by the product of the rate of slowing down $q \, dV \, dt$ and the time Δt which it takes for the neutrons to slow down through the interval, or

$$n \, dV \, du \, dt = q \, dV \, dt \, \Delta t \qquad (2\text{-}5\text{-}2)$$

The time taken to traverse the lethargy interval du is given by the product of the number of collisions in the interval and the time between collisions. The number of collisions is given by the ratio du/ξ, where ξ is the average logarithmic decrement of energy per collision. The time between collisions is the ratio of the mean free path between collisions to the velocity of the neutrons, or λ_s/v. Hence the time Δt spent in the interval du is $du \, \lambda_s/\xi v$. Equation 2-5-2 becomes

$$n \, dV \, du \, dt = \frac{q\lambda_s}{\xi v} dV \, du \, dt \qquad (2\text{-}5\text{-}3)$$

The slowing-down density, q, can now be defined in terms of the neutron density, n, as

$$q = \frac{nv\xi}{\lambda_s} = nv\xi\Sigma_s \qquad (2\text{-}5\text{-}4)$$

since $\lambda_s = 1/\Sigma_s$. The number of neutrons lost from the differential element due to the slowing-down process can now be written as

$$dS = \frac{\partial(nv\xi\Sigma_s)}{\partial u}\, dV\, du\, dt \qquad (2\text{-}5\text{-}5)$$

Equation 2-5-5 accounts for the net number of neutrons in a differential volume which leave the lethargy interval between u and $u + du$ during the time interval dt because they are slowed down out of the lethargy interval under consideration, and into a new lethargy interval.

Let us consider for a moment the accuracy of Equation 2-5-5. If all the fast neutrons which were to be accounted for originated at the same energy (monoenergetic source of neutrons), the slowing-down process for neutrons at energies near to the energy of the source would require some special considerations. In an actual reactor, of course, not all the neutrons originate at the same energy, though they do tend to collect in the general region of 2 Mev. The difficulty with the neutrons from the monoenergetic source can be described somewhat as follows.

It was shown in Equation 1-11-8 that the maximum fractional energy, α, which can be lost in one collision with a nucleus of atomic weight A is given by

$$\alpha = \left[\frac{A-1}{A+1}\right]^2 \qquad (2\text{-}5\text{-}6)$$

If then the energy of source neutrons is designated by E_0, the lowest energy to which these source neutrons can be reduced in one collision is αE_0. The original source neutrons, after one collision, are scattered uniformly through all lethargy groups in the range of energies from E_0 to αE_0. All neutrons with energies less than αE_0 have been scattered at least twice. At energy αE_0 there is a discontinuity in the slowing-down density from the monoenergetic source. Just above this energy, neutrons are provided both from the collisions of original source neutrons and from multiple collisions. Just below this point there are no neutrons from the collisions of original source neutrons, and the slowing-down density here, being due only to multiple scatterings, is thereby depleted. At this point it would certainly not be correct, for the case of neutrons from a monoenergetic source, to consider the slowing-down density to be continuous, and to write a differential expression for the slowing-down density across the discontinuity.

For hydrogen, since the atomic weight A is unity, $\alpha = 1$, and a neutron can lose all its energy in one collision. In this case the neutrons from collisions at source energy are scattered uniformly into all lethargy groups from source energy to zero. There is, therefore, no discontinuity in the slowing-down density. For heavier moderating materials the slowing-down density becomes continuous below the point, αE_0. Equation 2-5-5 is correct for hydrogen, and gives a good approximation to the correct slowing-down density for all materials for all energies less than αE_0. For purposes of an engineering calculation of the slowing-down density for an actual reactor (not a mono-energetic source), an empirical correction can be made to the theoretical value of ξ used in the range of the fission energies of neutrons, if this is thought to be necessary. Since fission neutrons are, in fact, not a monoenergetic source, but distributed over a range of energies, the error which would be predicted by a theoretical calculation should be considerably smoothed out in an actual reactor. For most materials, moreover, the asymptotic solution is a very good approximation to the slowing-down density of neutrons. For instance, for graphite $\alpha E_0 = 0.72 E_0$. In the range of energies above αE_0 from $0.72 E_0$ to E_0, the maximum deviation from the asymptotic value of the slowing-down density from a monoenergetic source is about 44 percent. The deviation averaged over lethargy is about 12 percent. For deuterium, $\alpha = 0.111$. The maximum deviation from the asymptotic value is about 18 percent. The deviation, averaged over lethargy for the interval from $0.111 E_0$ to E_0, is about 6 percent. For engineering purposes these deviations would seem to be acceptable as outside limits on the deviation of the accuracy of calculations of slowing-down density.

2-6. Production

In a sense the most important item discussed in Section 2-2, so far as the reactor equations are concerned, is the production term. All the terms discussed previously represent losses of fission neutrons which must be restored to provide for a steady reaction. Production of neutrons is due to the process of fission. Let the density of neutrons per unit volume and per unit lethargy at lethargy u be n, the fission cross section at this lethargy, Σ_f, and the number of neutrons emitted per fission ν. Then the number of fissions occurring, per unit time and per unit volume, is given by the product $\nu n v \Sigma_f$. The total number of fissions occurring due to neutrons at all lethargies u_1 is given by the integral over the lethargy, or $\nu \int_0^\infty n_1 v_1 \Sigma_{fl}\, du_1$. The neutrons from fission are emitted with kinetic energies which vary over a wide range, the variation of the yield of fission neutrons as a function of energy or lethargy being called the fission spectrum. The production of fission neutrons at lethargy u in the differential element is

$$dP = s(u)\nu \int_0^\infty n_1 v_1 \Sigma_{fl} \, du_1 \, dV \, du \, dt \qquad (2\text{-}6\text{-}1)$$

where $s(u)$, called the fission spectrum, is the fraction of all fission neutrons produced in the lethargy interval du. By definition, the sum of the fractions of total neutron production in each lethargy interval must be equal to one, or $\int_0^\infty s(u) \, du = 1$. The fission spectrum for U-235 for the range up to 10 Mev is given approximately by the empirical formula

$$s(E) = 0.484e^{-E} \sinh \sqrt{2E} \qquad (2\text{-}6\text{-}2)$$

where E is the fission neutron energy in Mev.

2-7. Transients

To proceed to the last item mentioned in Section 2-2, the time rate of change in the number of neutrons in the differential element is

$$dT = \frac{\partial n}{\partial t} \, dV \, du \, dt \qquad (2\text{-}7\text{-}1)$$

2-8. Diffusion Equation

We are now ready to write the basic differential equation for the conservation of neutrons. It has five terms, one for each of the items discussed in the previous sections. This equation is

$$-dL - dA \quad + dP \qquad\qquad = dS \qquad + dT$$

$$\nabla \cdot D \, \nabla n - n v \Sigma_a + s(u)\nu \int_0^\infty n_1 v_1 \Sigma_{fl} \, du_1 = \frac{\partial(n v \xi \Sigma_s)}{\partial u} + \frac{\partial n}{\partial t} \quad (2\text{-}8\text{-}1)$$

Equation 2-8-1 is the equation for the diffusion of neutrons in a reactor. In this equation all coefficients, D, Σ_a, Σ_f, $\xi\Sigma_s$, may be functions of all three space variables and lethargy and time. It is subject to limitations, two of which have been discussed. One was that the diffusion theory is not strictly correct. The second was that the slowing-down term is not correct for neutrons at energies near the energy of a monoenergetic source from which they have emanated.

Possibly the most serious difficulty with Equation 2-8-1 is that it was written for continuous processes, as is indicated by its differential form, whereas actual neutron processes are discontinuous. Neutrons travel finite (and sometimes large) distances between collisions, and lose finite (and sometimes large) amounts of energy in single collisions. The validity of the approximation to this discontinuous process by a continuous process depends on the size of the discontinuities relative to various characteristics of the reactor. For heavy materials, where the energy loss per collision is small, and where there are, therefore, a large number of collisions in a given slowing-down interval, the continuous approximation is good. Also, for reactors in which there are a large number of mean free paths for neutrons in the smallest dimension of the reactor, as is generally required for criticality with a reasonable mass of fissionable material, the approximation of the continuous model is good. For the lightest moderating material, hydrogen, where it is possible for a neutron to lose all its energy in a single collision the continuous model for the slowing-down process is logically untenable. If it is desirable to preserve the form of Equation 2-8-1 for hydrogenous materials, it is necessary to use some quantity other than the calculated value for ξ in the term for the slowing-down density. Approximate values can be found from calculations based on a discontinuous model, or from empirical data for hydrogenous reactors. For a reactor containing mixtures of hydrogenous and other slowing-down media it is necessary to treat the neutrons which collide with the hydrogen somewhat separately from those which collide with the other materials.

It is proposed for the purpose of this book, and also for the calculation of the conservation of neutrons in actual reactors, to treat Equation 2-8-1 as adequate for engineering design, and to suppose that means will be found for evaluating the coefficients which are appropriate to any specific reactor configuration.

Equation 2-8-1 is subject to boundary conditions which are determined by the physical conditions of operation of a particular reactor which it is used to describe. From the form of the differentials in Equation 2-8-1 it is apparent that two spatial boundary conditions are needed, plus one for time and one for lethargy. The boundary condition which satisfies the spatial requirements, and is common to all reactors, is that the neutron flux (or neutron density) is zero, or some specified small amount, on the outermost boundary. The boundary conditions pertinent to the time and lethargy coordinates will be discussed later. In Section 9 various methods for the solution of Equation 2-8-1 will be considered.

One other factor should be mentioned at this point. In the term for the production of new neutrons from fission it was tacitly assumed that all the fission neutrons are emitted immediately at the time of fission, but it has been previously stated that about 0.7 percent of these neutrons are delayed by measurable periods after fission. These delayed neutrons are important during rapid transient variations in the neutron density. They will be treated in the next chapter in connection with the neutron kinetics of reactors, where it will be found that they exert a controlling influence on certain aspects of the control of reactors.

2-9. Analytical Solutions to the Diffusion Equation

Methods for the solution of equations like Equation 2-8-1 are often divided into two categories, analytical and numerical. This division is artificial in the sense that analytical solutions, in terms of circular, hyperbolic, Bessel, or other transcendental functions are analytical only because standardized tables have been previously prepared by numerical methods, in terms of which the solutions to certain classes of problems can be expressed without the necessity for repeating the numerical work. These solutions are not, in general, exact, since tabular values are not given to an infinite number of decimal points, any more than the numerical solutions arrived at without the use of prepared tables are exact. As correct a viewpoint as any is probably to maintain that the analytical solutions are those special cases, in a more general field of numerical solutions, which have occurred with sufficient frequency to justify their standardization and tabulation. Accordingly, the solution of Equation 2-8-1 will be treated in general as a numerical problem, and some common analytical special cases will be mentioned since they are useful where simplifications of the physical problem, allowing their use, are practical.

2-10. Critical Reactors

By definition a critical reactor is one in which the neutron density, and hence the power, is maintained at a steady level. For the critical reactor, then, the partial derivative of neutron density with respect to time, in Equation 2-8-1, disappears. For this case Equation 2-8-1 becomes

$$\nabla \cdot D \, \nabla n - n v \Sigma_a + s(u) v \int_0^\infty n_1 v_1 \Sigma_{f1} \, du_1 = \frac{\partial (n v \xi \Sigma_s)}{\partial u} \quad (2\text{-}10\text{-}1)$$

Since any reactor of importance for engineering purposes must, in general, be critical, Equation 2-10-1 is worthy of consideration. Let us investigate it for two idealized cases: (1) the fast reactor and (2) the thermal reactor.

2-11. Fast Critical Reactor

The idealized fast reactor is composed of atoms of materials so heavy that neutrons colliding with them bounce off without losing an appreciable amount of energy. To a close approximation, then, $\xi = 0$, and the slowing-down term on the right of Equation 2-10-1 disappears. If the further idealization be made that fission neutrons occur only at one energy, E_0, rather than over a spectrum of energies, all the neutrons in the reactor can be treated as being of one energy, E_0. The production term is then

$$s(u)\nu \int_0^\infty n_1 v_1 \Sigma_{f1}\, du_1 = \nu n v \Sigma_f \qquad (2\text{-}11\text{-}1)$$

Equation 2-10-1 becomes

$$\nabla \cdot D\, \nabla n + nv(\nu \Sigma_f - \Sigma_a) = 0 \qquad (2\text{-}11\text{-}2)$$

If it is assumed here that the contents of the reactor are uniform throughout the reactor, the coefficients D, $\nu \Sigma_f$, and Σ_a are constant throughout the reactor. These coefficients can then be combined into a single constant $\kappa_1{}^2$ and the equation for the fast reactor then becomes

$$\nabla^2 \varphi + \kappa_1{}^2 \varphi = 0 \qquad (2\text{-}11\text{-}3)$$

where, since $D = v/3\Sigma_t$,

$$\kappa_1{}^2 = 3\Sigma_t \Sigma_a \left(\frac{\nu \Sigma_f}{\Sigma_a} - 1\right) \qquad (2\text{-}11\text{-}4)$$

and $\varphi = nv$ is the neutron flux. For simple geometries, solutions in tabulated form exist for Equation 2-11-3. Consider, for example, a symmetrical spherical reactor, for which, in spherical polar coordinates,

$$\nabla^2 \varphi = \frac{1}{r^2}\frac{\partial}{\partial r}\left(r^2 \frac{\partial \varphi}{\partial r}\right) \qquad (2\text{-}11\text{-}5)$$

Let the reactor be subject to the condition that the neutron flux must vanish at the extrapolated boundary, $r = R$. It can be verified by substitution that the solution to Equation 2-11-3 of most general form for the sphere is

$$\varphi = A\,\frac{\sin \kappa_1 r}{r} + B\,\frac{\cos \kappa_1 r}{r} \qquad (2\text{-}11\text{-}6)$$

To satisfy the symmetry condition for the sphere the constant B must be assigned the value zero. To satisfy the boundary condition that $\varphi = 0$ when $r = R$ requires that $\sin \kappa_1 R = 0$, or that $\kappa_1 R = n\pi$, where n is an integer. Since negative flux densities are not allowed in the physical problem, only $n = 1$ is permissible, so that

$$\kappa_1 R = \pi \tag{2-11-7}$$

For the neutron distribution in a critical fast reactor, then, the solution is

$$\varphi = A \frac{\sin \dfrac{\kappa_1 r}{R}}{r} \tag{2-11-8}$$

It should be noted that the magnitude A is undetermined, signifying that, in the linear approximation on which this whole development is based, the neutron level, and hence the power level, of operation is indeterminate from the equations. In an actual reactor an upper limit to the power with a given set of coefficients is generally set by the non-linear departures of these coefficients from their constant values. It should be noted that there is only one size of spherical reactor which satisfies the differential equation 2-10-1 for a given set of physical conditions, for steady-state, or critical, operation. A larger reactor would continually increase its neutron density and power. A smaller reactor would not be able to support the continuous generation of neutrons. The critical size of the reactor is given by Equation 2-11-7. Substituting the value of κ_1 from its definition, we have the critical value for the radius (extrapolated radius):

$$R = \frac{\pi}{\kappa_1} = \frac{\pi}{\left\{ 3\Sigma_t \Sigma_a \left(\nu \dfrac{\Sigma_f}{\Sigma_a} - 1 \right) \right\}^{\frac{1}{2}}} \tag{2-11-9}$$

The larger the value of κ_1, the smaller is the resultant size of the critical reactor. Hence, the larger the macroscopic transport cross section, the macroscopic cross section for fission, and the number of neutrons per fission, and the smaller the macroscopic absorption cross section, the smaller is the reactor.

Similar solutions exist for other simple shapes if the same assumptions are made—namely, fast, uniform, one-energy reactors. The extrapolated critical dimension for these reactors can be generalized to $R = \alpha/\kappa_1$, where α is the lowest zero, or root, for the functional series appropriate to the geometry of the reactor. For instance, for the infinitely long cylinder, Bessel's function of the first kind, and of zero order, is the appropriate series, its lowest zero being $\alpha = 2.405$.

For a cube of side length $2R$, $\alpha = \sqrt{3}\,\pi$. It can be seen that, for several uniform reactors, α is of the order of π, the half dimension of these reactors then being of the order of π/κ_1.

2-12. Critical Thermal Reactor

For an idealized thermal reactor it is here assumed that all fission neutrons are emitted at one high energy E_0, that all absorptions occur at one energy, E_{th}, at which the neutrons are in thermal equilibrium with their surroundings, and that all coefficients are constant.

The analysis can be broken down into three parts, and Equation 2-10-1, describing the conservation of neutrons, can be written separately for each one. These parts are (a) conservation of neutrons in the thermal region, (b) slowing down of neutrons, and (c) the production of neutrons. These will now be discussed in order.

For the thermal region, the production term is zero. The slowing-down term requires some special treatment. It is apparent that, in the thermal region, the neutrons, since they are in kinetic equilibrium with their surroundings, will, on the average, neither gain nor lose energy in collisions. Hence no neutrons are lost to a different energy level as a result of elastic collisions. Owing to the production of neutrons at high energies and subsequent slowing down, new neutrons are continually being added to the thermal region. The rate at which neutrons cross a given energy level was defined in Section 2-6 as q, and is expressed in terms of neutron density by Equation 2-6-4, which at the threshold of thermal energy becomes

$$q_{th} = n_{th}v_{th}\xi\Sigma_{s\ th} \qquad (2\text{-}12\text{-}1)$$

q_{th} takes the place of the slowing-down term in Equation 2-10-1, which can now be written for the thermal region

$$D_{th}\,\nabla^2 n_{th} - n_{th}v_{th}\Sigma_{a\ th} + q_{th} = 0 \qquad (2\text{-}12\text{-}2)$$

or, using flux as a variable,

$$\frac{1}{3\Sigma_{t\ th}}\,\nabla^2\varphi_{th} - \varphi_{th}\Sigma_{a\ th} + q_{th} = 0 \qquad (2\text{-}12\text{-}3)$$

For the slowing-down phase of the reactor process, the assumptions of no absorptions, no production of fission neutrons, and constant coefficients reduce Equation 2-10-1 to two terms,

$$D\,\nabla^2 n = \frac{\partial(nv\xi\Sigma_s)}{\partial u} \qquad (2\text{-}12\text{-}4)$$

For the neutron production phase, the same assumptions reduce Equation 2-10-1 to two terms, the production term and a term defining the beginning of the slowing-down process. The production term is simplified, because all neutrons are produced at the same energy, to $\nu n_{th} v_{th} \Sigma_{f\ th}$. The rate at which neutrons enter the slowing-down region is defined as q_f. Equation 2-10-1 becomes for this phase,

$$q_f = \nu n_{th} v_{th} \Sigma_{f\ th} = \nu \varphi_{th} \Sigma_{f\ th} \qquad (2\text{-}12\text{-}5)$$

This set of three equations (Equations 2-12-3, 2-12-4, and 2-12-5) must be solved simultaneously to determine the solution for the idealized thermal reactor.

Since a new variable, q, appears in two of these equations, defining the upper and lower borders of the slowing-down process, it is convenient to rewrite the differential equations for the slowing region, Equation 2-12-4, in terms of this variable. Using the previously defined quantities,

$$D = v/3\Sigma_t \qquad (2\text{-}12\text{-}6)$$

and

$$q = nv\xi\Sigma_s \qquad (2\text{-}12\text{-}7)$$

we obtain from Equation 2-12-4

$$\frac{1}{3\xi\Sigma_t\Sigma_s} \nabla^2 q = \frac{\partial q}{\partial u} \qquad (2\text{-}12\text{-}8)$$

This equation can be simplified by defining a new variable,

$$d\tau = \frac{du}{3\xi\Sigma_s\Sigma_t} \qquad (2\text{-}12\text{-}9)$$

The quantity τ, defined by Equation 2-12-9, is called the *Fermi age*, or *age*, after its originator. A check will show that it has the dimensions of length-squared, or area. Substituting Equation 2-12-9 into 2-12-8 gives an equation for the slowing-down density in the idealized thermal reactor,

$$\nabla^2 q = \frac{\partial q}{\partial \tau} \qquad (2\text{-}12\text{-}10)$$

Equations 2-12-3, 2-12-5, and 2-12-10 will be used in the following development of an equation for the idealized critical thermal reactor.

Many reactors, particularly those employing good moderators, are described quite adequately by the idealized thermal reactor equations. These equations will be considered for two cases. The first case involves reactors which are uniform in all their properties throughout the volume of the reactor. These reactors are called uniform bare reactors, implying that fuel, and all other constituents, are distributed uniformly throughout the reactor and that there are no reflectors around the outside of the reactor. In this case the neutron flux is assumed to go to zero at the extrapolated boundary of the reactor. Simple solutions, for simple geometrical shapes, exist for these reactors in terms of tabulated functions, just as for the idealized fast reactors. The second case to be considered involves reactors which are not bare and uniform in the sense used above. In order to conserve neutrons it is often desirable to vary the distribution of fuel, moderator, and structural materials and coolants in such a way as to take advantage of the variations of neutron cross sections with lethargy. Unavoidable variations also are caused by structural and cooling requirements. These reactors will involve regions with and without fuel, and with differing properties of moderation and absorption. For these cases, considerations of dimensional analysis will be used to demonstrate some general characteristics of the neutron distribution and reactor criticality.

Let us now define a procedure for solving analytically the equations for a thermal reactor. First, Equation 2-12-10 is solved to give a relationship for the slowing-down density at the thermal limit of the slowing-down range to the slowing-down density at the fission limit. Since the equations are linear, this will have the form

$$q_{th} = F(\tau_{th})q_f \qquad (2\text{-}12\text{-}11)$$

where $F(\tau_{th})$ is a function of the Fermi age at the thermal limit (called thermal age) to be determined from the solution. The term q_f can be eliminated between Equations 2-12-11 and 2-12-5 to give an expression for q_{th} in terms of φ_{th}. This value for q_{th} is then substituted into Equation 2-12-3 to eliminate q_{th}, giving an equation involving only φ_{th}.

For the bare thermal reactor, let us start by assuming that the possible solutions to Equation 2-12-10 can be expressed in the form of a product, or sum of products, such as

$$q = S \cdot T \qquad (2\text{-}12\text{-}12)$$

where S is a function only of space coordinates, and T is a function only of the age, τ. It is necessary to show that the differential equation can be satisfied in a simple way by such product terms, and that these terms also can be made to satisfy the boundary conditions for the engineering problem of interest. Substituting the product into Equation 2-12-10, and dividing through by the product, $S \cdot T$, gives

$$\frac{1}{S} \nabla^2 S = \frac{1}{T} \frac{dT}{d\tau} \tag{2-12-13}$$

Since the left side of the equation, because of the nature of our assumptions concerning the product, must be a function only of space coordinates, whereas the right side must be a function only of neutron age, each side must be equal to some constant. Let this constant be assigned the value $-\kappa_2^2$. Equation 2-12-10 has now been separated into two ordinary differential equations, which are

$$\nabla^2 S + \kappa_2^2 S = 0 \tag{2-12-14}$$

and

$$\frac{1}{T} \frac{dT}{d\tau} = -\kappa_2^2 \tag{2-12-15}$$

The solution to Equation 2-12-15 is

$$\ln T = -\kappa_2^2 \tau \tag{2-12-16}$$

or

$$T = e^{-\kappa_2^2 \tau} \tag{2-12-17}$$

The slowing-down density, from Equation 2-12-12, is then

$$q = S e^{-\kappa_2^2 \tau} \tag{2-12-18}$$

At the thermal limit, from Equation 2-12-18,

$$q_{th} = S e^{-\kappa_2^2 \tau_{th}} \tag{2-12-19}$$

At the fission limit, from Equation 2-12-18, $\tau = 0$, so $q_f = S$. Eliminating S between these limits gives

$$q_{th} = e^{-\kappa_2^2 \tau_{th}} q_f \tag{2-12-20}$$

Eliminating q_f between Equations 2-12-20 and 2-12-5 gives

$$q_{th} = \nu \varphi_{th} \Sigma_{f\ th} e^{-\kappa_2^2 \tau_{th}} \tag{2-12-21}$$

Substituting Equation 2-12-21 into Equation 2-12-3 for the diffusion of thermal neutrons gives

$$-\frac{1}{\varphi_{th}} \nabla^2 \varphi_{th} = 3\Sigma_{t\ th} \Sigma_{a\ th} \left(\nu \frac{\Sigma_{f\ th}}{\Sigma_{a\ th}} e^{-\kappa_2^2 \tau_{th}} - 1 \right) \tag{2-12-22}$$

Because Equation 2-12-22 is of the same form as Equation 2-12-14, and is for the same physical reactor, the term on the left must equal the same constant, $\kappa_2{}^2$. Again we obtain two equations. As for the fast reactor the first equation is

$$\nabla^2 \varphi_{th} + \kappa_2{}^2 \varphi_{th} = 0 \qquad (2\text{-}12\text{-}23)$$

The second equation gives the value of $\kappa_2{}^2$ in terms of physical characteristics of the reactor,

$$\kappa_2{}^2 = 3\Sigma_{t\ th}\Sigma_{a\ th}\left(\nu\, \frac{\Sigma_{f\ th}}{\Sigma_{a\ th}}\, e^{-\kappa_2{}^2\tau_{th}} - 1\right) \qquad (2\text{-}12\text{-}24)$$

This equation can be simplified by using two constants which have physical meaning. The multiplication factor, k, was defined by Equation 2-1-3. For this reactor, having no fast fission effect, $\epsilon = 1$, and no absorption in the slowing-down range, $p = 1$, Equation 2-1-3 becomes

$$k = \nu\, \frac{\Sigma_f}{\Sigma_a} \qquad (2\text{-}12\text{-}25)$$

Another quantity, L, the thermal diffusion length, is defined by the equation below and is a measure of the average distance traveled by the thermal neutrons before they are absorbed.

$$L^2 = \frac{1}{3\Sigma_t\Sigma_a} \qquad (2\text{-}12\text{-}26)$$

With these substitutions, Equation 2-12-24 becomes

$$1 + \kappa_2{}^2 L^2 = k e^{-\kappa_2{}^2\tau_{th}} \qquad (2\text{-}12\text{-}27)$$

Equation 2-12-23 (or Equation 2-12-14, which is identically the same form) is still to be solved. For those reactors for which a solution to Equation 2-12-23 can be found, our assumption of a solution to the neutron distribution problem in terms of a product $S \cdot T$ has been justified. Equation 2-12-23 is seen to be of the same form as Equation 2-11-3 for the fast reactor, and has the same analytical solutions for the same types of geometry.

For large thermal reactors the product $\kappa_2{}^2\tau_{th}$ is small compared with unity, and the approximation, $e^{+\kappa_2{}^2\tau_{th}} = 1 + \kappa_2{}^2\tau_{th}$, is acceptable. In this case Equation 2-12-27 can be written

$$(1 + \kappa_2{}^2\tau_{th})(1 + \kappa_2{}^2 L^2) = k \qquad (2\text{-}12\text{-}28)$$

Solving for $\kappa_2{}^2$, approximately, gives

$$\kappa_2{}^2 = \frac{k-1}{L^2 + \tau_{th}} = \frac{k-1}{M^2} \qquad (2\text{-}12\text{-}29)$$

where M^2 is called the migration area. The migration length, M, is a measure of the average distance, in the idealized thermal reactor, which is traveled by a neutron, first in slowing down and then as a thermal neutron, before capture.

Let us assume that, as in the fast reactor, κ_2 is of the form

$$\kappa_2 = \alpha/R \qquad (2\text{-}12\text{-}30)$$

where, this time, R is a critical half dimension of the thermal reactor and α is a number of approximate magnitude π. What does Equation 2-12-29 tell us about the size of the reactor?

Substituting Equation 2-12-30 into 2-12-29, and solving for R^2, we have

$$R^2 = \frac{\alpha^2 L^2 \left(1 + \dfrac{\tau_{th}}{L^2}\right)}{k - 1} \qquad (2\text{-}12\text{-}31)$$

Since the value of L^2 is $1/(3\Sigma_{t\ th}\Sigma_{a\ th})$ and that of k is $\nu\Sigma_{f\ th}/\Sigma_{a\ th}$, this equation can be written

$$R^2 = \frac{\alpha^2 \left(1 + \dfrac{\tau_{th}}{L^2}\right)}{3\Sigma_{t\ th}\Sigma_{a\ th} \left(\dfrac{\nu\Sigma_{f\ th}}{\Sigma_{a\ th}} - 1\right)} \qquad (2\text{-}12\text{-}32)$$

Equation 2-12-32 can be made dimensionless by a rearrangement of terms, giving

$$\Sigma_{t\ th}\Sigma_{f\ th}R^2 = \frac{\alpha^2}{3} \frac{1 + \dfrac{\tau_{th}}{L^2}}{\nu - \dfrac{\Sigma_{a\ th}}{\Sigma_{f\ th}}} \qquad (2\text{-}12\text{-}33)$$

It can be seen that the terms on the right will become smaller as the terms τ_{th}/L^2 and $\Sigma_{a\ th}/\Sigma_{f\ th}$ become smaller. From the definitions of τ_{th} and L^2, their ratio, for constant values of the parameters in the slowing-down range, is

$$\frac{\tau_{th}}{L^2} = \frac{u_{th}\Sigma_{a\ th}}{\xi\Sigma_s} \qquad (2\text{-}12\text{-}34)$$

The term $\xi\Sigma_s/\Sigma_{a\ th}$ is called the moderating ratio. It is a measure of the ability of the particular combination of reactor materials to slow down the neutrons without absorbing them (note that $\Sigma_{a\ th}$ includes absorptions in structural materials, fuel, etc., as well as in the moderator). The ratio $\Sigma_{f\ th}/\Sigma_{a\ th}$ measures the ratio of fission absorptions to total absorptions in all materials, including fission.

Equation 2-12-29 is applicable, because of the specializations made, only to a very limited class of reactors, the idealized thermal reactors, which emphasize good moderators.

The physical size of such an idealized thermal reactor can be calculated, using appropriate data for the particular reactor configuration considered. For example, consider a bare spherical reactor in which the moderator, heavy water (D_2O), is mixed uniformly with fissionable uranium, U-235, in such a way that the space density of uranium is 10^{-4} times the density of solid uranium (19.0 grams per cubic centimeter). If there are negligible amounts, in a nuclear sense, of structural materials, etc., essentially all scattering and moderation will be due to heavy water and all absorptions to uranium. The following values are then appropriate:

$$\Sigma_{t\ th} = 0.42 \text{ cm}^{-1}$$

$$\sigma_{f\ th} = 545 \text{ barns}$$

$$\sigma_{a\ th} = 645 \text{ barns}$$

$$\nu = 2.5 \text{ neutrons per fission}$$

$$\tau_{th} = 120 \text{ cm}^2$$

$$\alpha = \pi$$

The macroscopic absorption cross section is

$$\Sigma_{a\ th} = \frac{0.602 \times 645 \times 19.0}{235 \times 10^4} = 0.0031 \text{ cm}^{-1}$$

From Equation 2-12-32 the extrapolated critical size is

$$R = \pi \left[\frac{1 + 3 \times 0.42 \times 0.0031 \times 120}{3 \times 0.42 \times 0.0031 \left(\dfrac{2.5 \times 545}{645} - 1 \right)} \right]^{1/2}$$

$$= 58 \text{ cm (3.8 feet diameter)}$$

The extrapolated dimension of an actual bare reactor would be somewhat larger than this owing to absorptions in structures and coolants, etc., as well as to allow for depletion. The actual physical radius is decreased by the extrapolation length, $0.71\lambda_{t\ th}$, or, in this case, $0.71/0.42 = 1.7$ cm. The critical mass of uranium is

$$M = \frac{4\pi(56.3)^3 \times 19.0}{3 \times 10^4 \times 10^3} = 1.4 \text{ kg (3.1 lb)}$$

The critical mass would be increased as the size was increased for absorptions in various parasitic materials and for depletion.

Some general characteristics of reactors can be found from a dimensional analysis of the reactor equations, without assigning specific values to the coefficients of the equations, and without finding a specific numerical solution to the equations. This procedure is applied in the following paragraphs to the equations for the thermal reactor.

2-13. Dimensional Analysis

Physical quantities are associated both with a number and with a dimension. Dimensional analysis makes a separate study of the relationships among the dimensions, leaving the numbers to be determined by experiment or calculation. There are three different possible situations in dimensional analysis, depending on the type of information which is available: (1) hunch or experiment, (2) differential equation, or (3) algebraic equation. In the first situation we have occasion to believe that a certain physical quantity of interest is dependent on certain other physical quantities. What are the possible combinations of these quantities which can express physical laws? Dimensional relationships can be found from dimensional analysis for this situation, but numbers to go with the dimensions must be found by another means. In the second situation a differential equation gives fairly explicit relationships among the dimensions of physical quantities, but numbers can be found only by integrating the equation. In the third situation a physical equation gives both physical relationships between dimensions and an algebraic equation for the numbers. The basis of dimensional analysis is just the statement that physical laws must be given in equations all of whose terms have the same dimensions, or units—the rule of unitary homogeneity. Not all equations have unitary homogeneity. Engineers often use equations which do not, one well-known example being the equation for the velocity of efflux from a nozzle,

$$v = 223.7\sqrt{h_1 - h_2} \tag{2-13-1}$$

where v is the velocity in feet per second and h is the enthalpy in Btu per pound. This equation has been derived from

$$v(\text{ft/sec}) = \sqrt{2g(h_1 - h_2)} = \sqrt{2 \times 32.2 \ (\text{ft/sec}^2) \times (h_1 - h_2)(\text{ft})}$$

$$(2\text{-}13\text{-}2)$$

Both sides of this equation have the units in feet per second. If we are to express $(h_1 - h_2)$ in the units Btu per pound, we have 1 Btu = 778 ft-lb, or 1 Btu/lb = 778 ft. Thus $(h_1 - h_2)(\text{Btu/lb}) = 778$ $(h_1 - h_2)(\text{ft})$, and the above equation becomes

$$v = \sqrt{2 \times 32.2 \times 778 \times (h_1 - h_2)} = 223.7\sqrt{h_1 - h_2} \quad (2\text{-}13\text{-}3)$$

where v is in feet per second and h is measured not in feet but in Btu per pound. This explanation is not offered in depreciation of the non-dimensional formula, since in engineering routine it is very handy, but as a warning for caution in its use. In the particular case mentioned here, elaborate charts are in existence from which $h_1 - h_2$ can be read directly in Btu per pound, whereas velocity is desired for engineering reasons in feet per second.

Let us see what we can find out about the equations for a thermal reactor from dimensional analysis. A check will show that all the reactor equations, as written, have unitary homogeneity. The terms in Equation 2-12-10, for instance, have the dimensions $L^{-5}T^{-1}$, where L represents the dimension of length and T the dimension of time. Notice that the dimensions of ∇^2 are L^{-2}, of q are $L^{-3}T^{-1}$, and of τ are L^2. If Equation 2-12-10 is multiplied through, term by term, by any quantity having the dimensions L^5T, the dimensionless parameters which result will give some measure of the characteristics of the reactor.

In the section which follows, the three differential equations describing the idealized thermal reactor will be written in dimensionless form to determine some significant dimensionless variables. These equations will be combined as before to produce one equation in terms of a dimensionless variable involving the neutron flux. Some conclusions will be drawn from the resulting equations regarding reactor size and critical mass required for this reactor type.

Let us rewrite Equation 2-12-10, describing the slowing-down process, for reference, and include a term for a small amount of absorption in the slowing-down range. This is

$$\nabla^2 q - 3\Sigma_t \Sigma_a \, q = \frac{\partial q}{\partial \tau} \qquad (2\text{-}13\text{-}4)$$

The multiplier chosen for Equation 2-13-4 is τ_{th}/q, which has the proper dimensions, L^5T. Equation 2-13-4 then becomes

$$\tau_{th}\frac{\nabla^2 q}{q} - 3\Sigma_t\Sigma_a\tau_{th} = \frac{\partial q/q}{\partial \tau/\tau_{th}} \qquad (2\text{-}13\text{-}5)$$

Let us now define a new dimensionless variable α by the expression

$$\alpha^2 = -\frac{\nabla^2 q}{q}R^2 \qquad (2\text{-}13\text{-}6)$$

where R is some reference dimension for the critical reactor (for instance, the radius of a sphere, or cylinder, or the half dimension of the side of a cube, etc.). Substituting the variable α into Equation 2-13-5 gives

$$-\frac{\tau_{th}}{R^2}\alpha^2 - 3\Sigma_t\Sigma_a\tau_{th} = \frac{d(\ln q)}{d(\tau/\tau_{th})} \qquad (2\text{-}13\text{-}7)$$

This expression can be integrated from fission age (zero) to thermal age to give

$$-\frac{\tau_{th}}{R^2}\int_0^1 \alpha^2 d(\tau/\tau_{th}) - \int_0^1 3\Sigma_t\Sigma_a\tau_{th}d(\tau/\tau_{th}) = \int_{q_f}^{q_{th}} d(\ln q) \quad (2\text{-}13\text{-}8)$$

or

$$\ln(q_f/q_{th}) = \frac{\tau_{th}}{R^2}\int_0^1 \alpha^2 d(\tau/\tau_{th}) + \int_0^1 3\Sigma_t\Sigma_a\tau_{th}d(\tau/\tau_{th}) \quad (2\text{-}13\text{-}9)$$

Rearranging, we obtain

$$(q_f/q_{th}) = \left[\exp\left\{\frac{\tau_{th}}{R^2}\int_0^1 \alpha^2 d(\tau/\tau_{th})\right\}\right]\left[\exp\left\{\int_0^1 3\Sigma_t\Sigma_a\tau_{th}d(\tau/\tau_{th})\right\}\right]$$

$$(2\text{-}13\text{-}10)$$

The expression in the first bracket of Equation 2-13-10 represents the fraction of neutrons which escape leakage during slowing down. It was previously discussed in this chapter as the factor, l_1, of the neutron cycle. The resonance escape probability, p, also previously discussed in this chapter, is by definition the fraction of the fission neutrons which escape capture during the slowing-down process. It is given analytically by the expression in the second bracket of Equation 2-13-10,

$$p = \exp\left\{-\int_0^1 3\Sigma_t\Sigma_a\tau_{th}d(\tau/\tau_{th})\right\} \qquad (2\text{-}13\text{-}11)$$

An average value of α^2 over the whole slowing-down range can be defined as

$$\bar{\alpha}^2 = \int_0^1 \alpha^2 d(\tau/\tau_{th}) \qquad (2\text{-}13\text{-}12)$$

Substituting Equations 2-13-11 and 2-13-12 into Equation 2-13-10 gives the ratio of the slowing-down densities at the fission and thermal limits,

$$\frac{q_f}{q_{th}} = \frac{1}{p} e^{\left(\bar{\alpha}^2 \frac{\tau_{th}}{R^2}\right)} \qquad (2\text{-}13\text{-}13)$$

This equation is in dimensionless form and can be used for numerical work. Likewise Equation 2-12-3 can be made dimensionless by multiplying through by any quantity having the dimensions $L^3 T$. The quantity chosen is $1/\Sigma_{a\ th}\varphi_{th}$. For reference, Equation 2-12-3 is

$$\frac{1}{3\Sigma_{t\ th}} \nabla^2 \varphi_{th} - \Sigma_{a\ th}\varphi_{th} + q_{th} = 0 \qquad (2\text{-}13\text{-}14)$$

Upon multiplying by $1/\Sigma_{a\ th}\varphi_{th}$, it becomes

$$\frac{1}{3\Sigma_{t\ th}\Sigma_{a\ th}} \frac{\nabla^2 \varphi_{th}}{\varphi_{th}} - 1 + \frac{q_{th}}{\Sigma_{a\ th}\varphi_{th}} = 0 \qquad (2\text{-}13\text{-}15)$$

The thermal diffusion length, L, was defined before as

$$L^2 = \frac{1}{3\Sigma_{t\ th}\Sigma_{a\ th}} \qquad (2\text{-}13\text{-}16)$$

As before, a new dimensionless variable, β^2, will now be defined, similar in form to Equation 2-13-6:

$$\beta^2 = -\frac{\nabla^2 \varphi_{th}}{\varphi_{th}} R^2 \qquad (2\text{-}13\text{-}17)$$

Now Equation 2-13-15 becomes

$$\frac{\beta^2 L^2}{R^2} + 1 = \frac{q_{th}}{\Sigma_{a\ th}\varphi_{th}} \qquad (2\text{-}13\text{-}18)$$

Equation 2-13-18 relates the slowing-down density at the thermal limit to the flux of thermal neutrons. This is also in a dimensionless form.

Before making the third equation dimensionless, it can be broadened so that it will be more useful. If some of the fissions in the reactor are caused by fast neutrons, the source term must be integrated over the whole range of lethargy, rather than just over the thermal range as in Equation 2-12-5. The ratio of the total number of fissions to those caused by thermal neutrons is called the fast effect, and is designated by ϵ. Equation 2-12-5, which describes the production of neutrons, then becomes

$$q_f = \epsilon \nu \varphi_{th} \Sigma_{f\ th} \qquad (2\text{-}13\text{-}19)$$

The thermal utilization factor, f, defined in Equation 2-1-6 can also be written

$$f = \frac{\Sigma_{f\ th}}{\Sigma_{a\ th}} \frac{\Sigma_{fuel}}{\Sigma_{f\ th}} \qquad (2\text{-}13\text{-}20)$$

Substituting the value of f into Equation 2-13-19 gives

$$q_f = \epsilon \nu f \varphi_{th} \Sigma_{a\ th} \frac{\Sigma_{f\ th}}{\Sigma_{fuel}} \qquad (2\text{-}13\text{-}21)$$

The number of neutrons per fission is related to the number of neutrons per absorption in fuel by the relationship (Equation 2-1-5),

$$\nu = \eta \frac{\Sigma_{fuel}}{\Sigma_{f\ th}} \qquad (2\text{-}13\text{-}22)$$

Substituting into Equation 2-13-21 gives

$$q_f = \epsilon \eta f \varphi_{th} \Sigma_{a\ th} \qquad (2\text{-}13\text{-}23)$$

Equation 2-13-23 is a statement relating the slowing-down density at the fission limit to the thermal flux, which utilizes three dimensionless numbers. If Equations 2-13-18 and 2-13-23 are combined to eliminate φ_{th},

$$\frac{q_f}{q_{th}} = \frac{\epsilon \eta f}{\left(\dfrac{\beta^2 L^2}{R^2} + 1\right)} \qquad (2\text{-}13\text{-}24)$$

Eliminating q_f/q_{th} between Equations 2-13-13 and 2-13-24 gives

$$\frac{\epsilon \eta p f}{\left(\dfrac{\beta^2 L^2}{R^2} + 1\right)} = e^{\left(\bar{\alpha}^2 \frac{\tau_{th}}{R^2}\right)} \qquad (2\text{-}13\text{-}25)$$

The multiplication factor, another dimensionless quantity, has been defined as $k = \epsilon \eta p f$ (Equation 2-1-7). Therefore Equation 2-13-25 can be written

$$k = e^{\left(\bar{\alpha}^2 \frac{\tau_{th}}{R^2}\right)} \left(\frac{\beta^2 L^2}{R^2} + 1\right) \qquad (2\text{-}13\text{-}26)$$

Equation 2-13-26 is of the same form as Equation 2-12-27, and the same general considerations apply to it. For our purposes at the moment, however, it can be put into a more useful form. We can use Equation 2-13-26 to find the mass of fissionable material which is needed in the reactor for criticality. The reactor is considered to be composed of a mass of fissionable material intermixed with other material required for cooling, moderation, structure, etc. Let us say that the cross section for absorption of thermal neutrons is composed of two parts: one Σ_{fuel} in uranium or other fissionable material; the other $\Sigma_{c\ th}$ in all other materials. Then

$$\Sigma_{a\ th} = \Sigma_{\text{fuel}} + \Sigma_{c\ th} \qquad (2\text{-}13\text{-}27)$$

and from our definition of f

$$f = \frac{\Sigma_{\text{fuel}}}{\Sigma_{\text{fuel}} + \Sigma_{c\ th}} \qquad (2\text{-}13\text{-}28)$$

Also, by the definition of the diffusion area,

$$L^2 = \frac{1}{3(\Sigma_{\text{fuel}} + \Sigma_{c\ th})\Sigma_{t\ th}} \qquad (2\text{-}13\text{-}29)$$

Substituting these values for f and L^2 into Equation 2-13-25 gives

$$\epsilon\eta p \frac{\Sigma_{\text{fuel}}}{\Sigma_{\text{fuel}} + \Sigma_{c\ th}} = e^{\left(\bar{\alpha}^2\frac{\tau_{th}}{R^2}\right)}\left[\frac{\beta^2}{3R^2(\Sigma_{\text{fuel}} + \Sigma_{c\ th})\Sigma_{t\ th}} + 1\right] \qquad (2\text{-}13\text{-}30)$$

Solving Equation 2-13-30 for the ratio of absorptions in fuel to transport collisions gives

$$\frac{\Sigma_{\text{fuel}}}{\Sigma_{t\ th}} = \frac{\dfrac{\beta^2}{3(\Sigma_{t\ th})^2 R^2} + \dfrac{\Sigma_{c\ th}}{\Sigma_{t\ th}}}{p\eta\epsilon e^{-\left(\bar{\alpha}^2\frac{\tau_{th}}{R^2}\right)} - 1} \qquad (2\text{-}13\text{-}31)$$

The macroscopic cross section for fuel can be expressed in terms of the microscopic cross section, the mass of fuel, and the total volume of reactor by

$$\Sigma_{\text{fuel}} = \sigma_{\text{fuel}}N_{\text{fuel}} = \sigma_{\text{fuel}}\frac{M_{\text{fuel}}}{V}\frac{N_0}{A_{\text{fuel}}} \qquad (2\text{-}13\text{-}32)$$

where N_{fuel} is the number of fissionable atoms per unit volume of the reactor, σ_{fuel} is the microscopic cross section for the absorption of neutrons in fuel, M_{fuel} is the mass of fuel in the reactor, N_0 is Avogadro's number, V is the volume of the reactor, given by $V = \gamma R^3$, where

γ is a constant depending on the shape of the reactor, and A_{fuel} is the atomic mass number of the fuel material. The ratio of absorptions in fuel to transport collisions is

$$\frac{\Sigma_{\text{fuel}}}{\Sigma_{t\ th}} = \frac{\sigma_{\text{fuel}}M_{\text{fuel}}N_0}{\gamma R^3 A_{\text{fuel}}\Sigma_{t\ th}} \tag{2-13-33}$$

Substituting Equation 2-13-33 into Equation 2-13-31, we obtain a dimensionless equation involving the mass of fuel in the reactor. This equation defines the critical mass required for reactor operation

$$\frac{\sigma_{\text{fuel}}M_{\text{fuel}}N_0}{\gamma\Sigma_{t\ th}R^3 A_{\text{fuel}}} = \frac{\dfrac{\beta^2}{3(\Sigma_{t\ th})^2 R^2} + \dfrac{\Sigma_{c\ th}}{\Sigma_{t\ th}}}{p\eta\epsilon\epsilon^{-\left(\alpha^2\frac{\tau_{th}}{R^2}\right)} - 1} \tag{2-13-34}$$

We will now examine Equation 2-13-34 to determine the variation of critical mass with the variables under the control of the designer. It should be repeated that this equation applies to an idealized thermal reactor based on the following assumptions. Fissions are caused primarily by thermal neutrons. Some fissions are caused by fast neutrons. All fission neutrons are produced at the same energy. All neutrons, except a small portion which is absorbed, slow down to thermal energy. The reactor is thermal throughout. We can separate Equation 2-13-34 into dimensionless class parameters of two kinds, geometrical and physical:

Geometrical, α, β, γ

Physical, $\left(\dfrac{\sigma_{\text{fuel}}M_{\text{fuel}}N_0}{\Sigma_{t\ th}R^3 A_{\text{fuel}}}\right)$, $((\Sigma_{t\ th})^2 R^2)$, $\left(\dfrac{\tau_{th}}{R^2}\right)$, p, η, ϵ, $\dfrac{\Sigma_{c\ th}}{\Sigma_{t\ th}}$

Certain general statements can be made about the geometrical factors. For instance, for all bare (or unreflected) reactors of practical interest, α, β, and γ are found to be of the order of π. Their accurate values can be found only by performing the integrations, generally numerically, of the differential equations; but for classes of reactors for which dimensionless parameters are the same, one calculation does for the whole class.

The choice of a fissionable material fixes A_{fuel} and σ_{fuel}. The additional choices of moderator and basic internal arrangement fix τ_{th}, ϵ, η, p, $\Sigma_{c\ th}$, and $\Sigma_{t\ th}$. Let us now examine the variation of the critical mass, M_{fuel}, with overall size of the reactor and for particular choices of the variables above. It is apparent that the critical mass approaches infinity for two values of the critical dimension, R. The first of these occurs when R approaches infinity, that is, a reactor of infinite size requires an infinite amount of fissionable material. The second occurs when

$$p\eta\epsilon e^{-\left(\bar{\alpha}^2\frac{\tau_{th}}{R^2}\right)} = 1 \tag{2-13-35}$$

or when

$$R^2 = \frac{\bar{\alpha}^2\,\tau_{th}}{\ln\,(p\eta\epsilon)} \tag{2-13-36}$$

Physically, this equation means that, as the reactor becomes very small, the total mass and, hence, the density of fissionable material must increase to offset the unfavorable leakage situation. This minimum dimension, at which the critical mass becomes infinite, decreases as the efficiency of production of neutrons increases (η, ϵ, p) and as the slowing-down process improves ($\xi\Sigma_s\Sigma_t$).

Between these two infinite values of the critical mass there is obviously a minimum. The least value of the critical mass occurs when the derivative of the critical mass with respect to the critical dimension is zero, or when

$$\frac{dM_{\text{fuel}}}{dR} = 0 \tag{2-13-37}$$

This minimum occurs when

$$0 = \frac{\dfrac{\beta^2}{3(\Sigma_{t\,th})^2 R_{\min}{}^2} + 3\dfrac{\Sigma_{c\,th}}{\Sigma_{t\,th}}}{\dfrac{\beta^2}{3(\Sigma_{t\,th})^2 R_{\min}{}^2} + \dfrac{\Sigma_{c\,th}}{\Sigma_{t\,th}}} - \frac{2\bar{\alpha}^2\dfrac{\tau_{th}}{R_{\min}{}^2}p\eta\epsilon}{p\eta\epsilon - e^{+\left(\bar{\alpha}^2\frac{\tau_{th}}{R_{\min}{}^2}\right)}} \tag{2-13-38}$$

Equation 2-13-38 is to be solved numerically for the critical dimension $R_{\min}$. Let us again consider the idealized, spherical, heavy-water reactor from the example in Section 2-12. Since, for this example, $\Sigma_{c\,th} = 0$, Equation 2-13-38 can be written

$$2p\eta\epsilon K = p\eta\epsilon - e^K \tag{2-13-39}$$

where

$$K = \frac{\bar{\alpha}^2\tau_{th}}{R_{\min}{}^2} \tag{2-13-40}$$

By trial-and-error solution it is found that $K = 0.208$, and therefore the extrapolated radius of the reactor having the minimum critical mass is $R_{\min} = 75.3$ cm.

When R is large compared with the value of $\bar{\alpha}^2 \tau_{th}$ (large size or efficient moderator) the denominator on the right side of Equation 2-13-34 approaches ($p\eta\epsilon - 1$). If, at the same time, values of the non-useful capture cross section $\Sigma_{c\ th}$ are kept small (efficient design to minimize absorbers), the first term of the numerator on the right of

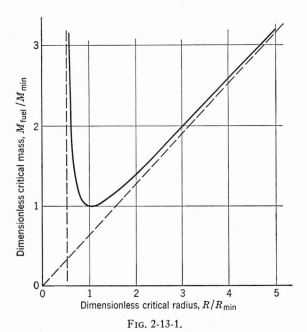

FIG. 2-13-1.

Equation 2-13-34 becomes large compared with the second. For this thermal reactor, Equation 2-13-34 becomes linear with respect to R, or

$$M_{\text{fuel}} = \frac{\gamma\beta^2 A_{\text{fuel}}}{3\Sigma_{t\ th}\sigma_{\text{fuel}}N_0(p\eta\epsilon - 1)} R \qquad (2\text{-}13\text{-}41)$$

For larger values of R, or for larger values of absorption, $\Sigma_{c\ th}$, the first term of the numerator becomes insignificant and the curve becomes a cubic,

$$M_{\text{fuel}} = \frac{\Sigma_{c\ th}\gamma A_{\text{fuel}}}{\sigma_{\text{fuel}}N_0(p\eta\epsilon - 1)} R^3 \qquad (2\text{-}13\text{-}42)$$

A typical critical mass curve is shown schematically in dimensionless form in Figure 2-13-1, for a reactor having a very low non-useful capture cross section outside the fuel ($\Sigma_{c\ th}$).

2-14. Numerical Methods for Critical Reactors

In the design of reactors it will generally be found that the conditions for which the reactor is intended will preclude its being readily adapted to solution in terms of functions which have already been tabulated. In many reactors a significantly large fraction of the fissions are caused by neutrons which are somewhat above thermal energy. In general the constituents of the reactor are not uniform throughout its volume. It is usually desirable to surround the reactor with a reflector to conserve neutrons. There are probably many cases where it is desirable to place materials in locations within the reactor with due regard to their effects on the neutron distribution. For all these cases, and many others, it is necessary to resort to some one, or more, of the methods known as numerical.

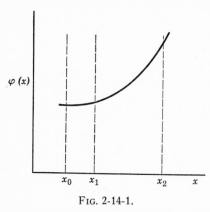

FIG. 2-14-1.

Many types of numerical methods are available for the solution of differential equations. Many of these involve finite difference approximations to the differentials in the equations. The variations in method have primarily to do with the form in which the difference approximation is cast, and the manner of solution of the finite difference equations which result from the approximation. The attempt will be made here to demonstrate the finite difference approximation, to show the effects of some of the differences of form in which it can be cast on the numerical work involved in solution of the difference equation, to show the effect of these differences in form on the convergence, or lack of it, of the solution, and finally to apply the finite difference approximation to the solution of the problem of neutron distribution and reactor criticality. It will be found that the amount of work required to solve a problem for which prepared tabular values do not exist is larger than for those for which such tables do exist. The numerical method, however, will be found to afford flexibility to adapt to the intricate necessities of the engineering design of a reactor.

The finite difference procedure begins with the definition of a derivative as the limit of the ratio of the change in a dependent variable to the change in the independent variable, as the latter becomes indefinitely small. Let it be supposed that the neutron flux, φ, is a function of the distance, x, through a reactor. This functional relationship is shown schematically in Figure 2-14-1. The first derivative of the function $\varphi(x)$ at x_0 is defined as

$$\frac{d\varphi}{dx} = \lim_{x_2 \to x_0} \frac{\varphi(x_2) - \varphi(x_0)}{x_2 - x_0} \tag{2-14-1}$$

where the limit symbol signifies that the interval between x_2 and x_0 is allowed to become indefinitely small. In the finite difference procedure, the limiting process is not carried out. For a small, but still finite, interval from x_2 to x_0, the first derivative of the function $\varphi(x)$ in the interval $x_0 < x < x_2$ is expressed in terms of the finite differences approximately as

$$\left.\frac{d\varphi}{dx}\right]_{x_0 < x < x_2} = \frac{\varphi(x_2) - \varphi(x_0)}{x_2 - x_0} \tag{2-14-2}$$

To the same degree of approximation, the second derivative is given by

$$\frac{1}{2}\left.\frac{d^2\varphi}{dx^2}\right] = \frac{\varphi(x_2)}{(x_2 - x_1)(x_2 - x_0)} + \frac{\varphi(x_0)}{(x_1 - x_0)(x_2 - x_0)}$$

$$- \frac{\varphi(x_1)}{(x_2 - x_1)(x_1 - x_0)} \tag{2-14-3}$$

The finite difference approximations of Equations 2-14-2 and 2-14-3 represent average values of the derivatives in the interval $x_0 < x < x_2$. To the degree of approximation inherent in the finite difference procedure, these equations can be said to represent the derivatives at any point in the interval to which we choose to assign them. In the limit of indefinitely small intervals, of course, the distinction among the three named points disappears. It will be shown by analysis, however, that, when the finite difference approximation is applied to the solution of differential equations, the association of the finite difference expression with specific points in the region of approximation has a direct bearing on the results achieved. This association of difference expressions will determine (1) whether the numerical computations converge to a solution to the problem, or diverge therefrom, (2) the type of numerical procedure which is appropriate to the solution, if one exists, and (3) the amount of computational effort necessary to carry out the individual steps of the solution.

As an example let us consider the simplest possible neutron equation for the slowing-down region, namely, Equation 2-12-10 in one-dimensional spherical space coordinates. This is

$$\frac{\partial^2 \psi}{\partial r^2} = \frac{\partial \psi}{\partial \tau} \qquad (2\text{-}14\text{-}4)$$

where $\psi = rq$. The term on the left of Equation 2-14-3 is expressed in difference form, in the interval, $r_0 < r < r_2$, and for the neutron age, τ:

$$\frac{1}{2}\frac{d^2\psi}{dr^2} = \frac{\psi(r_2, \tau)}{(r_2 - r_1)(r_2 - r_0)} + \frac{\psi(r_0, \tau)}{(r_1 - r_0)(r_2 - r_0)}$$
$$- \frac{\psi(r_1, \tau)}{(r_2 - r_1)(r_1 - r_0)} \qquad (2\text{-}14\text{-}5)$$

The term on the right, by analogy with Equation 2-14-2, at r and in the age interval, $\tau_0 < \tau < \tau_2$, is

$$\frac{dq}{d\tau} = \frac{\psi(r, \tau_2) - \psi(r, \tau_0)}{\tau_2 - \tau_0} \qquad (2\text{-}14\text{-}6)$$

At which points in the coordinate system, within the stated difference intervals, should the unspecified τ in Equation 2-14-5 and the unspecified r in Equation 2-14-6 be placed? Altogether, six combinations are possible. Let the unspecified r be placed at the middle point, r_1, and the unspecified τ in turn at τ_0, τ_1, and at τ_2. This results in three different forms of the difference equation for Equation 2-14-4, which are somewhat simplified in form if evenly spaced intervals are used. Let these intervals be expressed: $2(r_2 - r_1) = 2(r_1 - r_0) = (r_2 - r_0) = 2h$, and $2(\tau_2 - \tau_1) = 2(\tau_1 - \tau_0) = (\tau_2 - \tau_0) = 2k$. The three difference equations are then

$$\frac{\psi(r_2, \tau_0) + \psi(r_0, \tau_0) - 2\psi(r_1, \tau_0)}{h^2} = \frac{\psi(r_1, \tau_2) - \psi(r_1, \tau_0)}{2k} \qquad (2\text{-}14\text{-}7)$$

and

$$\frac{\psi(r_2, \tau_1) + \psi(r_0, \tau_1) - 2\psi(r_1, \tau_1)}{h^2} = \frac{\psi(r_1, \tau_2) - \psi(r_1, \tau_0)}{2k} \qquad (2\text{-}14\text{-}8)$$

and

$$\frac{\psi(r_2, \tau_2) + \psi(r_0, \tau_2) - 2\psi(r_1, \tau_2)}{h^2} = \frac{\psi(r_1, \tau_2) - \psi(r_1, \tau_0)}{2k} \qquad (2\text{-}14\text{-}9)$$

It is desired to investigate the convergence of the three equations to find whether they can actually be used as bases for the numerical solution to the problem of the slowing down of neutrons in the idealized thermal reactor. Let a trial solution to the problem be assumed. This trial solution can be considered to be made up of a "true" solution plus a departure from the true solution which can be considered to be the error in the trial solution. If the numerical procedure is to converge to the true solution, it is required that the error become smaller, or at least not grow, as the numerical work progresses. If the true solution is $\psi(r, \tau)$ and the error is $\delta(r, \tau)$, it is apparent that both ψ and δ must satisfy whichever difference equation is to be used. Assume that the error δ can be represented by a series of terms like $\delta = e^{i\beta r} e^{\alpha \tau}$, where α and β can have any numerical values.* The three equations, representing three choices for specifying τ, can then be rewritten in terms of δ:

$$e^{i\beta h} + e^{-i\beta h} - 2 = \frac{h^2}{2k} (e^{2\alpha k} - 1) \qquad (2\text{-}14\text{-}10)$$

$$e^{\alpha k}(e^{i\beta h} + e^{-i\beta h} - 2) = \frac{h^2}{2k} (e^{2\alpha k} - 1) \qquad (2\text{-}14\text{-}11)$$

$$e^{2\alpha k}(e^{i\beta h} + e^{-i\beta h} - 2) = \frac{h^2}{2k} (e^{2\alpha k} - 1) \qquad (2\text{-}14\text{-}12)$$

The term $e^{\alpha k}$, represents the magnification of the error due to carrying the process of computation from the age τ to the age $\tau + k$. If the process is to converge, the numerical value of this magnification must be less than, or at most equal to, unity, or $|e^{\alpha k}| \leqq 1$. Let us consider each of Equations 2-14-7, 2-14-8, and 2-14-9 for convergence.

The left side of Equation 2-14-10 is equivalent to $2(\cos \beta h - 1)$, or to $-4 \sin^2 (\beta h/2)$. Letting $e^{2\alpha k} = \xi^2$, and solving for the ratio, $2k/h^2$, gives

$$\frac{2k}{h^2} = \frac{1 - \xi^2}{4 \sin^2 \left(\dfrac{\beta h}{2}\right)} \qquad (2\text{-}14\text{-}13)$$

Putting in the limits, $-1 \leqq \xi^2 \leqq 1$, since $2k/h^2$ must in any case be a real, positive number, we find that, for convergence, $2k/h^2$ must be between the limits.

$$0 \leqq \frac{2k}{h^2} \leqq \frac{1}{2 \sin^2 \left(\dfrac{\beta h}{2}\right)} \qquad (2\text{-}14\text{-}14)$$

---

* G. G. O'Brien, M. A. Hyman, and S. Kaplan, "A Study of the Numerical Solution of Partial Differential Equations," *Journal of Mathematics and Physics*, Vol. XXIX, No. 4, January, 1951.

Hence the difference form represented by Equation 2-14-10, in which r is identified with the middle point and τ with the lowest point of the interval, will converge to a solution if, and only if, the size of the age increment k is less than, or at most equal to, one-fourth the square of the space increment chosen. In some reactors this may result in an inconveniently large number of age intervals.

The same analysis, applied to Equation 2-14-11, gives

$$\xi \frac{2k}{h^2} = \frac{1 - \xi^2}{4 \sin^2 \left(\dfrac{\beta h}{2}\right)} \tag{2-14-15}$$

Solving for the magnification,

$$\xi = -A \pm \sqrt{A^2 + 1} \tag{2-14-16}$$

where

$$A = 2 \left(\frac{2k}{h^2}\right) \sin^2 \left(\frac{\beta h}{2}\right) \tag{2-14-17}$$

It is seen that ξ can have the value unity only when $A = 0$, and hence when the ratio $2k/h^2 = 0$. For all values of this quantity other than zero, one root of ξ has a value greater than unity in absolute magnitude. For all finite values of the ratio $2k/h^2$, then, the magnitude of any error present in the numerical work will increase as the work progresses. Therefore the numerical system which identifies both r and τ with the middle point of the finite interval is of no use in the solution of the problem of neutron distribution during the slowing-down process.

From Equation 2-14-12, in which r is identified with the middle point and τ with the lowest point of the interval,

$$\xi^2 \frac{2k}{h^2} = \frac{1 - \xi^2}{4 \sin^2 \left(\dfrac{\beta h}{2}\right)} \tag{2-14-18}$$

Solving for ξ^2, we obtain

$$\xi^2 = \frac{1}{4 \dfrac{2k}{h^2} \sin^2 \left(\dfrac{\beta h}{2}\right) + 1} \tag{2-14-19}$$

For all values of the ratio $2k/h^2$, ξ^2 has values less in magnitude than unity, and convergence of the numerical procedure is obtained.

Since Equations 2-14-7 and 2-14-9 have been found to give convergent numerical solutions, Equation 2-14-7 in the range $2k/h^2 = \frac{1}{2}$ and Equation 2-14-9 for all values of $2k/h^2$, either can be used for the solution of Equation 2-14-4 by numerical procedures. Some techniques for solving these two equations will be considered. We will look at Equation 2-14-7 first.

Equation 2-14-7 gives an explicit solution for the value of $\psi(r_1, \tau_2)$ in terms of the values at a previous age τ_0. If the slowing-down density is known at any age, the slowing-down density at all subsequent ages can be calculated directly from Equation 2-14-7. For the limiting case, $2k/h^2 = \frac{1}{2}$, Equation 2-14-7 takes an especially simple form, since the term $\psi(r_1, \tau_0)$ disappears, leaving

$$\psi(r_1, \tau_2) = \frac{\psi(r_2, \tau_0) + \psi(r_0, \tau_0)}{2} \tag{2-14-20}$$

It is seen that the value of the slowing-down density at the age τ_2 can be found from averaging the values of the slowing-down density at the previous age τ_0. This scheme is shown in Figure 2-14-2, in a

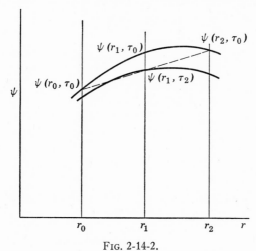

FIG. 2-14-2.

graphical interpretation. The averaging procedure is carried out by drawing straight lines connecting the points to be averaged. Such a graphical method is due to E. Schmidt,* and is called a *Schmidt plot*. It has been used principally in the solution for the transient temperature distribution in thermally conducting solids, for which the equation is identical to Equation 2-14-4, except that time replaces age as an independent variable. For example, let us consider a spherical re-

* E. Schmidt, *Thermodynamics*, Oxford Press, 1949, p. 428. L. M. K. Boelter, V. H. Cherry, H. A. Johnson, and R. C. Martinelli, *Heat Transfer Notes*, University of California Press, Berkeley, California, 1948, p. V-36. E. R. G. Eckert, *Introduction to the Transfer of Heat and Mass*, McGraw-Hill Book Co., 1950.

actor with an outer radius, R, such that $R^2 = 40\tau_{th}$, composed of a
central core of radius $r = 0.6R$, having a constant density of moderator
and fissionable material, and a surrounding reflector having the same
moderating properties as the core. Since it is assumed that there are
no absorptions in the slowing-down region, the central core of this re-

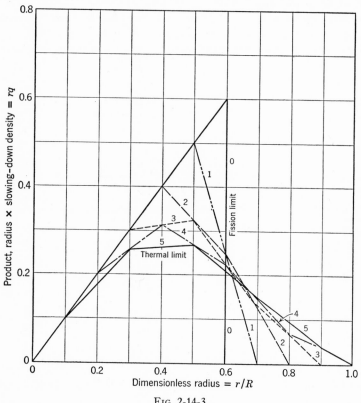

Fig. 2-14-3.

actor acts as a source of fission neutrons, which are scattered and
slowed down by the moderating and reflecting material. Let the
length of the space interval be $h = 0.1R$. The problem set is to find
the slowing-down density of neutrons at the thermal limit, due to a
slowing-down density at the fission limit arbitrarily assumed constant, using the graphical procedure. Since $2k/h^2 = \frac{1}{2}$, the age interval is $2k = [(0.1)^2 \times 40/2]\tau_{th} = 0.2\tau_{th}$. There are then five intervals
in the slowing-down range. The values of ψ found from the graphical
procedure are shown in Figure 2-14-3, for the arbitrary assumption of
the distribution at the fission limit. Since $\psi = rq$, the assumption of

constant q means a straight-line variation of ψ with r at the high energy limit. These assumptions also amount incidentally to the assumption of constant density of thermal power. This is, however, an assumption, subject to later examination.

For evaluating this example it should be remembered that the limitations on diffusion theory cause the solution to be incorrect in the immediate vicinity of the discontinuity in fast slowing-down density. The interval of space used in the example is rather large, and the solution is therefore subject to some error. The easiest check on the error due to the size of interval is to repeat the solution with a different interval, and to compare the results of the two calculations. For the spherical reactor, since $q = \psi/r$, in order to have a finite value for the slowing-down density at the origin, it is necessary that $\psi = 0$ when $r = 0$. One further comment is needed. Since the ratio, $2k/h^2 = \frac{1}{2}$, is on the borderline of the region of convergence, rather minor changes in the problem may cause divergence difficulties. The addition of absorbing materials, for instance, will cause divergence, as well as complicate the graphical procedure.

Other relationships between space and age variables also make a graphical solution possible, and give more definite convergence, though at the expense of somewhat more work. For instance, the relationship

$$\frac{2k}{h^2} = \frac{1}{4} \tag{2-14-21}$$

gives the expression

$$\psi(r_1, \tau_2) = \frac{\psi(r_2, \tau_0) + 2\psi(r_1, \tau_0) + \psi(r_0, \tau_0)}{4} \tag{2-14-22}$$

Equation 2-14-22 can be solved graphically by the scheme shown in Figure 2-14-4. This scheme is seen to involve three construction lines, instead of one, to progress by one-half the age interval of Figure 2-14-2.

Besides the convergence difficulty with schemes of the type of Equation 2-14-7, there is another. Although a similar graphical scheme can be developed for the solution of the equation for thermal neutrons, it is tedious, partly due to the necessity of accounting for absorptions in the thermal range. Probably the main advantage of the graphical procedure for our present purposes is that it gives a visual presentation of an approximation to the slowing-down procedure. A system of equations which guarantees convergence for all circumstances and which handles both the equations for slowing down and for thermal neutrons by a uniform procedure is desirable. Such a system of equations is available and will be discussed next.

Let us now examine the other equations which will produce convergence for all interval spacings. Equation 2-14-9 is a non-homogeneous, linear, second-order difference equation. It is subject to many of the same conditions and restrictions which apply to a non-homogeneous, linear, second-order differential equation, and some of the methods for solving the differential equation are also of help for the

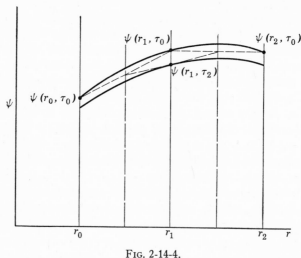

Fig. 2-14-4.

difference equation. In each case it is necessary to satisfy two arbitrary boundary conditions on the spatial distribution of the slowing-down density. For instance, for the sphere, it is required the $\psi = rq$ $= 0$, for $r = 0$ and for $r = R$. The solution to the difference equation which satisfies the physical problem is given by that particular solution to the difference equation which also satisfies these two boundary conditions. Two ways of obtaining this particular solution will be discussed.

Let Equation 2-14-9 be rewritten for convenience as

$$\psi_2 + \psi_0 - (2 + \alpha)\psi_1 = s_1 \qquad (2\text{-}14\text{-}23)$$

where $\psi_2 = \psi(r_2, \tau_2)$, etc., $\alpha = (h^2/2k)$, and $s_1 = (h^2/2k)\psi(r_1, \tau_0)$. The most general solution to Equation 2-14-23 is

$$\psi = C_1 H_1 + C_2 H_2 + P \qquad (2\text{-}14\text{-}24)$$

where H_1 and H_2 are any two independent solutions to the homogeneous equation which result when s_1 is set equal to zero, and P is any solution to the complete equation, with $s_1 \neq 0$, called a particular integral of the equation. All these functions are independent of the boundary conditions, these boundary conditions being satisfied by adjusting C_1 and C_2. In general, for the numerical problem, it is possible to pick a solution for both the homogeneous and particular integrals in such a way that one of the boundary conditions is automatically satisfied, and it is then necessary only to write

$$\psi = CH + P \tag{2-14-25}$$

The arbitrary constant C is adjusted in such a way that when the two functions are added together, the second of the two boundary conditions, which neither of the functions satisfies by itself, is finally satisfied. This result is the required solution to the physical problem.

To demonstrate, let us consider the same spherical geometry which was used to demonstrate the graphical solution. Let the source be the same as in the previous example. The problem is to compute the slowing-down density which results at the first lethargy step. As before, take ten space intervals and five lethargy intervals to thermalize the neutrons. The functions ψ, P, and H are assigned the value zero at $r = 0$, to satisfy the first of the boundary conditions. To make Equation 2-14-23 determinate for P_2 or H_2, it is necessary to assign a value also to P_1 and H_1 for the first step of the calculation. It might be mentioned that if exactly the right value were chosen for the starting values of P_1, the particular integral so found would also satisfy the second boundary condition, and there would be no need for a calculation of the homogeneous integral. Since we cannot anticipate being so fortunate, and since a poor choice results in awkwardly small differences in large numbers for satisfying the second boundary condition, perhaps the best general procedure is to make the starting P_1 equal to ψ_1, from the previous age calculation, and to adjust its value later if the magnitude of numbers to be subtracted becomes too large. The computations based on this procedure are shown in Table 2-14-1.

TABLE 2-14-1. SOLUTION TO EQUATION 2-14-25

r	s	P	H	$-CH$	ψ
0.0	0.0	0.0	0.0	0.00	0
0.1	0.2	0.1	0.1	0.00	0.10
0.2	0.4	0.2	0.4	0.00	0.20
0.3	0.6	0.3	1.5	0.00	0.30
0.4	0.8	0.4	5.6	0.02	0.38
0.5	1.0	0.5	20.9	0.09	0.41
0.6	1.20	0.6	78.0	0.33	0.27
0.7	0	1.3	291.1	1.23	0.07
0.8	0	4.6	1086.4	4.57	0.03
0.9	0	17.1	4054.5	17.09	0.01
1.0	0	63.8	15131.6	63.80	0

To show the derivation of the numbers in the table, let us calculate P and H at $r = 0.5$, from Equation 2-14-23:

$$P_5 = -s_4 - P_3 + (2 + \alpha)P_4$$

Since $\alpha = h^2/2k$ has been arbitrarily made equal to two, this becomes

$$P_5 = -0.8 - 0.3 + 4 \times 0.4 = 0.5$$

Likewise,

$$H_5 = -H_3 + 4H_4 = -1.5 + 4 \times 5.6 = 20.9$$

The value of the constant C is given by

$$C = -\frac{P_{1.0}}{H_{1.0}} = -\frac{63.8}{15131.6} = -0.00422$$

A comparison of this solution with that of the graphical solution for ψ made previously shows that the effect of the discontinuity has been spread out over a larger area than in the graphical solution. This numerical procedure must, of course, be repeated four more times to determine the function of ψ, at the thermal limit, as was done in the graphical example.

A second method * for the solution of Equation 2-14-23 uses the solution to the homogeneous equation to find the particular integral which satisfies the boundary conditions on the physical problem. It is assumed that the solution for ψ can be expressed in the form of a product

$$\psi = Ht \qquad (2\text{-}14\text{-}26)$$

where, as before, H is a solution to the homogeneous equation which satisfies one of the boundary conditions, and t is a function which is to be adjusted so as to satisfy the second boundary condition. Substituting Equation 2-14-26 into Equation 2-14-23 gives

$$H_2 t_2 + H_0 t_0 - (2 + \alpha)H_1 t_1 = -s_1 \qquad (2\text{-}14\text{-}27)$$

From the solution to the homogeneous equation

$$H_2 + H_0 - (2 + \alpha)H_1 = 0 \qquad (2\text{-}14\text{-}28)$$

Eliminating H_1 between Equations 2-14-27 and 2-14-28, we obtain

$$H_2(t_2 - t_1) = -s_1 + H_0(t_1 - t_0) \qquad (2\text{-}14\text{-}29)$$

With $t_2 - t_1 = \delta_2$, and $t_1 - t_0 = \delta_1$,

$$H_2 \delta_2 = -s_1 + H_0 \delta_1 \qquad (2\text{-}14\text{-}30)$$

---

* R. Ehrlich and H. Hurwitz, Jr., *Multigroup Methods for Neutron Diffusion Problems*, Knolls Atomic Power Laboratory, KAPL-P-1063. Also published in *Nucleonics*, February, 1954, Vol. 12, No. 2, pp. 23–30.

The computations for ψ at the end of the first lethargy step according to this scheme are shown in Table 2-14-2, for the same example treated in the last problem. H is computed from Equation 2-14-28, with an assumption for H_1. S is computed from Equation 2-14-30. It is to be noted that the quantity δ is computed from the top of the column, where $r = 0$, whereas t is computed starting at the bottom of the column, where $r = 1.0$. This procedure would be varied to suit different

TABLE 2-14-2. SOLUTION TO EQUATION 2-14-26

r	H	s	δ	t	ψ
0.0	0.0	0.0	0.0	0.995	0
0.1	0.1	0.2	0.0	0.995	0.10
0.2	0.4	0.4	−0.5	0.495	0.20
0.3	1.5	0.6	−0.3	0.195	0.29
0.4	5.6	0.8	−0.128	0.0670	0.38
0.5	20.9	1.0	−0.0473	0.0197	0.41
0.6	78.0	1.2 / 0	−0.0162	0.00347	0.27
0.7	291.1	0	−0.00322	0.000249	0.07
0.8	1086.4	0	−0.000231	0.0000178	0.02
0.9	4054.5	0	−0.0000166	0.000001188	0.00
1.0	15131.6	0	−0.000001188	0	0

boundary conditions. Because of the very large variation in H over the whole region, and the desire to achieve a uniform accuracy for the product $H \times t$, it is necessary to carry a given number of significant figures, rather than a given number of decimal places, in t. The minor differences in the values of ψ in Tables 2-14-1 and 2-14-2 are due to the differences in the accumulation of rounding-off errors in the two calculations.

A great many other variations of the difference equations for Equation 2-14-4 could be considered. For instance, in Equation 2-14-6, the unspecified r could have been associated with r_0 or r_2 instead of with r_1, giving another set of three equations. Still other difference equations can be obtained by adding together expressions like Equations 2-14-7, 2-14-8, and 2-14-9. Each of these variations changes the convergence problem, as well as the amount of computation required to complete a step of the procedure.

DIFFERENCE EQUATIONS FOR NON-UNIFORM REACTORS

Let us now develop a more general set of difference equations for the conservation of neutrons, to allow a solution for non-uniform reactors in which the properties of the reactor which influence the behavior of neutrons are functions both of position in the reactor and of neutron lethargy. The coefficients for these differential equations are then functions of space and lethargy. For this purpose let us rewrite the reactor equation, Equation 2-10-1, into two parts, by analogy with Equations 2-12-3 and 2-12-4. For the slowing-down region, allowing absorptions and fissions during slowing down, we have

$$\frac{1}{3} \nabla \cdot \frac{1}{\Sigma_t} \nabla \varphi - \Sigma_a \varphi = \frac{\partial(\xi \Sigma_s \varphi)}{\partial u} - s(u)F \qquad (2\text{-}14\text{-}31)$$

where

$$F = \nu \varphi_{th} \Sigma_{f\ th} + \nu \int_0^{u_{th}} \varphi_1 \Sigma_{f1}\, du_1 \qquad (2\text{-}14\text{-}32)$$

For the thermal region

$$\frac{1}{3} \nabla \cdot \frac{1}{\Sigma_{t\ th}} \nabla \varphi_{th} - \Sigma_{a\ th} \varphi_{th} - \xi \Sigma_{s1} \varphi_1 = 0 \qquad (2\text{-}14\text{-}33)$$

where φ_{th} is the thermal neutron flux and φ_1 is the flux of neutrons at the thermal end of the slowing-down region.

Equations 2-14-31 and 2-14-33 will be developed, in finite difference form for numerical solution, for geometries which allow reasonable approximation to some engineering configurations of reactors. The simplest of these is the symmetrical sphere, a one-dimensional geometry, involving symmetry of all variables about a point in space, in which all quantities can be expressed as functions only of distance from the point (and lethargy). For this first case, the vectorial notation, $\nabla \cdot (1/\Sigma_t)\, \nabla \varphi$ becomes

$$\frac{1}{r^2} \frac{\partial}{\partial r} \left(\frac{r^2}{\Sigma_t} \frac{\partial \varphi}{\partial r} \right) \qquad (2\text{-}14\text{-}34)$$

The next complication is a two-dimensional case, involving symmetry about a line (cylindrical polar coordinates), in which all variables are functions not only of distance from the line of symmetry but also of distance from some plane of reference normal to the line. For this case the vectorial notation, $\nabla \cdot (1/\Sigma_t)\nabla \varphi$ becomes

$$\frac{1}{r} \frac{\partial}{\partial r} \left(\frac{r}{\Sigma_t} \frac{\partial \varphi}{\partial r} \right) + \frac{\partial}{\partial z} \left(\frac{1}{\Sigma_t} \frac{\partial \varphi}{\partial z} \right) \qquad (2\text{-}14\text{-}35)$$

The third case is three dimensional, involving no symmetries at all. The vectorial notation in Cartesian coordinates is

$$\frac{\partial}{\partial x} \left(\frac{1}{\Sigma_t} \frac{\partial \omega}{\partial x} \right) + \frac{\partial}{\partial y} \left(\frac{1}{\Sigma_t} \frac{\partial \varphi}{\partial y} \right) + \frac{\partial}{\partial z} \left(\frac{1}{\Sigma_t} \frac{\partial \varphi}{\partial z} \right) \qquad (2\text{-}14\text{-}36)$$

All the terms of Equations 2-14-34, 2-14-35, and 2-14-36 can be expressed in a standard form:

$$\frac{1}{x^m}\frac{\partial}{\partial x}\left(\frac{x^m}{\Sigma_t}\frac{\partial\varphi}{\partial x}\right) \quad \text{or} \quad \frac{1}{\Sigma_t}\frac{\partial^2\varphi}{\partial x^2} + \left[\frac{\partial}{\partial x}\left(\frac{1}{\Sigma_t}\right) + \frac{m}{x\Sigma_t}\right]\frac{\partial\varphi}{\partial x} \quad (2\text{-}14\text{-}37)$$

where the exponent m has the following values:

Symmetry	Value of m
None	0
About a line	1
About a point	2

Substituting the difference expressions from Equations 2-14-2 and 2-14-3 into Equation 2-14-37 gives

$$\frac{1}{x^m}\frac{\partial}{\partial x}\left(\frac{x^m}{\Sigma_t}\frac{\partial\varphi}{\partial x}\right)\bigg]_{x_0 < x < x_2} =$$

$$\frac{1}{h^2\Sigma_t(x_1)}[(a_2 + \delta)\varphi(x_2) + (a_1 - \delta)\varphi(x_0) - 2a_1a_2\varphi(x_1)] \quad (2\text{-}14\text{-}38)$$

where

$$4\delta = \frac{x_2 - x_0}{x_1}m + \frac{\dfrac{1}{\Sigma_t(x_2)} - \dfrac{1}{\Sigma_t(x_0)}}{\dfrac{1}{\Sigma_t(x_1)}} \quad (2\text{-}14\text{-}39)$$

$$h = \frac{x_2 - x_0}{2} \quad (2\text{-}14\text{-}40)$$

$$2a_1 = \frac{x_2 - x_0}{x_1 - x_0} \quad 2a_2 = \frac{x_2 - x_0}{x_2 - x_1} \quad (2\text{-}14\text{-}41)$$

The other differential term in Equation 2-14-31 can be written, to the same degree of approximation,

$$\frac{\partial(\Sigma_s\varphi)}{\partial u}\bigg]_{u_0 < u < u_2} = \frac{\Sigma_s(u_2)\varphi(u_2) - \Sigma_s(u_0)\varphi(u_0)}{k} \quad (2\text{-}14\text{-}42)$$

where $k = u_2 - u_0$. Now we can write Equation 2-14-31 in difference form if we associate the unspecified space point with x_1, and the unspecified lethargy point with u_2. Equation 2-14-31 for the case of spherical symmetry, in difference form, becomes

$$\frac{1}{3h^2\Sigma_t(r_1, u_2)}[(a_2 + \delta)\varphi(r_2, u_2) + (a_1 - \delta)\varphi(r_0, u_2) - 2a_1a_2\varphi(r_1, u_2)]$$

$$- \Sigma_a(r_1, u_2)\varphi(r_1, u_2) = \frac{\xi\Sigma_s(r_1, u_2)\varphi(r_1, u_2) - \xi\Sigma_s(r_1, u_0)\varphi(r_1, u_0)}{k}$$

$$- s(u_2)F(r_1) \quad (2\text{-}14\text{-}43)$$

Equation 2-14-43 can be put into simpler form for ease of numerical handling:

$$(a_2 + \delta)\varphi(r_2, u_2) + (a_1 - \delta)\varphi(r_0, u_2)$$

$$- (2a_1a_2 + \alpha)\varphi(r_1, u_2) = -\sigma(r_1) \quad (2\text{-}14\text{-}44)$$

where

$$\frac{\alpha}{3} = h^2\Sigma_t(r_1, u_2)\Sigma_a(r_1, u_2) + \frac{h^2\Sigma_t(r_1, u_2)\Sigma_s(r_1, u_2)\xi}{k} \quad (2\text{-}14\text{-}45)$$

and

$$\frac{\sigma(r_1)}{3} = \frac{h^2\Sigma_t(r_1, u_2)\Sigma_s(r_1, u_0)\xi}{k}\varphi(r_1, u_0) - s(u_2)F(r_1)h^2\Sigma_t(r_1, u_0)$$

$$(2\text{-}14\text{-}46)$$

For evenly spaced increments, $a_1 = a_2 = 1$. It can be seen that Equation 2-14-44 is a non-homogeneous difference equation, similar in form to Equation 2-14-23. It is solved analogously to Equation 2-14-23, the difference in the details of the solution being due to variations in increment size, in physical properties of the reactor materials, in the geometrical symmetries, and in the source distribution in lethargy. These differences show up in the calculations of the coefficients, $a_2 + \delta$, $a_1 - \delta$, $2a_1a_2 + \alpha$, and $\sigma(r_1)$.

The difference equation for the thermal range, developed from Equation 2-14-33, has the same form as Equation 2-14-44, with all values of physical quantities now pertaining to the flux of thermal neutrons, except that now

$$\alpha_{th} = 3h^2\Sigma_{t\ th}(r_1)\Sigma_{a\ th}(r_1) \quad (2\text{-}14\text{-}47)$$

and

$$\sigma_{th}(r_1) = 3h^2\Sigma_{t\ th}(r_1)\Sigma_s(r_1, u_1)\xi\varphi(r_1, u_1) \quad (2\text{-}14\text{-}48)$$

where the subscript th designates thermal neutron conditions.

The procedure for the numerical solution to the criticality problem is given in the following steps:

1. A source distribution of fission neutrons is assumed.

2. The fission source is distributed properly among the lethargy groups, according to the fission spectrum.

3. Equation 2-14-44 is solved for the neutron distribution in the lowest lethargy group, using the fission neutrons as the source.

4. Equation 2-14-44 is solved for the neutron distribution in the next to lowest lethargy group, using the fission neutrons and the neutrons slowed down from the previous group as the source. This is repeated for all groups, including the thermal group.

5. The fissions from all the groups are summed to give a new source distribution.

6. The calculated source distribution is checked against the prior assumed distribution. It will in general be found that these distributions differ in two respects. First, the level of the calculated distribution will be higher or lower than the assumed distribution. If it is higher, the reactor as designed had too much fissionable material and was therefore supercritical. For the next trial less fissionable material should be used. The converse is also true for a calculated distribution lower than that assumed. Second, the detailed shapes of the distribution curves will differ. If the method converges, this difference in detail will disappear with successive trials.

7. Use the calculated source, corrected for the amount of fissionable material, as the basis for a new trial, and repeat steps 1 to 6. The calculated reactor is critical when the new calculated distribution agrees with the assumed distribution at all points.

The above discussion does not include all the numerical methods * which are available for the solution of the problem of neutron distribution. The methods presented here should be considered as representative of the numerical approach to the solution of physical problems.

REFERENCES

Glasstone, S., and M. C. Edlund, *Nuclear Reactor Theory*, D. Van Nostrand Co., New York, 1952.

Grinter, L. E., *Numerical Methods of Analysis in Engineering*, The Macmillan Co., New York, 1949.

Langhaar, H. L., *Dimensional Analysis and Theory of Models*, John Wiley and Sons, New York, 1951.

* A. S. Thompson, "Numerical Computation of Neutron Distribution and Critical Size," *Journal of Applied Physics*, Vol. 22, No. 10, October, 1951.

Margenau, H., and G. M. Murphy, *The Mathematics of Physics and Chemistry*, D. Van Nostrand Co., New York, 1943.

Milne, W. E., *Numerical Solution of Differential Equations*, John Wiley and Sons, New York, 1953.

Scarborough, J. B., *Numerical Mathematical Analysis*, The Johns Hopkins Press, Baltimore, 1930.

Soodak, H., and E. C. Campbell, *Elementary Pile Theory*, John Wiley and Sons, New York, 1950.

Willers, Fr. A., *Practical Analysis*, Dover Publications, New York, 1948.

CHAPTER 3

REACTOR KINETICS

3-1. Transient Behavior of Reactors

Any power plant, to be useful, must be susceptible to control. It must start and rise reliably to some predetermined power level, and must respond properly to any changes in operating conditions which are imposed on it, deliberately or otherwise, during its lifetime. It must be dynamically stable, so that oscillations in power (or temperature or pressure) of such magnitude as to damage apparatus or limit performance unduly cannot occur. Catastrophic accidents must be impossible, or at least limited in extent, so that radioactive materials cannot be scattered in inhabited areas, or in watersheds of inhabited areas. Provision must be made to correct for changes in the operating characteristics of the reactor as it ages that are due to depletion of fissionable materials and to the accumulation of "poisons."

Some difficulties exist in the design of the control system for a nuclear reactor which stem primarily from the fact that reactors are so expensive that they are built in limited quantities, and in general cannot be built for such purposes as testing control systems. Most of the estimates of the operating characteristics of a reactor which are pertinent to the design of a control system are based on mathematical analyses. These operating characteristics are so complicated that it is not practical to attempt to write mathematical equations to describe their behavior completely, and even if they were written they would be too complicated to be feasible for solution. The simplified equations which can be solved contain many assumptions concerning the behavior of the reactor which may represent sufficiently close approximations to actual behavior, but which can be justified only by empirical means. This is different from the usual engineering situation primarily in the increased difficulty of obtaining empirical verification of the validity of assumptions and in the disastrous nature of some of the consequences which can be imagined for a catastrophic failure of a reactor due to the inadequacy of the control system.

The power reactor is thermodynamically coupled to the rest of the power system. For a discussion of the control of the power system it is necessary to find first the special characteristics of a reactor which determine its kinetic response to transient disturbances within the critical reactor, and then to consider the reactor as a part of the power system. The transient response of the reactor to external stimuli requires the solution, at least approximately, to the problem of the time-dependent equation for reactor power. The coupling of the reactor with the system involves the thermodynamic characteristics of the reactor cooling fluid and the performance characteristics of the system components.

The power in a nuclear reactor is determined by the rate at which fissions occur. In a given reactor the rate of fissioning is proportional to the amount of fissionable material present and to the average neutron density. Hence, a change in the neutron density in the reactor results directly in a change in the power level of the reactor. Control of the reactor is accomplished by regulating the density of neutrons. If the density of neutrons is neither increasing nor decreasing, it is said that the reactor is critical, or has a multiplication factor of unity. The amount by which the multiplication factor exceeds unity is called the excess multiplication factor, or excess reactivity.

Modern control systems are generally of the type called *closed-loop systems*. A closed-loop system includes a sensing device for the quantity (for example, a rotating speed of a shaft) to be controlled; a reference signal, say the desired speed of the shaft; an error-sensing device to measure the differences between the quantity measured and that desired; an amplifier to increase the strength of the error signal; and an actuator which moves a control in such a direction as to cancel out the error.

In a nuclear reactor the most direct and immediate quantity which indicates the reactor performance is the density of neutrons in the reactor. The most obvious sensing device is then an instrument capable of counting (in a statistical sense) the number of neutrons in the reactor at a given time. The signal from the counter is compared with the level desired, the error signal being amplified and used in the control system to return the reactor to the desired operating level.

Control of the supply of neutrons can be accomplished (1) by moving a strong absorber, such as boron, into or out of strategic areas of the reactor, (2) by moving a reflector material nearer to, or farther from, the reactor, or (3) by adding or subtracting fissionable material in the reactor.

The most basic assumption of the usual control analysis of any power system is the assumption of linearity of the differential equations describing the system. This means that the dependent variable, in this case reactor power, occurs in all terms only to the first power (if the equation is homogeneous) or is absent in some terms (if the equation is complete, or non-homogeneous). This assumption accomplishes important simplifications in analytical and experimental control procedures. The primary advantage of the assumption of linearity stems from the fact that solutions can be built up by superposition, or adding, of other known solutions. For the control problem this means that the response of a linear system to a total disturbance, which is the sum of several individual disturbances, is given by the sum of the responses to the individual disturbances. The methods for solution of the equations for transients in linear systems have been highly formalized.* Where these methods are applicable they are rapid and powerful in achieving results. The linearized equations are, in general, applicable to descriptions of small departures from equilibrium conditions.

For a reactor it is found experimentally that as the departure of the reactor power from equilibrium increases, some of the coefficients of the differential equations do not remain constant, but are dependent on reactor power (the dependent variable). Many situations can be envisioned in which large departure from steady-state conditions in a reactor exist, for instance, during start-up or shut-down of the reactor, or during large changes in the operating power, or temperature or density, of the reactor due to outside causes such as changes in the external load on the reactor. It is found empirically (as would be expected for theoretical reasons) that the excess reactivity depends on the thermodynamic variables, temperature and pressure, in the reactor, which are in turn dependent on reactor power. The reactor power, hence, enters the equations to powers other than the first, and the equations are non-linear. This precludes the assumption of linearity, and solution by superposition of terms, for large variations of reactor power from equilibrium. For such large variations from equilibrium it is necessary to solve non-linear equations.

It is not the purpose of this chapter to duplicate the systematic analysis of linear systems, or of the servomechanisms for their control. It is the purpose to discuss those features of the transient behavior of nuclear reactors which are peculiar and non-linear, and which, under some circumstances, make conventional control analysis inadequate.

* See references at the end of the chapter.

In the usual analytical or experimental investigations of the transient behavior of power systems it is customary to impose an impulse of known magnitude on the operating system and to determine its response to that impulse. Customarily two distinct types of impulse are used. The first type, called the step impulse, consists in a sudden change δ at time t, of some operating variable. This might be plotted against time as shown in Figure 3-1-1.

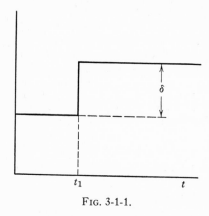

FIG. 3-1-1.

The second type of impulse consists of a sinusoidal variation with time of an operating variable. This is shown in Figure 3-1-2.

The advantages of these impulses for the study of linear systems lie partly in the fact that the analysis of such systems for these impulses has been formalized and standardized to the point where much information on system behavior can readily be found, and partly because, particularly by the use of superposition of solutions, a good approximation to many actual physical situations can be made. For the non-linear system these advantages largely disappear. It seems expedient, then, for the non-linear system, to try to pick an impulse function

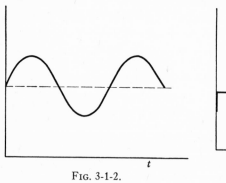

FIG. 3-1-2.

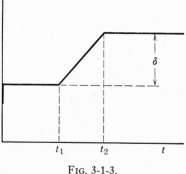

FIG. 3-1-3.

which may more closely represent an actual operating situation without superposition. It is obvious that the step function represents a limit to an actual process, since it involves finite motion in zero time, or infinite accelerations and decelerations, which are not physically attainable. In general, also, it will not be desirable to impose a sinusoidal motion on a non-linear control system. Rates of motion of control apparatus, or rates at which accidental situations can build up are important quantities. These can be expressed by "ramp" functions which can be pictured as in Figure 3-1-3. Here an impulse starts building up at a linear rate at t_1, leveling off again at t_2. The total impulse height can be represented again by δ.

The purpose of an analysis will be to consider first the linear approximation to the transient behavior of reactor power, which is valid only for small departures from steady state, or critical operation. Then an approximation to the non-linear system, with excess reactivity dependent on reactor power, will be considered. Also an approximate analysis of the effect of the delayed neutrons on reactor control will be made.

For the purpose of our analysis the reactor system considered will be quite limited in scope and will be subject to several symplifying assumptions.

The system considered for an example is an idealized reactor which has the following characteristics. It is made up of a multiplicity of parallel cooling tubes, all identical. The power density generated in the reactor is uniform throughout the reactor volume. The transient reactivity in the reactor depends only on the average temperature of the cooling fluid in the reactor; the cooling fluid is incompressible. The transient distribution of neutrons in space and lethargy is the same as the distribution in the critical reactor. The temperature of the cooling fluid entering the reactor will be considered fixed. The reactor will be considered to be followed by a heat exchanger which is capable of absorbing all the thermal energy dumped into it by the reactor.

The procedure to be followed in developing the control analysis will be the following. The differential equation for the non-critical, or transient, distribution of neutrons in a reactor will first be simplified by defining average values of the neutron density and the diffusion operator over lethargy, for a reference point in space. This leaves an equation for the variation of this average neutron density in time. The equation is then written in terms of the operating power of the reactor and the excess reactivity, or excess multiplication factor. This equation is then specialized for several cases; they are the linearized case with no delayed neutrons, the linearized case with delayed neutrons, and finally the non-linear case. To develop the non-linear case a discussion is given of the dependence of the multiplication factor on average reactor temperature, density, and operating power. Some numerical solutions to the non-linear case are presented.

TRANSIENT EQUATIONS FOR A REACTOR WITH NO DELAYED NEUTRONS

To describe the transient behavior of a reactor we need an expression for the transient variation of reactor power in a non-critical reactor. As we have seen, we can find the transient behavior of reactor power if we know the transient behavior of the neutrons. Equation 2-8-1 of Chapter 2 gives the transient behavior of neutrons in a nuclear reactor in which it is assumed that all neutrons are prompt (no delayed neutrons). For reference, this equation is

$$\nabla \cdot D \, \nabla n - nv\Sigma_a + s(u)\nu \int_0^\infty n_1 v_1 \Sigma_{f1} \, du_1 = \frac{\partial(nv\xi\Sigma_s)}{\partial u} + \frac{\partial n}{\partial t} \quad (3\text{-}1\text{-}1)$$

In Chapter 2, Equation 3-1-1 was treated only for the critical reactor $\frac{\partial n}{dt} = 0$. It was desired there to determine primarily the spatial and lethargy distribution of neutrons and the conditions for criticality which the coefficients must fulfill. For our present purpose the spatial and lethargy distribution are not of primary interest. We desire here, for simplicity, to describe the transient behavior of the reactor in terms of appropriate averages, over space and lethargy, of the coefficients of the equation. We will first average overall values of lethargy by integrating Equation 3-1-1. This gives

$$\int_0^\infty \nabla \cdot D_1 \, \nabla n_1 \, du_1 + \int_0^\infty (\nu\Sigma_{f1} - \Sigma_{a1})n_1 v_1 \, du_1 = \frac{\partial}{\partial t}\left(\int_0^\infty n_1 \, du_1\right)$$

$$(3\text{-}1\text{-}2)$$

since, by definition, the source term is such that

$$\int_0^\infty s(u) \, du = 1 \quad (3\text{-}1\text{-}3)$$

and since

$$\int_0^\infty \frac{\partial(n_1 v_1 \xi \Sigma_{s1})}{\partial u_1} \, du_1 = 0 \quad (3\text{-}1\text{-}4)$$

Equation 3-1-3 states that the fissions at given lethargies can be summed over all lethargies to give the total number of fissions. Equation 3-1-4 states that, since all the neutrons are contained between the limits zero and infinity, the densities at the two limits are zero.

In Equation 3-1-2 let the total density of neutrons of all lethargies at some reference point in space be N, or

$$N = \int_0^\infty n_1 \, du_1 \quad (3\text{-}1\text{-}5)$$

Also, let an average (over lethargy) diffusion operator κ^2 be defined at the same point in space, where D_0 is the diffusion coefficient at the same point:

$$-\kappa^2 D_0 N = \int_0^\infty \nabla \cdot D_1 \, \nabla n_1 \, du_1 \qquad (3\text{-}1\text{-}6)$$

and

$$(\nu\Sigma_{f0} - \Sigma_{a0})v_0 N = \int_0^\infty (\nu\Sigma_{f1} - \Sigma_{a1})n_1 v_1 \, du_1 \qquad (3\text{-}1\text{-}7)$$

where the subscript zero indicates an average over the whole lethargy range. Now averages are defined so that Equation 3-1-2 can be written only in terms of space and time variables:

$$\frac{1}{\Sigma_{a0}v_0} \frac{1}{N} \frac{\partial N}{\partial t} = -\kappa^2 \frac{D_0}{\Sigma_{a0}v_0} + \left(\frac{\nu\Sigma_{f0}}{\Sigma_{a0}} - 1\right) \qquad (3\text{-}1\text{-}8)$$

In Equation 3-1-8 N is the total number of neutrons, of all lethargies, at a particular point in space. The factor $1/\Sigma_{a0}v_0$ is the mean lifetime of neutrons from one generation of fissions to the next. The quantity $D_0/\Sigma_{a0}v_0$ is the migration area. This, as defined in Chapter 2, is the mean square distance traveled by a neutron from its birth to its capture. The quantity $\nu\Sigma_{f0}/\Sigma_{a0}$ is the multiplication factor, or the ratio of the neutrons produced during a neutron cycle to those absorbed. For simplicity let the inverse of the mean lifetime, or the neutron life cycle frequency, λ, be

$$\lambda = \Sigma_{a0}v_0 \qquad (3\text{-}1\text{-}9)$$

Also let the migration area be represented by M^2 or

$$M^2 = \frac{D_0}{\Sigma_{a0}v_0} \qquad (3\text{-}1\text{-}10)$$

and the multiplication factor by k, where

$$k = \nu \frac{\Sigma_{f0}}{\Sigma_{a0}} \qquad (3\text{-}1\text{-}11)$$

Equation 3-1-8 can now be written

$$\frac{1}{\lambda} \frac{1}{N} \frac{\partial N}{\partial t} = -\kappa^2 M^2 + k - 1 \qquad (3\text{-}1\text{-}12)$$

Since the reactor power density, p, is proportional to the neutron density, N, Equation 3-1-12 can be rewritten in terms of reactor power density:

$$\frac{1}{\lambda}\frac{1}{p}\frac{\partial p}{\partial t} = -\kappa^2 M^2 + k - 1 \qquad (3\text{-}1\text{-}13)$$

Equation 3-1-13 is the form of the transient power equation which will be used to investigate the transient behavior of reactors. For many cases it is possible to express Equation 3-1-13 in terms of the parameters for a critical reactor.

For the steady-state (critical) conditions, we can write for Equation 3-1-13

$$0 = -\kappa_1{}^2 M_1{}^2 + k_1 - 1 \qquad (3\text{-}1\text{-}14)$$

For small departures of the neutron density from the steady state, due to a change of the multiplication factor, k, from the steady-state value, k_1, it can be assumed that the diffusion operator, κ^2, and the migration area, M^2, will change by a negligibly small amount from their steady-state values. Subtracting Equation 3-1-14 from Equation 3-1-13 therefore gives

$$\frac{1}{\lambda}\frac{1}{p}\frac{\partial p}{\partial t} = \delta(t) \qquad (3\text{-}1\text{-}15)$$

where

$$\delta = k - k_1 \qquad (3\text{-}1\text{-}16)$$

represents the excess of the multiplication factor over its critical value. It can be seen that Equation 3-1-15 is dimensionless. To recapitulate, the factor λ is the mean lifetime cycle frequency of the neutron from fission in one generation to its absorption in fission to start a new generation of neutrons. The factor $\delta(t)$ is the fractional increase (plus sign) or decrease in the number of neutrons (or reactor power) in one generation.

3-2. Linear Behavior of Reactors—No Delayed Neutrons

If the mean lifetime, λ, is assumed to be constant and if δ is assumed to be independent of the reactor power and the time, Equation 3-1-15 can be integrated to give

$$p = p_0 e^{\delta \lambda t} \qquad (3\text{-}2\text{-}1)$$

Equation 3-2-1 gives the linear transient response of a reactor to an excess multiplication factor, δ. The inverse of the product $\delta\lambda$ is called the *time constant* for the reactor. It measures the time for an increase in power by the exponential factor, e. Expansion of the exponential term gives

$$p = p_0 \left[1 + \delta\lambda t + \frac{\delta^2\lambda^2 t^2}{2} + \cdots \right] \qquad (3\text{-}2\text{-}2)$$

Equation 3-2-1 states that, if an excess multiplication factor is added to an already critical reactor, the power density will increase indefinitely with time on an exponential curve, the rate of increase being determined by the product of the neutron cycle frequency λ and the excess multiplication factor δ. Since the neutron cycle frequency is generally of the order of 10^4 per second, or more, it is seen that an excess multiplication factor of 10^{-2} (about one percent, since the multiplication factor is of the order of unity) will result in an increase in power density by the exponential factor e every 0.01 second, or sooner. The control of such a reactor, considering the danger from radioactivity in a catastrophic accident, would be very hazardous, unless it were possible to limit the excess multiplication factor which could be added to the reactor to very small values.

There are two major, and some minor, faults with Equation 3-1-13 insofar as its ability to describe a true physical situation is concerned. The minor faults have to do with the averaging processes necessary to evaluate the coefficients for the equation. The major faults stem from (1) neglect of the role played by the delayed neutrons in the transient behavior of a reactor, and (2) the dependence of the excess multiplication factor on the power density in the reactor, which causes Equation 3-1-13 to be non-linear. Let us investigate these effects.

3-3. Linear Behavior of Reactors—with Delayed Neutrons

The delayed neutrons which are available at time t are due to fissions which occurred at an earlier time $t - t_1$. Therefore, their quantity reflects the power level which existed at that previous time. The delayed neutrons, then, must be subtracted from the calculated effect at time t and added as an effect at time $t + t_1$. Equation 3-1-15 then becomes, if there are n groups of delayed neutrons,

$$\frac{dp}{dt} = \lambda\left[(\delta - \beta)p + \sum_{m=1}^{n} \beta_m p(t - t_m)\right] \qquad (3\text{-}3\text{-}1)$$

where β_m is the fraction of the neutrons which is delayed by the time $t - t_m$, and β is the total fraction of delayed neutrons,

$$\beta = \sum_{m=1}^{n} \beta_m \qquad (3\text{-}3\text{-}2)$$

For the fission of U^{235}, $\beta = 0.0075$, the five most important groups of delayed neutrons being $\beta(0.62) = 0.00084$, $\beta(2.19) = 0.0024$, $\beta(6.50) = 0.0021$, $\beta(31.7) = 0.0017$, and $\beta(80.2) = 0.00026$, where the numbers in the parentheses are the mean lifetime (in seconds) of the delayed neutron groups. For changes in reactor power which are rapid compared with the mean lives of the delayed neutrons, it seems reasonable to assume that the response due to the delayed neutrons will depend on some appropriate average of the power over the delayed period, p_{av}. Equation 3-3-1 then becomes

$$\frac{dp}{dt} = \lambda[(\delta - \beta)p + \beta p_{av}] \tag{3-3-3}$$

Equation 3-3-3 can be rearranged for integration by dividing through by the factor $\left(p + \frac{\beta}{\delta - \beta} p_{av} \right)$, giving

$$\frac{d\left(p + \dfrac{\beta}{\delta - \beta} p_{av} \right)}{p + \dfrac{\beta}{\delta - \beta} p_{av}} = \lambda(\delta - \beta)\, dt \tag{3-3-4}$$

Performing the integration of Equation 3-3-4, we obtain

$$p = p_0 e^{\lambda(\delta - \beta)t} + \frac{\beta p_{av}}{\delta - \beta} (e^{\lambda(\delta - \beta)t} - 1) \tag{3-3-5}$$

where p_0 is the power at time $t = 0$. If the reactor has been operating for some time at a steady level of power, prior to the sudden change in activity, then $p_{av} = p_0$, and

$$p = p_0 \left[\frac{\delta}{\delta - \beta} e^{\lambda(\delta - \beta)t} - \frac{\beta}{\delta - \beta} \right] \tag{3-3-6}$$

From a comparison of Equations 3-2-1 and 3-3-6, we can see that the delayed neutrons cause the exponential rise to be much slower than it would otherwise be. Expansion of the exponential term gives for Equation 3-3-6.

$$p = p_0 \left[1 + \delta\lambda t + \frac{\delta(\delta - \beta)\lambda^2}{2} t^2 + \cdots \right] \tag{3-3-7}$$

It can be seen from the third term on the right that the curvature of the power rise is positive or negative, depending on whether the excess activity δ is greater than or less than the fraction of delayed neutrons

β in the reactor. If δ is less than β, the reactor power approaches a finite limit as time passes. As was stated, the maximum value of β, if all delayed neutrons are kept in the reactor, is 0.007. For control purposes, since a negative curvature is desirable, it would seem that δ should be kept less than β, and, therefore, in all cases less than 0.007. The effect of delayed neutrons on the rise (and fall) of power density

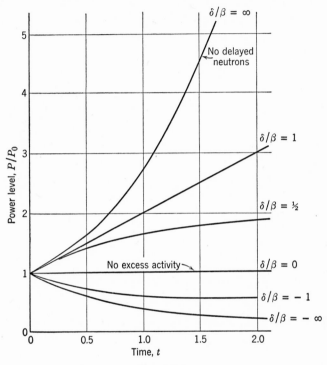

Fig. 3-3-1.

is shown in Figure 3-3-1 for various ratios of excess activity to delayed neutron effect, and for times short compared with the delay time of neutrons.

Both Equation 3-2-1 and Equation 3-3-6 result from the assumption of linearity of the equations from which they are derived. Because of this assumption they are applicable only to small departures from steady-state values of the reactor power. Also, after a lapse of time large compared to the delay time of fission neutrons, the assumption that the quantity of delayed neutrons is dependent on the steady-state operating power of the reactor, $p_{av} = p_0$, is no longer valid. Let us investigate the linear equation for periods long compared with the delay times of the neutrons. Consider Equation 3-3-1 for the case of one delayed group of neutrons having a delay time of t_1. Equation 3-3-1 then becomes

$$\frac{dp}{dt} = \lambda[(\delta - \beta)p + \beta p(t - t_1)]$$
(3-3-8)

The solution to Equation 3-3-8 can be written

$$p = p_0 e^{\alpha t}$$
(3-3-9)

where

$$\alpha = \lambda\delta - \lambda\beta\left(1 - \frac{1}{e^{\alpha t_1}}\right)$$
(3-3-10)

As the ratio δ/β is varied from zero to infinity, the value of α ranges from zero to the value $\lambda\delta$. It can be seen then, by comparison with Equation 3-2-1, that the power build-up at a given time is always less with delayed neutrons than without.

Let us now consider the non-linear behavior of reactors.

3-4. Reactivity Coefficients

It was stated that the excess multiplication factor depended on the operating power of the reactor. There are several kinds of dependence of multiplication factor on power. A change in the operating power of a reactor generally results in a change in the temperature distribution through the reactor. The change in temperature results in two effects on the multiplication factor, or reactivity. First, the energy distribution of neutrons in equilibrium with their surroundings is altered by the change in temperature. Since cross sections for the absorption of neutrons are dependent on neutron energy, and some of them strongly in a resonance region, the neutron distribution is changed by the change in temperature, resulting in a change in the multiplication factor. Second, most materials expand with rising temperature. Since the macroscopic cross sections are proportional to the densities of the materials with which the neutrons react, such changes in density result in changes of the multiplication factor. These effects of temperature are expressed in terms of temperature coefficients of reactivity. If the temperature coefficient for a particular part of the reactor is α_1, the change in excess activity due to a small change in the average temperature of this part is expressed by

$$\delta - \delta_0 = \alpha_1(\bar{T} - \bar{T}_0)$$
(3-4-1)

where the subscript zero refers to an initial condition. Because of the capacity of materials to store heat, not all parts of the reactor will have the same transient rise in temperature, and the total coefficient, which is the sum of the separate effects, will depend on the momentary operating conditions of the reactor.

If compressible fluids are used to cool a reactor, changes in the power of the reactor may result in changes in density independently of changes in temperature, and these in turn will cause changes in the reactivity. These changes can be expressed in terms of a small change in density as a coefficient of reactivity, by

$$\delta - \delta_0 = \alpha_2(\bar{\gamma} - \bar{\gamma}_0) \qquad (3\text{-}4\text{-}2)$$

During the operation of a reactor, due to the fission process, certain products, mainly xenon-135 and samarium-149, are formed which are strong absorbers of neutrons. Xenon is formed in larger quantities and has a much larger cross section than samarium, and is thus a much more important poison.

Such materials, as has been mentioned before, because of their deleterious effect on the continued operation of the reactor, are called "poisons." The higher the reactor power, the more rapidly the fission products are formed. Since xenon and samarium are caused by the decay of fission fragments, they are made at some time after the fission which caused them. In absorbing neutrons, xenon and samarium are changed to different materials which are not bad neutron poisons. Hence the higher the reactor power, the greater is the rate at which xenon and samarium are being consumed. It can be seen that the rate at which these poisons are being formed depends on the operating power of the reactor at some past time, whereas the rate of their destruction depends on the present power. Since xenon-135 itself is radioactive, it is destroyed by its own spontaneous disintegration, in addition to that caused by neutron absorption.

At the time of start-up of the reactor, the poison products are not present. As the reactor operates, the quantities of xenon and samarium increase, eventually approaching some equilibrium amount which in the case of xenon depends on the operating power and in the case of samarium is independent of operating power. After the reactor is shut down, the quantities of these materials increase considerably, since their production from decay continues and there are no longer neutrons produced to convert them to non-absorbing materials. Eventually, after shutdown of the reactor, the quantities of xenon and samarium will approach a maximum, the xenon then decreasing, because it is itself unstable. The samarium is not radioactive and does not decrease from the maximum accumulation. The maximum build-up after shutdown of a high power reactor is so large as to make it impractical to provide sufficient multiplication factor to override it, in many cases. There is then a period of time depending on reactor power after shutdown, in which it is impossible to restart.

Another effect of these fission product poisons is to cause the reactivity to be sensitive to the reactor power directly. Suppose the reactor is operating at an equilibrium concentration of fission product poisons. Then, if the reactor power increases, there are immediately more neutrons available to use up the poisons, while the source of the poisons from the decay of prior decay products is not immediately increased. There is then an increase in the reactivity due to the decreased quantity of neutron poison and, hence, also a further increase in reactor power. The effect can be expressed by a power coefficient of reactivity, α_3,

$$\delta - \delta_0 = \alpha_3(\bar{p} - \bar{p}_0) \qquad (3\text{-}4\text{-}3)$$

These three effects on the excess multiplication factor can be summed up

$$\delta - \delta_0 = \alpha_1(\bar{T} - \bar{T}_0) + \alpha_2(\bar{\gamma} - \bar{\gamma}_0) + \alpha_3(\bar{p} - \bar{p}_0) \qquad (3\text{-}4\text{-}4)$$

Equation 3-4-4 gives an expression for the change in excess activity due to changes of temperature, density, or power in the reactor. Of course these effects are not always independent. A change in power generally causes a change in both temperature and density, and in turn a change in temperature generally causes a change in density. A case of interest in reactor design is a boiling fluid, in which the density may change without a change in temperature, and the power may change, within limits, without changing either.

So far as effects on reactivity are concerned, the largest changes are due to density changes of either the fuel or the moderating material. Changes in microscopic cross section due to changes in temperature are relatively small, much the largest effect of changes in temperature being through changes in density. The effect of poisons is generally of a slow nature which does not cause problems of control stability, but does require rather large, but slow, motions of control rods.

The changes in reactivity of a reactor cause types of behavior different from those usually met in problems involving the kinetics and control of power plants. For purposes of illustration, let us discuss in more detail two of these effects on reactivity, that due to the accumulation of reactor poisons and that due to changes of the reactor temperature, taking first that due to poisons. For discussion purposes an idealized thermal reactor is assumed.

By definition, from the four-factor formula of Equation 2-1-7 of Chapter 2, the multiplication factor is given by

$$k = pf\eta\epsilon \tag{3-4-5}$$

Equation 3-4-5 gives the dependence of the multiplication factor on the nuclear characteristics of the reactor materials. The excess multiplication factor was defined in Equation 3-1-16 as $\delta = k - k_1$, where k_1 is the local multiplication factor at the reference point in the critical reactor. The power coefficient of reactivity can be defined in differential form, by analogy with Equation 3-4-3,

$$\alpha_3 = \frac{\partial \delta}{\partial p} \tag{3-4-6}$$

or assuming for the moment that k_1 does not change

$$\alpha_3 = \frac{\partial k}{\partial p} \tag{3-4-7}$$

The reactor power is related to the average flux of thermal neutrons, φ_{th}, the total number of atoms of fissionable uranium in the reactor, U, and the fission cross section, σ_f, by the expression

$$p = A\sigma_f\varphi_{th}\, U \tag{3-4-8}$$

where A is a dimensional constant. Assuming that the quantity of uranium stays essentially constant, combining Equations 3-4-7 and 3-4-8, we obtain

$$\alpha_3 = \frac{1}{A\sigma_f\, U}\frac{\partial k}{\partial \varphi_{th}} \tag{3-4-9}$$

Assuming that the primary effect of changes in the amounts of poisons is on the thermal utilization factor, f (there would also generally be some effect on the resonance escape probability, p), we have

$$\alpha_3 = \frac{p\eta\epsilon}{A\sigma_f\, U}\frac{\partial f}{\partial \varphi_{th}} \tag{3-4-10}$$

The thermal utilization factor was defined as the ratio of absorptions in fuel to total absorptions, or

$$f = \frac{\Sigma_{\text{fuel}}}{\Sigma_{\text{fuel}} + \Sigma_c} \tag{3-4-11}$$

where Σ_c represents the absorption cross section for parasitic, or non-useful, captures in the reactor. Equation 3-4-10 can be rearranged:

$$f = \frac{1}{1 + c} \tag{3-4-12}$$

where c represents the ratio of parasitic captures outside of fuel to the captures in fuel. The change in thermal utilization with neutron flux is, then,

$$\frac{\partial f}{\partial \varphi_{th}} = -\left(\frac{1}{1 + c}\right)^2 \frac{\partial c}{\partial \varphi_{th}} = -f^2 \frac{\partial c}{\partial \varphi_{th}} \tag{3-4-13}$$

Substituting into Equation 3-4-9

$$\alpha_3 = -\frac{pf\eta\epsilon}{A\sigma_f \, U} f \frac{\partial c}{\partial \varphi_{th}} = -\frac{kf}{A\sigma_f \, U} \frac{\partial c}{\partial \varphi_{th}} \tag{3-4-14}$$

If the poison is uniformly distributed throughout the reactor, the ratio c is given by

$$c = \frac{\sigma_N N \varphi_{th}}{\sigma_f \, U \, \varphi_{th}} = \frac{\sigma_N N}{\sigma_f \, U} \tag{3-4-15}$$

where the symbol N designates the number of atoms of poison and σ_N the poison cross section. Let us then find how the ratio c depends on the reactor flux, φ_{th}. To do so requires a study of the decay series by which the elements xenon-135 and samarium-149 are formed and the formulation of equations describing their formation and destruction.

The decay series for the formation and decay of xenon-135 is as follows:

$$\text{Te}^{135} \xrightarrow{\text{2 min}} \text{I}^{135} \xrightarrow{\text{6.7 hr}} \text{Xe}^{135} \xrightarrow{\text{9.2 hr}} \text{Cs}^{135} \xrightarrow{2 \times 10^6 \text{ yr}} \text{Ba}^{135} \text{ (stable)}$$

This series results from about 5.6 * percent of all fissions of uranium-235 due to slow neutrons. The absorption cross section for thermal neutrons for xenon-135 is very large, about 3.5×10^6 barns, whereas for the other products in the series the cross section is relatively small. The decay series for the formation of samarium-149 is

$$\text{Nd}^{149} \xrightarrow{\text{1.7 hr}} \text{Pm}^{149} \xrightarrow{\text{47 hr}} \text{Sm}^{149} \text{ (stable)}$$

This series results from about 1.4 percent of all fissions of uranium-235. The absorption cross section for thermal neutrons, for samarium-149, is about 5.3×10^4 barns.

* Xenon-135 is also produced directly in about 0.3 percent of fissions.

Let us now write equations for the formation and destruction of xenon-135 in a reactor.

By reference to Equation 1-6-4 of Chapter 1 a set of simultaneous differential equations can be written to describe the changes in the quantities of xenon or samarium. Letting the chemical symbols for the elements involved represent also the quantities of the chemicals involved and λ (with a subscript) their decay rates, we can write for the xenon-135 series:

$$0.003\sigma_f\varphi_{th}\, U + \lambda_I\, I - (\lambda_{Xe} + \sigma_{Xe}\varphi_{th})\, Xe = \frac{d\, Xe}{dt} \quad (3\text{-}4\text{-}16)$$

$$\lambda_{Te}\, Te - \lambda_I\, I = \frac{d\, I}{dt} \quad (3\text{-}4\text{-}17)$$

$$0.056\sigma_f\varphi_{th}\, U - \lambda_{Te}\, Te = \frac{d\, Te}{dt} \quad (3\text{-}4\text{-}18)$$

where σ_{Xe} stands for the absorption cross section of xenon-135. The decay constant λ is given in terms of the half-life, $T^{\frac{1}{2}}$, by Equation 1-6-3 as $\lambda = 0.693/T^{\frac{1}{2}}$.

These equations can be combined by eliminating I and Te to give a third-order differential equation in Xe. Let us, however, look at the steady-state solution for which all time derivatives are zero. We find for the steady-state quantity of xenon-135,

$$Xe = \frac{0.059\sigma_f\varphi_{th}\, U}{\lambda_{Xe} + \sigma_{Xe}\varphi_{th}} \quad (3\text{-}4\text{-}19)$$

Substituting Equation 3-4-19 into 3-4-15 with $\sigma_N = \sigma_{Xe}$ and $N = Xe$, we find for the steady-state ratio, c, of absorptions in xenon-135 to fissions

$$c = 0.059\, \frac{\varphi_{th}}{\dfrac{\lambda_{Xe}}{\sigma_{Xe}} + \varphi_{th}} \quad (3\text{-}4\text{-}20)$$

It can be seen that as the neutron flux, φ_{th}, approaches zero, the steady-state quantity of xenon approaches zero. For large values of the flux ($\varphi_{th} \gg \lambda_{Xe}/\sigma_{Xe}$, or about 0.6×10^{13}) approximately

$$c \sim 0.059 \quad (3\text{-}4\text{-}21)$$

For large values of the flux, the steady-state quantity of xenon is almost independent of the flux (or power) level. At this level, for every 100 neutrons absorbed in fission, about 5.9 neutrons are absorbed in xenon-135 (unless the xenon is continuously removed from the reactor). Since the decay constant, λ_{Sa}, for samarium-149 is zero (stable element) a similar calculation for the samarium series would give for the steady-state accumulation

$$c \sim 0.014 \qquad (3\text{-}4\text{-}22)$$

For all operating flux levels, the steady-state quantity of samarium is independent of the flux (or power) level.

Let us find the dependence of the rate of change in the quantity of xenon-135 on a sudden departure, $\delta\varphi_{th}$, of the neutron flux from its steady-state value. For this case, from Equation 3-4-16, assuming that the accumulated quantities of xenon and iodine have not had time to change, approximately

$$\frac{d\,\mathrm{Xe}}{dt} = -(\sigma_{Xe}\,\mathrm{Xe} - 0.003\sigma_f\,\mathrm{U})\,\delta\varphi_{th} \qquad (3\text{-}4\text{-}23)$$

Substituting the equilibrium value of xenon from Equation 3-4-19 and the value of c from Equation 3-4-15, we obtain

$$\frac{dc}{dt} = -\frac{(0.056\sigma_{Xe}\varphi_{th} - 0.003\lambda_{Xe})\,\delta\varphi_{th}}{\lambda_{Xe}/\sigma_{Xe} + \varphi_{th}} \qquad (3\text{-}4\text{-}24)$$

For large values of the flux

$$\frac{dc}{dt} = -0.056\sigma_{Xe}\,\delta\varphi_{th} \qquad (3\text{-}4\text{-}25)$$

Thus, if the power (flux) is suddenly increased from a large steady-state value, φ_{th}, to a new value $\varphi_{th} + \delta\varphi_{th}$, the amount of xenon in the reactor will immediately start to decrease at the rate prescribed by Equation 3-4-25, tending to increase the power still further. This is an inherent instability in the reaction to large power changes which must be overcome by the motion of control mechanisms.

It is now interesting to know the history of xenon build-up and decay after shutdown of the reactor from an equilibrium condition. By solution of Equations 3-4-16, 3-4-17, and 3-4-18 it can be shown that the quantity of xenon-135, present at a time t after shutdown from operation at a steady neutron flux, φ_{th}, with a steady-state accumulation of all the materials in the xenon series, is related to the steady-state quantity of xenon, Xe_0, by

$$\frac{\mathrm{Xe}}{\mathrm{Xe}_0} = e^{-\lambda_{Xe}\,t} + A_1(e^{-\lambda_{Xe}\,t} - e^{-\lambda_I\,t}) + A_2(e^{-\lambda_{Te}\,t} - e^{-\lambda_{Xe}\,t}) \qquad (3\text{-}4\text{-}26)$$

where

$$A_1 = \frac{0.056}{0.059} \frac{\lambda_{Te}(\lambda_{Xe} + \sigma_{Xe}\varphi_{th})}{(\lambda_I - \lambda_{Xe})(\lambda_{Te} - \lambda_I)}$$

and

$$A_2 = \frac{0.056}{0.059} \frac{\lambda_I(\lambda_{Xe} + \sigma_{Xe}\varphi_{th})}{(\lambda_{Te} - \lambda_I)(\lambda_{Te} - \lambda_{Xe})}$$

Since the third term in Equation 3-4-26 is generally small compared with the second (due to the larger values of λ_{Te} compared with both λ_I and λ_{Xe}), it can be neglected for our present purposes. For the same reason the ratio $\lambda_{Te}/(\lambda_{Te} - \lambda_I)$ in the parameter A_1 can be taken equal to unity. Equation 3-4-26 can then be written

$$\frac{Xe}{Xe_0} = e^{-\lambda_{Xe} t} + A_1(e^{-\lambda_{Xe} t} - e^{-\lambda_I t}) \qquad (3\text{-}4\text{-}27)$$

where

$$A_1 = \frac{0.056}{0.059} \frac{\lambda_{Xe} + \sigma_{Xe}\varphi_{th}}{\lambda_I - \lambda_{Xe}}$$

This function has a maximum value when

$$t = \frac{1}{\lambda_I - \lambda_{Xe}} \ln\left(\frac{A_1}{1 + A_1} \frac{\lambda_I}{\lambda_{Xe}}\right) \qquad (3\text{-}4\text{-}28)$$

For very large neutron flux ($\varphi_{th} \gg \lambda_{Xe}/\sigma_{Xe}$), the ratio $A_1/(1 + A_1)$ is approximately unity, so that the time after shutdown when the maximum concentration of xenon occurs is

$$t = \frac{1}{\lambda_I - \lambda_{Xe}} \ln \frac{\lambda_I}{\lambda_{Xe}} \qquad (3\text{-}4\text{-}29)$$

or, with numerical values of the half-lives, 6.7 hours for iodine-135 and 9.2 hours for xenon-135, and with the cross section for xenon-135 of 3.5×10^6 barns, $t = 11.3$ hours. For these same conditions, $A_1 = 4.25 \times 10^{13}\varphi_{th}$. Substituting these values into Equation 3-4-27 for very large fluxes (greater than about 10^{14} neutrons per square centimeter per second) for which $\varphi_{th} \gg \lambda_{Xe}/\delta_{Xe}$, we obtain

$$\frac{Xe}{Xe_0} = 0.497 \times 10^{-13}\varphi_{th} \qquad (3\text{-}4\text{-}30)$$

It can be seen from Equation 3-4-30 that the accumulation of xenon-135 poisoning, for very large reactor power (neutron flux greater than 10^{14}) becomes very large indeed after shutdown. There is a period, of the order of a day, in which start-up of the reactor requires the addition of large amounts of reactivity to overcome the xenon poisoning. For smaller powers the time required to reach the maximum amount of xenon becomes shorter, the build-up at this point also being much smaller.

For a high-power reactor, xenon (and to a lesser extent samarium) poisoning causes three main problems. Excess reactivity over that required for starting the reactor must be provided to override the steady-state accumulation. Even more reactivity must be supplied to start the reactor during a period of the order of a day after shut-down. Control apparatus must be provided to adjust for the variations in the quantity of xenon which accompany excursions in reactor power. All these changes are relatively slow compared with other requirements on control apparatus. In the following paragraphs some effects will be discussed which are not necessarily slow compared with the capabilities of control apparatus.

We will now discuss in detail the temperature effects and derive an expression for α_1 in terms of reactor characteristics for an idealized thermal reactor. The temperature coefficient can be defined as

$$\alpha_1 = \frac{\partial \delta}{\partial T} \tag{3-4-31}$$

When k_1 can be considered constant, this is equivalent to

$$\alpha_1 = \frac{\partial k}{\partial T} \tag{3-4-32}$$

Substituting Equation 3-4-5 into Equation 3-4-32 gives

$$\alpha_1 = \frac{\partial (pf\eta\epsilon)}{\partial T} \tag{3-4-33}$$

Since the resonance escape probability, p, neutron production efficiency, η, and the fast fission effect, ϵ, are essentially independent of the temperature, this can be written

$$\alpha_1 = p\eta\epsilon \frac{\partial f}{\partial T} \tag{3-4-34}$$

From Equation 3-4-12 the change in the thermal utilization with temperature is

$$\frac{\partial f}{\partial T} = -\left(\frac{1}{1+c}\right)^2 \frac{\partial c}{\partial T} = -f^2 \frac{\partial c}{\partial T} \tag{3-4-35}$$

Substituting into Equation 3-4-34 gives

$$\alpha_1 = -pf\eta\epsilon f \frac{\partial c}{\partial T} = -kf \frac{\partial c}{\partial T} \qquad (3\text{-}4\text{-}36)$$

In general, the product kf will be close to unity in a nearly critical reactor and the temperature coefficient α_1 will be measured approximately by $-\dfrac{\partial c}{\partial T}$, which is the measure of the rate of change with temperature of the ratios of captures outside the fuel to captures in the fuel. This ratio will not change rapidly with temperature except near a region of large resonance capture where microscopic cross sections from some particular material are changing rapidly. The temperature coefficient, then, as has been previously stated, is not usually strongly dependent on changes in nuclear characteristics of the reactor.

The magnitude of the temperature coefficient is also dependent on the physical size of the reactor. This size can be determined from the criticality condition of Equation 3-1-14, which can be written

$$k_1 = 1 + \kappa^2 M^2 \qquad (3\text{-}4\text{-}37)$$

The temperature coefficient is then, from Equations 3-1-16 and 3-4-32,

$$\alpha_1 = -\frac{\partial k_1}{\partial T} = -\frac{\partial(\kappa^2 M^2)}{\partial T} \qquad (3\text{-}4\text{-}38)$$

Expanding the derivative term gives

$$\alpha_1 = -\left[\kappa^2 \frac{\partial M^2}{\partial T} + M^2 \frac{\partial \kappa^2}{\partial T}\right] \qquad (3\text{-}4\text{-}39)$$

κ^2 was previously defined in Chapter 2 as α^2/R^2, where α is a dimensionless ratio characteristic only of the overall shape of the reactor and the distribution of materials in it. The derivative of κ^2 can then be written

$$\frac{\partial \kappa^2}{\partial T} = -\frac{2\alpha^2}{R^3} \frac{\partial R}{\partial T} \qquad (3\text{-}4\text{-}40)$$

The derivative of M^2 will now be derived. In Chapter 2 the migration area for a thermal reactor was given approximately as

$$M^2 = \frac{1}{3\Sigma_t \Sigma_a} + \frac{u_{th}}{3\xi\Sigma_s \Sigma_t} \qquad (3\text{-}4\text{-}41)$$

It is found experimentally that the logarithmic decrement does not change rapidly with temperature. Since the thermal lethargy is a logarithmic function of temperature, its change with temperature will be quite small for reasonable changes in temperature (dependent on ratio of change in temperature to absolute temperature). The macroscopic cross section has been defined in terms of microscopic cross section as

$$\Sigma = \frac{N_0 \rho \sigma}{A} \tag{3-4-42}$$

Where N_0 is Avogadro's number, ρ is the density of material in space, σ is the microscopic cross section, and A is the atomic mass number. It has been found experimentally that the microscopic scattering and transport cross section do not usually change rapidly with temperature. The largest changes in macroscopic cross section, then, will be due to changes in the densities of scattering and absorbing materials. Designating absorbing material by the subscript a, and scattering material by subscript s (or t), we have

$$M^2 = \frac{A_s}{3N_0^2 \sigma_t} \frac{1}{\rho_t} \left[\frac{A_a}{\sigma_a \rho_a} + \frac{u_{th} A_s}{\xi \sigma_s \rho_s} \right] \tag{3-4-43}$$

The temperature derivative is

$$\frac{\partial M^2}{\partial T} = - \frac{A_s}{3N_0^2 \sigma_t} \frac{1}{\rho_t} \left[\left\{ \frac{A_a}{\rho_s \sigma_a \rho_a} + \frac{2u_{th} A_s}{\xi \sigma_s \rho_s^2} \right\} \frac{\partial \rho_s}{\partial T} + \frac{A_a}{\sigma_a \rho_a^2} \frac{\partial \rho_a}{\partial T} \right] \tag{3-4-44}$$

Substituting Equation 3-4-42 into Equation 3-4-44

$$\frac{\partial M^2}{\partial T} = - \frac{1}{3\Sigma_t} \left[\left\{ \left(\frac{1}{\Sigma_a} + \frac{2u_{th}}{\xi \Sigma_s} \right) \frac{1}{\rho_s} \right\} \frac{\partial \rho_s}{\partial T} + \frac{1}{\Sigma_a \rho_a} \frac{\partial \rho_a}{\partial T} \right] \tag{3-4-45}$$

From Equations 3-4-40 and 3-4-39, we can see that an increase in reactor radius with an increase in temperature gives a positive temperature coefficient (due to decreased leakage from the large reactor). From Equations 3-4-39 and 3-4-44, we can see that a decrease in density of either reflectors (or moderators) or absorbers (fuel has been assumed to be the primary absorber) with increasing temperature results in a negative temperature coefficient. There are thus two compensating effects of changes in physical dimensions of the reactor on the temperature coefficient. One which is due to the overall increase in reactor size with increasing temperature is positive, and one which is due to the decrease in density of internal materials is negative. For a given reactor a detailed accounting is needed.

It should be observed that not all temperature effects are simultaneous. Fuel materials are heated very directly by the fission process whereas structural materials and coolants, for instance, are generally heated more slowly by thermal diffusion. Hence rapid transients will be quite different for these two cases.

The behavior of a reactor with an excess multiplication factor is strongly dependent on the reactivity coefficients. Particularly important is the sign of the coefficient in question. Let us consider the effect of the temperature coefficient. First for a positive temperature coefficient, the reactivity increases as the temperature rises; since the temperature is normally higher for higher power, the reactor power will rise on an ever-increasing exponential. For a negative temperature coefficient, on the other hand, as the power, and therefore also the temperature, rises, the reactivity becomes ever less. At some point, therefore, the excess multiplication factor becomes zero, and the reactor power can no longer increase. A negative temperature coefficient is thus to be preferred to a positive coefficient, since the potential increase in power due to excess activity would seem to be limited in the first case but not in the second.

Two serious questions arise, however, that are due to the negative temperature coefficient. First, if the reactor is capable of operation at a high temperature, then owing to the negative temperature coefficient it has an excess multiplication factor when it is cold. The larger the numerical value of the coefficient, the greater must be the excess multiplication factor in the cold reactor. Aside from the added fissionable material required to provide the excess multiplication for bringing the reactor up to operating temperature, adequate precautions are necessary to insure that this excess will never be added too rapidly. Second, the reactor is rendered susceptible to the possibility of an oscillating, or dynamic, type of instability. The negative temperature coefficient acts to some extent like a restoring force in a mechanical system undergoing self-induced oscillations. Since a large amount of energy (from fissions) is available to support such self-induced oscillations if they are possible, the dynamic stability of the reactor would seem possibly to be tied in with the numerical magnitude of the negative temperature coefficient. This question of dynamic stability is complicated by two facts. The equations of the simplest form possible to approximate much of the physical phenomena of the transient behavior of the reactor are non-linear, and are time-consuming in their solution. Also the most complicated equations which can be solved are still probably not adequate to describe the intricate details of the system of which the reactor is a part, and which govern its stability. Experiments, in the early stages of the design of the reactor power system, should be run with apparatus which is capable of duplicating as closely as possible the dynamic behavior of the system. Despite these difficulties, let us investigate analytically at least the rudimentary behavior of an elementary system, being constantly aware of the inadequacies of our investigation.

3-5. Non-linear Behavior of Reactors

Equation 3-3-3 gives a relationship between the excess multiplication factor and the rate of increase of power. Equation 3-4-4 gives the dependence of the multiplication factor on the temperatures, densities, and power densities in various parts of the reactor. The excess multiplication factor can be eliminated to give an expression for reactor power P in terms of reactor average temperature $\bar{T}$ and reactor density ρ. For example, let us assume a reactivity coefficient which can be expressed entirely in terms of temperatures, so that

$$\delta = \delta_1(t) + \alpha(\bar{T} - \bar{T}_0) \tag{3-5-1}$$

where $\delta_1(t)$ is the excess multiplication factor provided by the motion of control rods, etc., and $\bar{T}_0$ is the average temperature, as defined before, for a critical reactor, with $\delta_1(t) = 0$. By combining Equations 3-3-3 and 3-5-1 to eliminate the excess multiplication factor, an equation is obtained relating power and average temperature. This is

$$\frac{dP}{dt} = \lambda\{[\alpha(\bar{T} - \bar{T}_0) - \beta + \delta_1]P + \beta P_{av}\} \tag{3-5-2}$$

Equation 3-5-2 is one equation in two dependent variables, the reactor power P, and the average reactor temperature $\bar{T}$. Since these dependent variables appear as a product on the right side of the equation, Equation 3-5-2 is non-linear. It can be rearranged for future convenience of solution by dividing both sides by the reactor power P, giving

$$\frac{d \ln P}{dt} = \lambda \left\{\alpha(\bar{T} - \bar{T}_0) - \beta + \delta_1 + \beta \frac{P_{av}}{P}\right\} \tag{3-5-3}$$

In order to solve Equation 3-5-3 it is necessary to eliminate the average reactor temperature $\bar{T}$ from the equation. It is evident that another relationship is needed to relate reactor power to reactor temperature. For the purpose of obtaining such a relationship it is necessary to solve the thermodynamic equations which describe the transient behavior of the heat-extracting medium in the reactor, subject to boundary conditions which are determined by the system of which the reactor is one part. These thermodynamic equations will be written for a compressible fluid. Then, for the sake of an example, these will be specialized to an incompressible fluid. These equations will then be rearranged to give the desired expression for reactor power and average temperature.

The thermodynamic equations describing the transient behavior of a compressible fluid, to which heat is being added and by which work is being done, are four equations stating the conservation of (1) mass, (2) momentum, and (3) energy, and (4) an equation of state for the fluid. The conservation of mass for the transient case requires

$$\frac{\partial}{\partial x}(\gamma v A) + A\frac{\partial \gamma}{\partial t} = 0 \tag{3-5-4}$$

where γ is the fluid weight density, v is its velocity, and A is the area of the passage in which the fluid flows. Conservation of momentum for the transient case requires

$$-dw = \frac{v\,dv}{g} + \frac{1}{\gamma}\frac{\partial p}{\partial x}dx + df \tag{3-5-5}$$

where dw is the external work done by unit weight of fluid, p is the pressure, and df is the friction energy lost per unit weight of fluid. The conservation of energy for the transient case requires

$$dq - dw = \frac{v\,dv}{g} + dh - \frac{1}{\gamma}\frac{\partial p}{\partial t}dt \tag{3-5-6}$$

where dq is the heat added to unit weight of fluid and h is the enthalpy per unit weight of fluid. An appropriate equation of state might take the form

$$h = h(p, \gamma) \tag{3-5-7}$$

Equations 3-5-4 to 3-5-7 are non-linear, and in general susceptible only to numerical solution. Certain linearizing approximations can sometimes be made to render these equations susceptible to analytical solution. The simplest of these assumptions, which will be used for example here, is that the fluid is incompressible (density dependent on temperature only—not on pressure). This assumption is acceptable for liquids, and for the steady-state flow of gases at low velocities. It is not at all acceptable for gases for transient flow or for flow at velocities near acoustic.

Let us consider an incompressible fluid flowing in a cylindrical passage at uniform velocity through the reactor and heated uniformly along the reactor passage. For this passage Equation 3-5-4 is satisfied trivially. Equations 3-5-5 and 3-5-6 combine to give

$$dq + df = dh - \frac{1}{\gamma}dp \tag{3-5-8}$$

Since all the pressure variation in the passage for an incompressible fluid is due to friction, $df = -\frac{1}{\gamma} dp$, and Equation 3-5-8 becomes

$$dq = dh \tag{3-5-9}$$

For the incompressible fluid (or a perfect gas) in which there is no latent heat involved the equation of state can be written

$$dh = c_p \, dT \tag{3-5-10}$$

where c_p is the specific heat of the fluid at constant pressure. Combining Equations 3-5-9 and 3-5-10 gives

$$dq = c_p \, dT \tag{3-5-11}$$

Since dq gives the heat added to unit weight of the fluid, the power density is given by the product of $\frac{dq}{dt}$ by the weight of fluid in the passage, or by

$$dP = c_p \frac{dT}{dt} \gamma A \, dx \tag{3-5-12}$$

If there are m passages in the reactor, and if the flow rate and temperature rise are the same for all passages, then the total power developed in the reactor is given by

$$P = \frac{1}{S} \int_0^1 \frac{dT}{dt} d\xi \tag{3-5-13}$$

where $S = \dfrac{1}{c_p \gamma A L m}$ and where A is the total area for flow through the reactor passage, L is the length of the reactor passage, and ξ is a dimensionless length through the reactor, $\xi = x/L$.

We now have a second equation relating power and temperature. Before the equation can be combined with Equation 3-5-3 it is necessary to eliminate the space variable ξ and to write the equation in terms of the average temperature. The total derivative of temperature can be expanded into

$$\frac{dT}{dt} = \frac{\partial T}{\partial t} + \frac{1}{\tau} \frac{\partial T}{\partial \xi} \tag{3-5-14}$$

where $\tau = L/v$ is the transit time for the cooling fluid through the reactor. Substituting Equation 3-5-14 into Equation 3-5-13, we obtain

$$P = \frac{1}{S} \left[\int_0^1 \frac{\partial T}{\partial t} d\xi + \frac{1}{\tau} \int_0^1 \frac{\partial T}{\partial \xi} d\xi \right] \tag{3-5-15}$$

Because the temperature coefficient is expressed in terms of the average reactor temperature, it is desirable to express the power also in the same terms. The average temperature is defined:

$$\bar{T}(t) = \int_0^1 T(\xi, t)\, d\xi \tag{3-5-16}$$

Since the average temperature is a function only of time, its total derivative, from Equation 3-5-16, is

$$\frac{d\bar{T}}{dt} = \int_0^1 \frac{\partial T}{\partial t}\, d\xi \tag{3-5-17}$$

Substituting Equation 3-5-17 into Equation 3-5-15 and performing the integration with respect to ξ, we obtain

$$SP = \frac{d\bar{T}}{dt} + \frac{1}{\tau}(T_1 - T_0) \tag{3-5-18}$$

where T_1 is the temperature at the outlet of the reactor and T_0 the temperature at the inlet. Differentiating Equation 3-5-18 with respect to t, since for later convenience the second derivative of average temperature is needed, we have

$$S\frac{dP}{dt} = \frac{d^2\bar{T}}{dt^2} + \frac{1}{\tau}\left(\frac{dT_1}{dt} - \frac{dT_0}{dt}\right) \tag{3-5-19}$$

We now have eliminated the space variable in our second expression relating power and average reactor temperature. However, before we can use this equation, it is necessary to express the temperatures at the end of the passage, T_1 and T_0, in terms of power and average temperature. Since we have assumed that the power density is uniform along the length of the reactor passage, Equation 3-5-13 can be written also

$$P = \frac{1}{S}\frac{dT}{dt} \tag{3-5-20}$$

Or, substituting Equation 3-5-14, we have

$$P = \frac{1}{S}\left(\frac{\partial T}{\partial t} + \frac{1}{\tau}\frac{\partial T}{\partial \xi}\right) \tag{3-5-21}$$

In terms of values at the end of the passage, Equation 3-5-21 becomes

$$\frac{dT_1}{dt} = SP(t) - \frac{1}{\tau}\frac{\partial T}{\partial \xi}\Bigg]_{\xi=1,\ t=t} \tag{3-5-22}$$

Also owing to the uniformity of the power density, the spatial derivative of the temperature at the outlet end of the passage at time t is the same as the spatial derivative at the beginning of the passage at a previous time, earlier by the transit time of the fluid through the reactor, τ, or

$$\frac{\partial T}{\partial \xi}\bigg]_{\xi=1,\ t=t} = \frac{\partial T}{\partial \xi}\bigg]_{\xi=0,\ t=t-\tau} \qquad (3\text{-}5\text{-}23)$$

Substituting this into Equation 3-5-22 gives

$$\frac{dT_1}{dt} = SP(t) - \frac{1}{\tau}\frac{\partial T}{\partial \xi}\bigg]_{\xi=0,\ t=t-\tau} \qquad (3\text{-}5\text{-}24)$$

The spatial derivative at $t = t - \tau$ can be expressed in terms of the power generated at time $t = t - \tau$, by use of Equation 3-5-21:

$$\frac{1}{\tau}\frac{\partial T}{\partial \xi}\bigg]_{\xi=0,\ t=t-\tau} = SP(t-\tau) - \frac{dT_0}{dt}\bigg]_{t=t-\tau} \qquad (3\text{-}5\text{-}25)$$

Let

$$\zeta = \frac{1}{SP_0}\frac{dT_0}{dt} \qquad (3\text{-}5\text{-}26)$$

where P_0 is the power generated at time $t = 0$. Substitute Equations 3-5-24, 3-5-25, and 3-5-26 into Equation 3-5-19:

$$\frac{d^2\overline{T}}{dt^2} = S\left(\frac{dP}{dt} - \frac{1}{\tau}[P(t) - P(t-\tau) - P_0\{\zeta(t) - \zeta(t-\tau)\}]\right) \qquad (3\text{-}5\text{-}27)$$

Equation 3-5-27 gives the second relationship between average temperature and power output for a reactor in which the inlet temperature is a variable. The first term on the right is due to the heat stored in the reactor; the second term (in square brackets) is due to the heat dumped into the piping downstream from the reactor during the transient variation of power.

We can now combine Equation 3-5-27 and Equation 3-5-3 to produce an equation relating reactor power with time. This will be used to discuss the transient behavior of reactors, after first simplifying and regrouping the terms. Eliminating the average temperature from Equations 3-5-27 and 3-5-3 gives a differential equation for the reactor power:

$$\frac{d^3 \ln P}{dt^3} = \lambda\beta\frac{d^2}{dt^2}\left(\frac{P_{av}}{P}\right) + \lambda\frac{d^2\delta_1}{dt^2} + \alpha\lambda S\left(\frac{dP}{dt} - \frac{1}{\tau}[P(t) - P(t-\tau)\right.$$
$$\left. - P_0\{\zeta(t) - \zeta(t-\tau)\}]\right) \qquad (3\text{-}5\text{-}28)$$

It is convenient to express this equation in terms of dimensionless variables. Let

$$\eta = t/\theta$$

$$\rho = \frac{P}{P_0}$$

$$\delta_1(t) = \delta_0 f(t)$$

where θ is a characteristic time for the reactor, which may be, for example, the transit time of the fluid through the reactor ($\theta = \tau$) or the period of the power oscillation, if there is such an oscillation. Thus η is a dimensionless time for reactor transients. The quantity ρ is dimensionless reactor power density in terms of power at time t_0. The function $f(t)$ relates the excess activity at time t, $\delta_1(t)$, to the excess activity applied at time t_0. For convenience of handling Equation 3-5-28, also let

$$A = \lambda \delta_0 \theta$$

$$B = -\alpha \lambda S P_0 \theta^2$$

$$a = \frac{\beta}{\delta_0} \frac{P_{av}}{P_0}$$

$$b = \frac{\tau}{\theta}$$

$$c = \frac{\beta}{\delta_0}$$

Now Equation 3-5-28 becomes, if we neglect changes in inlet temperature, for simplicity,

$$\frac{d^3 \ln \rho}{d\eta^3} = A \left[a \frac{d^2}{d\eta^2} \left(\frac{1}{\rho} \right) + \frac{d^2 f}{d\eta^2} \right] - B \left\{ \frac{d\rho}{d\eta} - \frac{1}{b} [\rho(\eta) - \rho(\eta - b)] \right\}$$

$$(3\text{-}5\text{-}29)$$

Here A is the dimensionless initial excess activity and B is the dimensionless operating power level at time $\eta = 0$, whereas the parameters a and c measure the effect of delayed neutrons and the parameter b is the dimensionless transit time for the reactor fluid. Neglecting changes in inlet temperature to the reactor amounts to the assumption that there are no important transient couplings with the external power system. This assumption is not justified where transients arising in the reactor are propagated around the entire power system and fed back again into the reactor. It is also not justified if transients arising in the external power system are propagated into the reactor.

Equation 3-5-29 is a non-linear relation between reactor power and time which will now be used to discuss the transient behavior of our simplified reactor. Before considering the solution of the non-linear equation, let us consider the limiting form for very small changes in the operating power level, for which the linear approximation can be used. This linear approximation will establish a limit to the non-linear equation for small amplitudes, and will help us decide what to look for in the non-linear case. Let us assume that there are no delayed neutrons, and that no control rods are moved after the time $t = 0$. The linear approximation to Equation 3-5-29 for this case becomes

$$\frac{d^3\rho}{d\eta^3} = -B\left(\frac{d\rho}{d\eta} - \frac{1}{b}[\rho(\eta) - \rho(\eta - b)]\right) \qquad (3\text{-}5\text{-}30)$$

In the linear approximation all terms of the equation are reduced to linear terms. For instance,

$$\frac{d \ln \rho}{d\eta} = \frac{1}{\rho_0}\frac{d\rho}{d\eta} = \frac{d\rho}{d\eta}$$

since ρ_0 is by definition $P_0/P_0 = 1$.

Let us try a solution to Equation 3-5-30 of the form

$$\rho = 1 + (\rho_{max} - 1) \sin \sqrt{B}\, \eta + K\eta \qquad (3\text{-}5\text{-}31)$$

where ρ_{max} is the maximum amplitude of the sinusoidal oscillation about a mean line of power variation. Substitution of Equation 3-5-31 into Equation 3-5-30 demonstrates that this solution can apply only if $\sqrt{B}\, b = 2\pi n$, where n is any integer. The solution is good for all values of K. This gives the interesting result that, for variations of power small enough to allow the linear approximation, oscillations of a resonant nature are possible, not only periodically ($K = 0$), but also about a mean line of slope K. The linear approximation, of course, holds only for small values of K. Physically, what is happening is that the rising power in the reactor is being used to heat up the power apparatus behind the reactor, rather than heating the reactor itself. Thus, for however long this process can continue, the limiting effect of the negative temperature coefficient of reactivity on power is not being applied. It can be shown by including the term for the delayed neutrons in the linearized equation that the delayed neutrons have the effect of damping the oscillations. To consider the reactor as a part of a specific reactor system it would be necessary to balance this damping effect against whatever forcing or feedback effect might be fed in from the rest of the system by the term involving motion of control rods, etc. It must be remembered here, too, that the assumption of constant power density in the reactor is probably very unrealistic, and may well exclude some physical phenomena of interest for the transient behavior of particular nuclear reactors. Within the limitations which have been set on the problem, we have found the result that the reactor can maintain small oscillations only if delayed neutrons are dissipated outside the reactor, so that none are left inside, and if the combination of variables involved in $\sqrt{B}\, b$ has the value $2\pi n$, or, if, for definiteness, b is set equal to unity (the characteristic time for the reactor is then identified with the transit time), $\sqrt{B} = 2\pi n$, giving

$$-\alpha\lambda SP_0\tau^2 = 4\pi^2 n^2 \qquad (3\text{-}5\text{-}32)$$

Since all other quantities in this equation are positive, the temperature coefficient, α, is required to be negative to support oscillations, as is to be expected from intuitive considerations. Since the lowest non-trivial solution is for $n = 1$, oscillations cannot exist unless B, the dimensionless reactor operating power at time zero, is greater than $4\pi^2$, or about 40.

Consideration of the non-linear case by numerical procedures is probably most easily accomplished by integrating Equation 3-5-29 three times, which, when boundary conditions (here taken to be $\rho = 1$ and $\dfrac{d\overline{T}}{dt} = 0$ for $\eta = 0$) are applied, gives the following integral equation:

$$\ln \rho = A\left[a\int_0^\eta \frac{1}{\rho}\,d\eta_1 + \int_0^\eta (f - c)\,d\eta_1\right] - B\left\{\int_0^\eta d\eta_1 \int_0^{\eta_1} (\rho - 1)\,d\eta_2\right.$$

$$\left. - \frac{1}{b}\int_0^\eta d\eta_1 \int_0^{\eta_1} d\eta_2 \int_0^{\eta_2} [\rho(\eta_3) - \rho(\eta_3 - b)]\,d\eta_3\right\} \qquad (3\text{-}5\text{-}33)$$

Let us consider two types of impulse often used in studies of transient response and previously discussed in this chapter, the unit step and the linear ramp. Remembering the definition of f in terms of the excess activity, $\delta(t) = \delta_0 f(t)$, we see that for a unit step increase of multiplication factor at $\eta = 0$, $f = 1$. For a linear ramp, starting at $f(\eta) = 0$, $\eta = 0$ and ending at $f(\eta) = 1$, $\eta = 1$, then $f(\eta) = \eta$ for $0 < \eta < 1$ and $f(\eta) = 1$ for $1 < \eta < \infty$. Equation 3-5-33 can be used both to find possible non-linear periodic solutions and to find the transients which exist after the motion of control rods or any sudden change in the operating conditions in the reactor. In its present form, it is limited to a constant inlet temperature, though this limitation is not a necessary one, for solution of the problem.

Let us now repeat a general description of a reactor to which Equation 3-5-33 may be applied. It will be recognized that this description applies to a very much simplified version of an actual reactor power system. The following assumptions have been made. The reactor consists of a system of parallel and uniform heat-transfer passages. Power density in the reactor is uniform. The time for heat generated in nuclear fuel to be transferred to the cooling fluid is negligible compared with transient times in the reactor. The cooling fluid is incompressible, so that density changes are attributable only to temperature, not to pressure. The inlet temperature of the cooling fluid does not change with time; or the reactor is coupled with an external power system which accepts all transient exit conditions established by the reactor and feeds none of these back into the reactor inlet.

There are three requirements for a periodic solution to Equation 3-5-33. These can be taken, for convenience, to be the following: (1) The function ρ has the value unity at $\eta = 0$. (2) The function ρ has the value unity also at $\eta = 1.0$. (3) The slope of the function $\ln \rho$ has the same value at $\eta = 0$ and at $\eta = 1.0$. The first of these conditions is satisfied by taking

$$\ln \rho]_{\eta=0} = 0 \qquad (3\text{-}5\text{-}34)$$

From Equation 3-5-33 the second condition is then satisfied by

$$\frac{A}{B} =$$

$$\frac{\int_0^1 d\eta_1 \int_0^{\eta_1} (\rho - 1)\, d\eta_2 - \frac{1}{b} \int_0^1 d\eta_1 \int_0^{\eta_1} d\eta_2 \int_0^{\eta_2} [\rho(\eta_3) - \rho(\eta_3 - b)]\, d\eta_3}{a \int_0^1 \frac{1}{\rho}\, d\eta_1 + \int_0^1 (f - c)\, d\eta_1}$$

$$(3\text{-}5\text{-}35)$$

The third condition is satisfied by differentiating Equation 3-5-33 with respect to η. The values of the derivative at $\eta = 0$ and at $\eta = 1$ are equated to give

$$\int_0^1 (\rho - 1)\, d\eta_1 - \frac{1}{b} \int_0^1 d\eta_1 \int_0^{\eta_1} [\rho(\eta_2) - \rho(\eta_2 - b)]\, d\eta_2$$

$$= \frac{A}{B} [f(\eta_1) - f(\eta_0)] \quad (3\text{-}5\text{-}36)$$

Since for a periodic solution, the excess reactivity must also be periodic, $f(\eta_1) = f(\eta_0)$, and Equation 3-5-36 becomes

$$\int_0^1 (\rho - 1)\, d\eta_1 - \frac{1}{b}\int_0^1 d\eta_1 \int_0^{\eta_1} [\rho(\eta_2) - \rho(\eta_2 - b)]\, d\eta_2 = 0 \quad (3\text{-}5\text{-}37)$$

Equations 3-5-34, 3-5-35, and 3-5-37 are to be satisfied in a numerical solution of Equation 3-5-33.

Because of the non-linearity of the system these conditions for periodicity are most easily satisfied by trial-and-error methods, where, for instance, a solution is made with a trial value of B, and the departure from the zero value in Equation 3-5-37 is used as a measure of the departure from periodicity. Apparently the requirements for periodicity can be satisfied only for limited values of the coefficients of the equations, including the limitation that there must be no delayed neutrons. This is a familiar situation in problems of vibrations, in which vibrations, without forcing functions, are maintained only at natural frequencies, and die out when damping forces (in this case delayed neutrons) are applied. It is found, too, that the periods for periodic oscillations of reactor power are multiples of the transit time of the reactor cooling fluid ($b = 1, 2, 3, \cdots$). For an oscillatory change in power about some mean line of rising or falling power it is not necessary to satisfy Equation 3-5-35, and b is not required to be an integer. It should be noted that for a periodic solution, with $b = 1, \rho(\eta) = \rho(\eta - b)$ and the difference $[\rho(\eta) - \rho(\eta - b)]$ is zero wherever it occurs.

Several numerical solutions to Equation 3-5-33 have been made, using different values of the controlling parameters. Figure 3-5-1 shows the combinations of parameters for which periodic solutions to the non-linear equation exist as found by numerical solution to Equation 3-5-33, in the range from $B = 20$ to $B = 120$, with the factor $b = 1$, $2, 3, \cdots$. The low end of the curve gives an approximate check on the value $B = 40$ for the linearized approximation to the equations. As the amplitude of the periodic oscillation increases, the value of B which is necessary to make the oscillation possible also increases as would be expected of a non-linear oscillation.

Also on Figure 3-5-1 is plotted the maximum value of the dimensionless excess multiplication factor which occurs during the oscillation. The approximate shapes of the curves for several of these oscillations are plotted as a function of time in Figure 3-5-2. Since only ten time points were used in these calculations, the results can be considered as indicative. It can be seen that, as the maximum amplitude of the oscillation increases, the reactor spends less of the time at powers above

the operating level. A sample calculation for a periodic oscillation is
shown in Table 3-5-1. In this calculation a and c are zero, and for
every point $\rho(\eta) = \rho(\eta - b)$. A set of trial values of ρ are assumed for
Equation 3-5-33, and the integrations are performed using the trap-
ezoidal rule for integration. Values of A and B are chosen so as to

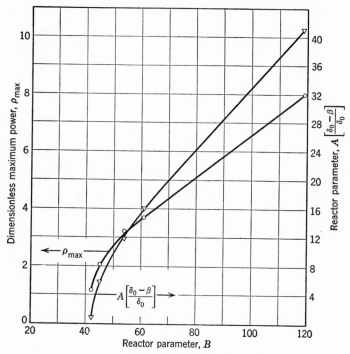

FIG. 3-5-1.   Required relationships for periodic oscillations.

$$a = c = 0$$
$$b = 1, 2, 3, \cdots$$

satisfy the conditions for a periodic oscillation from Equations 3-5-35
and 3-5-37. For instance, in Table 3-5-1, the value of the ratio A/B
is given by the ratio of the last number in column 4 (0.1288) to the
last number in column 1 (1.0) (since $\int_0^1 f \, d\eta_1 = 1.0$, with $f = 1$).
The value of B is found by trial and error to make $\int_0^1 (\rho - 1) \, d\eta = 0$
within the limits of accuracy of the calculations. (As shown, the net
sum of the terms of column 12 is 0.02, which was considered satisfactory.) The calculation is stopped when the calculated values for ρ on

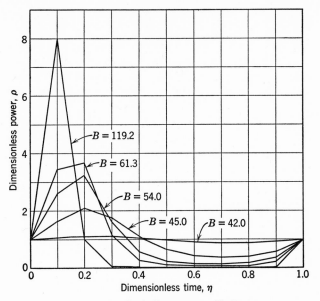

FIG. 3-5-2. Periodic power oscillations.

$$a = c = 0$$
$$b = 1, 2, 3, \cdots$$

TABLE 3-5-1. PERIODIC OSCILLATION

0	1	2	3	4	5	6	7	8	9	10	11	12
η	ρ	$\rho - 1$	$\int (2)$	$\int (3)$	$\begin{array}{c}0.1288 \\ \times \eta\end{array}$	$\begin{array}{c}(5) \\ \times (4)\end{array}$	$\begin{array}{c}40 \\ \times (5)\end{array}$	ρ	$\rho - 1$	$\begin{array}{c}45 \\ \times (5)\end{array}$	ρ	$\rho - 1$
0	1.00	0	0	0	0	0	0	1.00	0	0	1.00	0
0.1	1.65	0.65	0.033	0.0017	0.0129	0.0112	0.45	1.57	0.57	0.50	1.65	0.65
0.2	2.08	1.08	0.120	0.0094	0.0257	0.0163	0.65	1.92	0.92	0.73	2.08	1.08
0.3	1.75	0.75	0.212	0.0260	0.0386	0.0126	0.50	1.65	0.65	0.57	1.77	0.77
0.4	1.11	0.11	0.255	0.0494	0.0515	0.0021	0.08	1.08	0.08	0.09	1.09	0.09
0.5	0.64	−0.36	0.242	0.0743	0.0643	−0.0100	−0.40	0.67	−0.33	−0.45	0.65	−0.35
0.6	0.42	−0.58	0.195	0.0962	0.0772	−0.0190	−0.76	0.47	−0.53	−0.86	0.42	−0.58
0.7	0.36	−0.64	0.134	0.1127	0.0901	−0.0226	−0.90	0.41	−0.59	−1.02	0.36	−0.64
0.8	0.40	−0.60	0.072	0.1230	0.1031	−0.0199	−0.80	0.45	−0.55	−0.90	0.41	−0.59
0.9	0.59	−0.41	0.021	0.1277	0.1160	−0.0117	−0.47	0.63	−0.37	−0.53	0.59	−0.41
1.0	1.00	0	0	0.1288	0.1288	0	0	1.00	0	0	1.00	0

$A/B = 0.1288$
$B = 45$

$$\int (\rho - 1) = -0.15$$

$= +0.02$

the left side of the equation are the same as the assumed values on the right.   Figure 3-5-3 shows the damping effect of the delayed neutrons on a periodic oscillation.   During the period, $-\infty < \eta < 0$, the power is supposed to have undergone a periodic oscillation as shown, no delayed neutrons being present.   At $\eta = 0$ delayed neutrons are ad-

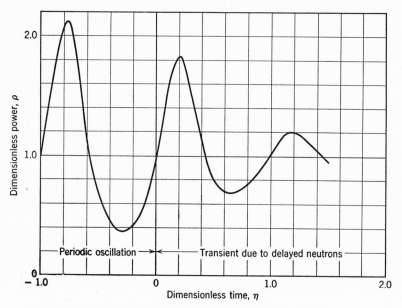

FIG. 3-5-3.   Transient effect of delayed neutrons on reactor power.

For periodic oscillation:	For transient oscillation:
$A = 5.8$	$A = 9.85$
$B = 45$	$B = 45$
$a = c = 0$	$a = c = 0.7$
$b = 1, 2, 3, \cdots$	$b = 1.0$

mitted ($\beta = 0.007$), keeping the total excess activity (δ_0) the same, so that the slope of the power curve is continuous at $\eta = 0$.

Figure 3-5-4 shows a different kind of solution to the non-linear problem, with the parameter $b = 0.4$ rather than integer, suggestive of the solution in the linearized case in which the power oscillated about a mean line of slope K.   Here the power history prior to time zero is arbitrarily assumed as being due to a particular motion of a control rod, for instance.   The curve for reactor power ascends in a stepwise fashion to large values, executing a series of oscillations about a mean line.   The temperature coefficient apparently does not limit the rise because all the excess power generated during any oscillation is used to raise the temperature of the power apparatus behind the reactor rather than the reactor itself. Eventually this effect would be modified by the change in inlet temperature of the fluid which had made a complete circuit of the reactor system, if not by some prior effect.

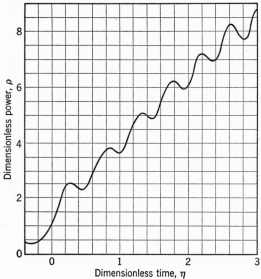

FIG. 3-5-4.   Transient effect of storage of energy in external heat exchangers.

$$A = 5.8 \qquad a = 0$$
$$B = 45.0 \qquad b = 0.4$$

3-6. Reactor Control

In this consideration of reactor kinetics the interrelationships of the reactor with the dynamics of the rest of the system, including the control apparatus, have been ignored. This is a more complicated problem. It is not likely that acceptable solutions to the combined problem can be found without experimental work.

It is obvious that the detailed analysis of a complicated, coupled reactor system is a time-consuming task, involving the use of high-speed computing machines. Since the solution to a non-linear equation is specific to the particular configuration to which it is applied, it is difficult to find general characteristics of a system by this means. For small variations of reactor power linearized equations give acceptable answers. For large variations it is necessary to solve non-linear equations. For normal control purposes it is anticipated that oscillations which are acceptable for engineering purposes are small enough to be considered linear. It may well be that the non-linear considerations are involved only in oscillations of such magnitude, in a power reactor, as to be only the result of an accident of which the consequences are very serious. In this case it is the prevention of the physical phenomenon which is important and not its mathematical analysis.

REFERENCES

Brown, Gordon S., and Donald P. Campbell, *Principles of Servomechanisms*, John Wiley and Sons, New York, 1948.

Gardner, Murray F., and John L. Barnes, *Transients in Linear Systems*, Vol. I, John Wiley and Sons, New York, 1942.

Glasstone, Samuel, and Milton C. Edlund, *The Elements of Nuclear Reactor Theory*, D. Van Nostrand Co., New York, 1952.

MacColl, LeRoy A., *Fundamental Theory of Servomechanisms*, D. Van Nostrand Co., New York, 1942.

CHAPTER 4

SHIELDING OF REACTORS

We have seen that nuclear reactors give off various types of radiation. This radiation is very intense from a reactor operating at high power.

The radiation from a reactor can cause damage to materials and interfere with the functioning of electric and electronic apparatus. However, by far the most serious effect of radiation is the damage caused to living tissue. The intensity of radiation which causes serious damage to living cells is a minute amount compared with the intensity emitted from a nuclear reactor. Consequently, it is necessary to shield a nuclear reactor for the protection of personnel in its vicinity by surrounding it with thick layers of materials to absorb most of the radiations which emanate from it.

It is the purpose of this chapter to discuss some of the elements which enter into the problem of shielding personnel from the radiations which emanate from a nuclear reactor. The types of radiation which must be considered are discussed, and the means available for absorbing these radiations.

4-1. Radiation Damage to Human Tissue

The effects of radiation on the human body are many and varied. High-energy particles, particularly neutrons and gamma rays, cause damage of three general kinds. The first is due to an actual displacement of struck atoms from their normal positions in a lattice structure of atoms. The second is due to ionization of the atoms in the path of a moving charged particle. Neutrons, being electrically neutral, are incapable of direct ionization, but do cause ionization indirectly by setting into motion the charged particles with which they collide. The third type of damage results from the ability of radiation, particularly neutrons and gamma rays, from a reactor to transmute atoms in the living tissue with which they interact into atoms of new materials, which are foreign to the tissue in which they are lodged, and which

131

may themselves be radioactive. The net result of these effects is a
path of damage and destruction of living tissue along the path of the
radiation. Apparently it takes only a small percentage of such dam-
aged tissue to cause serious sickness, or even death. The effects of
radiation applied over short intervals are cumulative, with some heal-
ing (replacement of destroyed cells) occurring over longer periods of
time.

4-2. Types of Radiation from Nuclear Reactors

The main radiations from a nuclear reactor are alpha and beta particles, neutrons, gamma rays, and neutrinos. Of these, the first two
have such low penetrating power that they are stopped easily by relatively insignificant amounts of any materials in their paths. It is
necessary to prevent the escape of alpha- and beta-emitting materials
from the reactor in fluids which might come into direct contact with
human beings or even be breathed into the lungs or ingested into the
stomach. If such radioactive materials become lodged in the body for
long periods of time they are capable of causing cumulative local damage to tissues. Certain alpha-emitting elements at the heavy end of
the chemical series, for instance, uranium and plutonium, tend, when
ingested into the body, to concentrate in the bone marrow where they
do damage to the blood-forming process. Such radioactive materials,
because of the short range of the alpha and beta particles which they
emit, are dangerous only when brought into close proximity to living
tissue. Hence protection must be provided against radioactive materials which are convected from the reactor, for instance, by the circulation of coolant carrying nuclear fuel outside the reactor, or the removal
of radioactive fuel elements or test specimens from the reactor. Neutrinos have no known interaction with any material through which
they pass, and hence are of no interest from the shielding point of view.
Neutrons and gamma rays have intermediate ranges of penetration
such that they are stopped in significant quantities by any materials
in their paths, including human tissue. Reductions in the quantities
of neutrons and gamma rays, of the order required in nuclear reactors
for the protection of personnel, necessitates the use of shielding several
feet in thickness. The neutrons and gamma rays then are the
radiations from a nuclear reactor of primary interest to the shield
designer.

The sources of radiation in a reactor, although all except alpha particles are a result of the fission process, are of several types so far as
shielding problems are concerned. As has been stated, the radiations

of main interest to the shielding designer are neutrons and gamma rays. It is necessary to know both the time and the place of origin of these radiations and their energy of emission.

In the fission process about 200 Mev of energy per fission is released. Of this energy, about 165 Mev is in the form of kinetic energy of the fission fragments. The kinetic energy of the fission fragments, because of their large masses, is absorbed in the immediate vicinity of the fission, and hence is of no interest to the shield designer. Owing to the decay of these fission fragments an additional 12 Mev of energy is given off at times subsequent to the time of fission, 7 Mev being due to beta particles and 5 Mev to gamma rays. As has been stated, since the beta particles are absorbed very close to their point of origin, they are of interest only if they are convected outside the reactor. At the time of fission, 6 Mev of energy in the form of gamma rays is given off. About 5 Mev of energy is given off in the form of kinetic energy of the fission neutrons. In a thermal reactor this kinetic energy is absorbed mostly in the moderator, although the neutrons, particularly fast neutrons, which are not absorbed are still of prime importance for shielding. Owing to the capture of neutrons in processes other than fission about 12 Mev of energy per fission is released in the form of gamma rays.

4-3. Radiation Dosage

Tolerance dosages of radiation for personnel are prescribed in terms of permissible dosage rates over long periods of exposure, and in terms of permissible cumulative dosages for shorter periods of time. The unit of measure for the permissible dose of radiation in common use is the Roentgen, or r unit. This is, by definition, the amount of radiation which will, on passing through pure air under standard conditions, produce one electrostatic unit of ions, of each sign, per cubic centimeter of air. Since the relative absorptivities of tissues for different radiations differ, and are not in general the same as that of air, it is apparent that the limit in the radiation dosage, expressed in r units, will be different for different forms of radiation, for different energies of the radiation, and for different kinds of tissue. The Roentgen unit was originally defined in connection with x-rays or gamma rays. Because the effects of other kinds of radiation from a reactor are similar to those of gamma rays, a unit was desired which could be applied more universally. Such a unit is the rem (Roentgen equivalent man), which is defined as the quantity of radiation which will produce the same amount of damage in human tissue as one r of gamma rays. For various radiations the tabulation below gives the approximate relative effects on human tissue.

Type of Radiation	rem
Gamma (or x-) rays	1
Beta particles	1
Fast neutrons	10
Thermal neutrons	5
Alpha particles	10–20

There are several reasons why it is difficult to establish permissible radiation dosage limits. To mention one, radiation damage to living tissue is not entirely proportional to the amount of radiation absorbed. Below some limit apparently no damage at all is sustained due to exposure to small amounts of radiation, since we are all exposed continuously to small amounts of radiation in the form of cosmic rays and from radioactive materials in the earth about us and even in our own bodies. Apparently, below some limit, radiation damage is completely healed by normal bodily processes, whereas, above this limit, damage is to some extent, at least, cumulative. Another source of difficulty in establishing permissible dosage limits is due to the fact that most of the radiation damage to human beings from radiation is not immediately apparent, some types of damage showing up only after long periods of time after exposure. Exposure of the whole body to radiation is, in general, considerably more damaging than exposure of small volumes, and different parts of the body are differently susceptible to radiation damage. Also the cumulative effects of a given amount of radiation are more serious if the exposure occurs over a shorter, rather than a longer, period of time.

The maximum safe limit for exposure, generally accepted by health physicists at the present time, has been set at 0.3 r per week of gamma rays, the relative acceptable dosages of other types of radiation being then established in terms of the rem by the tabulation above. Assuming that there are no periods of excessive exposure, then, we consider the safe limit for exposure to radiation of all kinds to be 0.3 rem per week.

4-4. Coefficients of Absorption for Radiation

It is customary to measure the capacity of a material to absorb radiation by a quantity called the coefficient of absorption for the material. The absorption coefficient is by definition the fractional rate of loss in intensity of an incident beam of radiation as it traverses

the absorbing material. Thus

$$\frac{1}{I}\frac{dI}{dx} = -\mu \qquad (4\text{-}4\text{-}1)$$

where I is the intensity of the incident beam, in units of energy per unit time and per unit area, x is the distance traversed through the absorber in the direction of motion of the beam, and μ is the coefficient

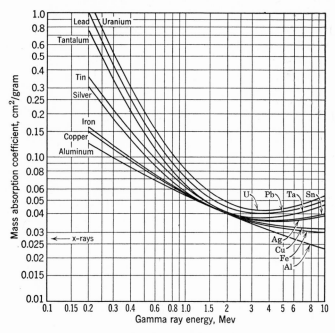

FIG. 4-4-1. Gamma ray absorption as a function of energy.

of absorption, having the dimensions of an inverse length. The numerical magnitude of the absorption coefficient is dependent on the type of radiation and on its energy, and on the properties of the absorbing material. In general the absorption coefficient for gamma rays increases with the density of the absorbing material, although some materials depart quite widely from this rule. Where space is a factor in shielding for gamma rays, therefore, there is an incentive for using dense materials for the shield. A measure of the effectiveness of a given mass of a material to absorb gamma rays is given by the ratio of its coefficient of absorption, μ, to its density, ρ, called the mass absorption coefficient. Approximate values of this ratio are shown in Figure 4-4-1.

The absorption coefficient for neutrons is the neutron cross section for the interactions of interest for shielding. The cross sections for absorption or inelastic scattering of fast neutrons are all low, whereas for neutrons at thermal energy the absorption cross sections for most materials are so high that thermal neutrons are very readily absorbed. For stopping neutrons, then, it is necessary to use light materials (moderators) to slow down the neutrons to energies at which they are readily absorbed. Those cross sections for neutrons which have been declassified are published in the so-called *Brookhaven Report.**

In order to acquire some feeling for the magnitude of the problem of shielding, let us estimate crudely the radiation dosage existing in the interior of a reactor having a total power of 10 megawatts and a surface area of 10,000 cm^2, and calculate the attenuation necessary to reduce the radiation at the surface to one r per month. Let it be assumed that 5 percent of the total energy generated in the reactor escapes from the core in the form of gamma rays of average energy 1 Mev. The energy escaping from unit area of the surface of the reactor is then 50 watts per cm^2. Since 1 ev = 1.6×10^{-19} watt second, the energy escaping from the surface can be expressed as 3.13×10^{14} Mev per cm^2-second. Since the absorption coefficient, μ, for 1 Mev gamma rays in air is about 3×10^{-5} cm^{-1}, the energy absorbed by the air at the surface of the reactor would be 0.94×10^{10} Mev per cm^3-second. One r per hour is equivalent to 18.6 Mev per cm^3-second. Therefore the surface radiation is equivalent to about 5×10^8 r per hour. For a tolerance dosage of 1 r per month, then, the required attenuation is about 8×10^{10}. Although the numbers chosen here may not be appropriate to a particular reactor design, nevertheless the result is such as to indicate that the attenuation required from the shielding of reactors is very large indeed. Compared with this large required attenuation, it becomes obvious that even small leakage through the shield because of holes or convection by circulating fluids may become of prime importance in an otherwise good shield design. Also, comparatively small quantities of very penetrating forms of radiation, such as very high energy neutrons, because of their very low absorption cross sections, may assume a disproportionate importance in the design of the shield.

4-5. Mechanisms for Absorption of Radiation

We have considered the radiation damage which can occur in the human body, and have stated the safe limits which must be set for the

* A.E.C. Neutron Cross Section Advisory Group, *Neutron Cross Sections*, AECU-2040, May 15, 1952, Office of Technical Services, Department of Commerce.

protection of personnel at any reactor establishment. It is the purpose of the shielding around a nuclear reactor to reduce the radiation emanating from it below this safe limit. The processes and the materials needed for absorption depend on the type of radiation to be absorbed. We have stated that the absorption of alpha and beta particles is accomplished by small amounts of practically any material interposed between the radiation source and the personnel to be protected. Let us now consider the shielding of the reactor against gamma rays and neutrons.

GAMMA RAYS

There are three main processes for the interaction of gamma rays with materials. These are called (1) the photoelectric effect, (2) Compton scattering, and (3) pair production. In the photoelectric effect, the gamma ray transfers all its energy to an electron, which is ejected from the atom to which it was attached and then loses energy by interaction with the surrounding material. The gamma ray is completely lost in the process. Since the coefficient for the photoelectric effect decreases as the energy of the incident gamma ray is increased, being insignificantly small at high energies, the photoelectric effect is important primarily at low energies. In the process of Compton scattering the gamma ray is scattered from an electron, changing both the energy and the direction of the gamma ray. In this process the gamma ray is not lost, but the reduction of its energy by the process makes it easier to annihilate subsequently. The coefficient for the Compton scattering effect also decreases as the energy of the incident gamma ray is increased, and is also therefore primarily important for low energy gamma rays. Since, in this process, the gamma ray does not disappear, but is only scattered, it is necessary in shielding calculations to keep track of scattered, as well as primary, gamma rays. The effect of these gamma rays which are scattered back into the incident beam is usually included in a quantity called the build-up factor, which will be discussed later. The necessity to account for the scattered gamma rays constitutes the main complicating factor in the design of shielding for gamma rays. In the process of pair production the gamma ray is destroyed, and gives rise to a pair of electrons of opposite electrical charge. This process occurs only if the incident gamma ray has an energy greater than about 1 Mev, the absorption coefficient rising as the gamma energy is increased above this threshold. At high incident energies, the pair production process accounts for most of the absorption of gamma rays. In this process, as in the photoelectric effect, the gamma ray disappears completely, although the positron again combines with an electron, producing gamma radiation. Figure 4-4-1 shows the summation of these effects for the three gamma ray processes in the form of the mass absorption coefficient, as a function of gamma ray energy, for primary gammas.

NEUTRONS

We have seen in Chapter 2 how, for purposes of neutron conservation and reactor criticality, the scattering and absorption of neutrons were computed. However, in view of the very large attenuations of neutron radiation required for shielding, it is apparent that quantities of neutrons which may be completely negligible in the calculation of criticality may be of major importance in the design of shielding. For instance, in a thermal reactor the fissions from the fast neutrons are not very important for achieving criticality, since they are much less plentiful than thermal neutrons and have much lower absorption cross sections. However, just because the fast neutrons do have such low absorption cross sections they are very penetrating compared with thermal neutrons, and hence assume a role of major importance among the neutrons which escape from the shield. It becomes important to know the spatial distribution of fast neutrons, and to provide means for slowing them down rapidly to energies at which they are easily absorbed. Because neutron capture, in most cases, produces secondary gamma rays, and in some cases high energy (hard) gamma rays produce neutrons (mostly in beryllium and in heavy water), the supplies of neutrons and gamma rays are not entirely independent. This interrelationship causes a second major complication in the design of reactor shielding.

4-6. Shielding Calculations

Although the idea of the absorption coefficient, or the absorption cross section, is a simple concept, picking appropriate values for all energies of both gamma rays and neutrons to use under the complicated geometrical and physical situations existing in actual reactors is made particularly difficult by the large attenuations of radiation which are required in shielding for reactors. In view of these difficulties there are three alternatives: (1) to design the shield for the worst conditions that could possibly exist; or if this results in too large, too heavy, or too expensive a shield, (2) to design and execute an appropriate experiment to find effective coefficients for an actual reactor configuration; or (3) to carry out a combination of detailed computations, along with the fundamental experimental measurements to support these calculations. The first of these is quick but may not be acceptable in many cases of interest. The second has the disadvantages of expense for experimental mock-ups for the reactor shielding, and inapplicability to designs which differ too much from the experimental mock-up. The third alternative has the disadvantage that the computations required are extensive, and therefore expensive, along with the advantage of a considerable amount of flexibility for solving the shielding problem for different designs. The experience gained from all these, as well as from the actual construction of reactors, is necessary for the design of shielding.

In the section which follows it is assumed that the problem of the shielding of gamma rays and fast neutrons can be calculated by means of equations like Equation 4-4-1. The burden of calculating the complicated interrelationships of gamma rays and neutrons which determine the appropriate accurate values of effective absorption coefficients for gamma rays, or cross sections for neutrons, for use in the application of Equation 4-4-1 to specific reactor applications is considered beyond the scope of this book.

Some references for the interactions of gamma rays and neutrons with matter are given at the end of the chapter. The examples which follow are meant to demonstrate particularly some effects of geometrical considerations on the solution of Equation 4-4-1 for distributed sources of radiation. To show the results of differing distributions of materials in the shield some assumptions of absorption coefficients will be made, without regard for their true relationship to any particular reactor. The examples used here are chosen primarily to present a method of formulation for the analysis of the geometry of shielding. Other, and different, examples could have been used.

As an example consider a source of gamma rays of total strength S concentrated at the center of a uniform sphere of material having a total absorption coefficient for all gamma ray processes, μ. This is an example of what is called a point isotropic source. Owing to the Compton scattering process a certain fraction of the gamma rays is scattered back into the beam. Let this fraction be K. Then the current of gamma rays crossing the surface of the sphere at radius R is given by analogy with Equation 4-4-1 as

$$I = \frac{S}{4\pi R^2} e^{-\mu(1-K)R} \qquad (4\text{-}6\text{-}1)$$

This can be written alternatively as

$$I = \frac{S}{4\pi R^2} B(R)e^{-\mu R} \qquad (4\text{-}6\text{-}2)$$

The factor $B(R)$, as used here, is often called the build-up factor.

Close to the source, where the factor μKR is small compared with unity, the build-up factor can be approximated,

$$B(R) = 1 + \mu KR \qquad (4\text{-}6\text{-}3)$$

If K is of the order of unity, Equation 4-6-3 can be approximated still further:

$$B(R) = 1 + \mu R \qquad (4\text{-}6\text{-}4)$$

The build-up factor as expressed in Equation 4-6-4 is sometimes used and has been called the *linear build-up factor*. Since K is of course less than unity, Equation 4-6-4 gives an overestimate of the build-up factor due to the Compton scattering effect close to the source. Since the exponential factor of Equation 4-6-1 increases more rapidly than linearly, there is some value of R farther from the source at which Equations 4-6-1 and 4-6-4 give the same answer.

If the concentrated source of gamma rays is located at the center of a spherical shell of outer radius R and thickness t, the current at the outer surface of the shell, from Equation 4-6-1, is

$$I = \frac{S}{4\pi R^2}\, e^{-\mu(1-K)t} \qquad (4\text{-}6\text{-}5)$$

At distances r from the source, where r is larger than R, the current is

$$I = \frac{S}{4\pi r^2}\, e^{-\mu(1-K)t} \qquad (4\text{-}6\text{-}6)$$

In a real reactor, of course, the sources are not concentrated, and it becomes necessary to integrate over all the distributed sources throughout the volume of the reactor. In general, also, the absorption coefficients are not uniform throughout the volume of the reactor, and are functions of the energy of the gamma rays. Add to this the fact that the build-up factor must be determined from a separate and complicated calculation, that the quantities of neutrons and gamma rays are interdependent, and that the calculations for neutrons are at least as complicated as those for gamma rays, and the complexity of any but a very approximate analysis becomes apparent. For most cases of actual reactors it is necessary to resort to approximations to the actual equations, and generally to numerical methods for their solution. Even the numerical solutions are of such complexity for most cases as to require the use of computing machines for handling them. The alternative to these computations is an experimental approximation to a reactor configuration of interest to determine the leakage of radiation. A second alternative, available when space and weight are not critical, is to use a simple approximation and to add sufficient thickness of shielding to provide a factor of safety.

Let us now consider the effect of a distributed source of gamma rays. As a second example, consider a source uniformly distributed throughout a sphere of radius R. Let the source density be designated by σ, so that the total generation of gamma ray energy in the sphere is

$$S = \tfrac{4}{3}\pi R^3 \sigma \qquad (4\text{-}6\text{-}7)$$

It is desired to find the current of gamma rays crossing the surface of the sphere. The coordinate scheme for the sphere is shown in Figure 4-6-1. The current from the surface of the sphere is given by the integral over the whole volume of the sphere,

$$I = \int \frac{\sigma d\tau}{4\pi\rho^2} \cos\theta e^{-\mu(1-K)\rho} \qquad (4\text{-}6\text{-}8)$$

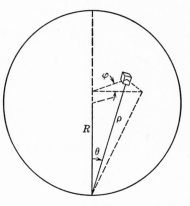

FIG. 4-6-1.

where $d\tau$ is the element of volume, given by $d\tau = \rho\, d\theta\, \rho \sin\theta\, d\varphi\, d\rho$. The factor $\cos\theta$ enters because the radiations are in general not perpendicular to the surface of the element of volume. Substituting the expression for the element of volume and applying limits of integration, we obtain

$$I = \frac{\sigma}{4\pi} \int_{\theta=0}^{\pi/2} \int_{\rho=0}^{2R\cos\theta} \int_{\varphi=0}^{2\pi} d\varphi\, e^{-\mu(1-K)\rho}\, d\rho \sin\theta \cos\theta\, d\theta \qquad (4\text{-}6\text{-}9)$$

Performing the indicated integrations gives for the leakage current

$$I = \frac{\sigma R}{2\alpha}\left[1 - \frac{2}{\alpha^2}\left(1 - \{1 + \alpha\}e^{-\alpha}\right)\right] \qquad (4\text{-}6\text{-}10)$$

where $\alpha = 2R\mu(1 - K)$. For large enough distances, compared with the mean distance traveled by gamma rays between interactions, that $\mu R \gg 1$, Equation 4-6-10 becomes

$$I = \frac{\sigma}{4\mu(1 - K)} \qquad (4\text{-}6\text{-}11)$$

The leakage ratio from the sphere can be defined as the ratio of the total leakage from the sphere to the total generation in the sphere, or

$$L = \frac{4\pi R^2 I}{\frac{4}{3}\pi R^3 \sigma} = \frac{3I}{R\sigma} \qquad (4\text{-}6\text{-}12)$$

The leakage ratio from the sphere is then

$$L = \frac{3}{2\alpha}\left[1 - \frac{2}{\alpha^2}(1 - \{1 + \alpha\}e^{-\alpha}) \right] \qquad (4\text{-}6\text{-}13)$$

Taking the limit on Equation 4-6-13 as α approaches zero gives the leakage ratio for the case of the absorption coefficient equal to zero. It is found that for this case $L = 1$, as it should. It should be noted that Equation 4-6-10 gives the current of gamma ray energy through the surface of the sphere. If it is desired to find the total gamma ray energy traversing a unit sphere on the surface of the radiating sphere, as is the case for dosage calculations, it is necessary to do the same calculations, except without the factor $\cos\theta$ in Equation 4-6-8. This quantity is the flux. Performing the integrations of Equation 4-6-8 for the uniform sphere gives for the flux

$$F = \frac{\sigma R}{\alpha^2}[\alpha + e^{-\alpha} - 1] \qquad (4\text{-}6\text{-}14)$$

The ratio of the flux to the current for the sphere is found by dividing Equation 4-6-14 by Equation 4-6-10, giving

$$\frac{F}{I} = 2\alpha\,\frac{\alpha + e^{-\alpha} - 1}{\alpha^2 - 2 + 2(1 + \alpha)e^{-\alpha}} \qquad (4\text{-}6\text{-}15)$$

Taking limits on this expression as α approaches zero and then infinity gives, respectively, the values 1.5 and 2. Care is necessary to avoid confusing flux and current in a shielding calculation. If the current is summed over the whole surface of a radiating body, this sum is equal to the total generated quantity of radiation which escapes from the surface. However, such a summation of flux over the surface would give a quantity larger than the total quantity escaping, owing to a multiple counting of the radiations. The flux is so defined that it includes all the radiation traversing a unit volume regardless of its direction of motion, which is the quantity of interest for dosage calculations.

In the previous example it was assumed that the source of radiations extended to the outside surface of the radiating body. In an actual case the radiating body would be surrounded by a layer of shielding material, in which the generation of radiations would be due only to secondary effects, and not to primary sources. Let us see what effect this shielding layer has on the leakage of radiations. Consider a third example: a sphere having a source of total strength S distributed uniformly throughout a central core of radius a, and an effective absorption coefficient μ_1, surrounded by a second region with no sources, of

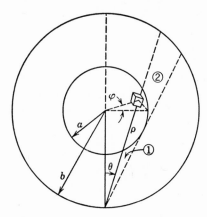

FIG. 4-6-2.

outside radius b, and with an effective absorption coefficient μ_2. The geometry for this case is shown schematically in Figure 4-6-2. The leakage ratio for this case is given by

$$L = \frac{3b^2}{4\pi a^3} \int_{\theta=0}^{\sin^{-1}(a/b)} \int_{\rho_1}^{\rho_2} \int_{\varphi=0}^{2\pi} e^{-\{\mu_1(\rho-\rho_1)+\mu_2\rho_1\}} \cos\theta \sin\theta \, d\varphi \, d\rho \, d\theta$$

(4-6-16)

Performing the integrations with respect to ρ and φ gives

$$L = \frac{3b^2}{2a^3\mu_1} \int_{\theta=0}^{\sin^{-1}(a/b)} e^{-\mu_2\rho_1}\{1 - e^{-\mu_1(\rho_2-\rho_1)}\} \cos\theta \sin\theta \, d\theta \quad (4\text{-}6\text{-}17)$$

From the geometry of the configuration and the law of cosines,

$$\cos\theta = \frac{\rho_2^2 + b^2 - a^2}{2b\rho_2} \quad \text{and} \quad \cos\theta = \frac{\rho_1^2 + b^2 - a^2}{2b\rho_1} \quad (4\text{-}6\text{-}18)$$

Eliminating $\cos\theta$ between these expressions gives a relationship for ρ_2 in terms of ρ_1,

$$\rho_2 = \frac{b^2 - a^2}{\rho_1} \quad (4\text{-}6\text{-}19)$$

Differentiating Equation 4-6-18 gives

$$\sin \theta \, d\theta = - \frac{1}{2b} \left\{ \frac{\rho_1^2 - (b^2 - a^2)}{\rho_1^2} \right\} d\rho_1 \qquad (4\text{-}6\text{-}20)$$

The limits of integration, in terms of ρ_1, become

$$\rho_1 = b - a, \quad \theta = 0 \qquad (4\text{-}6\text{-}21)$$

$$\rho_1 = \sqrt{b^2 - a^2}, \quad \theta = \sin^{-1}(a/b) \qquad (4\text{-}6\text{-}22)$$

Substituting Equations 4-6-18, 4-6-19, 4-6-20, 4-6-21, and 4-6-22 into Equation 4-6-17 gives

$$L = \frac{3}{8A^3} \int_{\sqrt{B^2 - A^2}}^{B-A} e^{-r} \left\{ \frac{1 - e^{-c\left(\frac{B^2 - A^2}{r}\right) - r}}{c} \right\} \left\{ r - \frac{(B^2 - A^2)^2}{r^3} \right\} dr$$

$$(4\text{-}6\text{-}23)$$

where $A = \mu_2 a$, $B = \mu_2 b$, $c = \mu_1/\mu_2$, and $r = \mu_2 \rho_1$. Equation 4-6-23 can be most easily handled by means of numerical integration. However, for shielding situations of interest, owing to the large attenuations of gamma rays required, the factor e^{-r} will generally vary rapidly, compared with the other factors in the integrand, over the whole region of integration. There will, therefore, be a relatively small error due to considering these remaining factors as constant, assigning to them the values pertinent to the limit of integration, $r = B - A$. Also the factor $\exp\left[-c\left(\frac{B^2 - A^2}{r}\right) - r \right]$ will generally be negligibly small compared with unity in the region of integration where e^{-r} is significantly large. These approximations give an upper limit to the possible values of the integrand. Furthermore, since e^{-r} changes so rapidly, the limit $r = \infty$ can, without appreciable error, be substituted for the lower limit, $r = \sqrt{B^2 - A^2}$. Equation 4-6-23 now becomes

$$L = \frac{3}{8A^3} \int_{\infty}^{B-A} e^{-r} \, dr \left[\frac{1}{c} \left\{ (B - A) - \frac{(B^2 - A^2)^2}{(B - A)^3} \right\} \right] \qquad (4\text{-}6\text{-}24)$$

or, by integration and simplification,

$$L = \frac{3B e^{-(B-A)}}{2A^2(B - A)c} \qquad (4\text{-}6\text{-}25)$$

This approximation is always larger than the answer given by an accurate integration of Equation 4-6-23. Whether the approximation is acceptable must be checked for any given set of shielding calculations.

Let us consider a uniform spherical source of 1 Mev gamma rays embedded in a beryllium matrix. Neglecting the effects of neutrons, we desire to find the thickness of the layer of lead by which the source must be surrounded to attenuate the gamma rays by a factor of 10^{12} ($L = 10^{-12}$). From the references, for 1 Mev gamma rays, the absorption coefficient for beryllium (density = 1.84 grams per cc) is 9.13 cm^{-1}, and for lead (density = 11.34 grams per cc) is 0.80 cm^{-1}. Let the radius of the source be 50 cm. For these conditions $A = 0.80 \times 50 = 40$, and $c = 0.13/0.80 = 0.16$. A trial-and-error solution to Equation 4-6-25 yields the value $B = 63.5$, giving an outer radius of the lead layer of about 80 cm, or a thickness of the layer of about 30 cm. This layer of lead weighs about 20 tons.

A more accurate numerical integration of Equation 4-6-23 for the case considered above, with $B = 63.5$, gives for the leakage ratio for our example $L = 0.88 \times 10^{-12}$. A closer analytical approximation still to the correct value for the integral can be found, for the case where $B - A$ is large compared with unity, by carrying out to two terms the integration by parts. This gives for the leakage ratio

$$L = \frac{3Be^{-(B-A)}}{2A^2(B-A)c}\left(1 - \frac{3}{B-A}\right) \qquad (4\text{-}6\text{-}26)$$

For the example considered above, this approximation gives $L = 0.87 \times 10^{-12}$. The differences in these approximations would seem to be unimportant for this problem.

The impression is not to be gained from the last example that 20 tons of lead around a reactor would provide an adequate shield. In the first place, the build-up factor was ignored in the calculation. From NDA Memo 15C-20, for 1 Mev gamma rays traversing 20 mean free paths in lead, the build-up factor is about 5. A more important factor for reactors, however, is the neglect of the effects of neutrons in the example. Owing to the absorption and inelastic scattering of neutrons secondary gammas are produced in quantities that are not insignificant compared with the primary source. These gamma rays are produced very strongly in most heavy materials, although lead produces less than most other heavy materials. The location of the sources of secondary gamma rays can be determined only by a detailed computation of the distribution of the neutrons in both space and lethargy. In general, though, it can be stated that avoiding excessive generation of secondary gammas requires that a good moderating material be distributed through the shield to slow down the fast neutrons elastically, and a strong absorber (only boron or lithium, among the strong absorbers, absorbs neutrons without giving off powerful gamma rays) to absorb them after they have been slowed down. Moderation of neutrons, as has been previously stated, requires the use of a light material. Because of the low cross sections of all materials for capturing fast neutrons, the fast neutrons assume a role of importance in shielding against radiation disproportionate to their numbers.

A very important consideration in any actual reactor is the leakage of radiations, or radioactive materials, through any holes which traverse the shield, such as coolant passages containing fluids which are poor absorbers of gamma rays or neutrons or are themselves radioactive. Any radioactive materials which pass outside the reactor require additional shielding. Considering the large attenuations required for shielding, mechanisms which bypass the shield require special attention.

REFERENCES

Cork, J. M., *Radioactivity and Nuclear Physics*, D. Van Nostrand Co., New York, 1950.

Glen, H. M., *Introduction to Nuclear Shielding for Engineers*, CF-51-10-221, Oak Ridge National Laboratory, Oak Ridge, Tenn.

Goldstein, H., and R. Aronson, *Status Report on Calculations of Gamma Ray Penetration*, NYO-3079, Nuclear Development Associates, Inc., White Plains, N. Y., August 20, 1953.

Goldstein, H., J. E. Wilkins, and S. Preiser, *Interim Report on the NDA-NBS Calculations of Gamma Ray Penetration*, NDA Memo 15C-20, Nuclear Development Associates, Inc., White Plains, N. Y., September 8, 1953.

Halliday, David, *Introductory Nuclear Physics*, John Wiley and Sons, New York, 1950.

Pollard, E., and W. L. Davidson, *Applied Nuclear Physics*, Second Edition, John Wiley and Sons, New York, 1951.

Spinney, K. T., *Some Approximate Formulae for Use in Neutron Shielding*, AERE T/R 1221, Atomic Energy Research Establishment, Ministry of Supply, Harwell, England, 1953.

CHAPTER 5

REACTOR MATERIALS

Materials for usual engineering purposes may be chosen to satisfy one, or a combination of several, criteria for their mechanical, electrical, or thermal sufficiency. For the selection of materials for a reactor for power purposes there are the usual problems of finding structural materials having satisfactory tensile, creep, and fatigue strength, and rigidity, and of finding coolants having thermodynamic properties of interest with acceptable corrosion limits. In addition new problems arise because of the fissioning of fuel material and the necessity to conserve neutrons. The reactor designer must relate his use of materials to the nuclear reactions in the reactor. In some cases the major characteristics of a reactor design may be determined primarily by the nuclear properties of the materials available.

The discussion of materials here is not meant to be exhaustive. In general those problems concerning the use of materials which fall within usual engineering categories are left out of the discussion entirely. The problems concerning materials which are discussed are problems which arise specifically because of the unique characteristics of nuclear reactors. These materials problems are arbitrarily divided, for discussion purposes, into four main categories: (1) conservation of neutrons; (2) control of reactor power; (3) shielding of reactors; and (4) radiation damage.

5-1. Conservation of Neutrons

It has been stated that the primary prerequisite for a power reactor is that it be critical—that the neutron density, and hence the power, should not be changing with time. It has been found that a reactor, to be critical, must be of a certain size, and that this size is determined by the nuclear properties of the materials of which the reactor is composed. Let us consider the properties of materials for a reactor in terms of the nuclear demands made on them. It is desired that neutrons be absorbed primarily in fissionable or fertile materials, with as few as possible lost in the competing, non-productive, absorption processes or leakage.

147

ABSORPTION OF NEUTRONS

The selection of structural and coolant materials for a reactor is guided by the necessity to conserve neutrons. Materials which are strong absorbers of neutrons must be used sparingly, especially in regions where the neutron flux is high. Many of the conventional structural and coolant materials are fairly strong absorbers of neutrons. On the other hand, many materials which have good nuclear properties were unknown in engineering development until they were studied for their potential use in reactors. Some of these new materials have proved to be of interest not only for their nuclear properties but also for structural properties. Some which are still laboratory curiosities may eventually be produced commercially for use in reactors. A few have already been brought to limited commercial production, largely because of the impetus supplied by reactor development, for instance, zirconium and beryllium.

The neutron-absorbing properties of several elements which are strong absorbers of neutrons are usually the result of only one strongly absorbing isotope, which may be present in the naturally occurring element in small quantity, the remaining isotopes being often very light absorbers. This strongly absorbing isotope can be separated from the element, at least on a laboratory scale, leaving behind those isotopes which are less strongly absorbing. Whether such a separation process is economically feasible on an engineering scale must be worked out in relationship to the value of the engineering aim that is to be accomplished by the material, and the costs of a specific process of separation. Many currently useful engineering alloys will have to be reconsidered for reactor purposes to determine whether in some cases small traces of highly absorbing impurities can be removed economically, and in others whether useful but highly absorbing trace materials in the alloys can be replaced by some less absorbing materials which perform equivalent functions.

Aside from fissionable and fertile material the materials used in reactors which use neutrons can be considered in four categories, although often the same material is used in more than one category. These are (1) reflectors, (2) moderators, (3) structural materials, and (4) coolants.

REFLECTORS AND MODERATORS

Reflectors are the containing materials for neutrons. Besides the requirement for a very low cross section for absorption, since they are used in large quantities in the reactor, reflectors are required to have large scattering cross sections. A large scattering cross section gives a short mean free path between collisions, and hence a large number of collisions in a given size of reactor prior to leakage of the neutrons from the reactor. Neutrons are thus made to spend a relatively long time in the vicinity of the fissionable material in the reactor, and the probability that a given neutron will cause fission is much increased. Reflecting materials can be used in relatively uniform mixtures with fuel materials in thermal reactors, or wrapped around the exterior surface of the reactor core of either thermal or fast reactors.

Moderators are materials used for slowing down neutrons. In thermal reactors it is desired to slow down fast neutrons as rapidly as possible to thermal energy. This is accomplished by the use of light, or moderating, materials both for external reflectors and mixed more or less uniformly throughout the volume of the reactor. The materials available for moderators are pretty much limited to beryllium, graphite, and compounds containing hydrogen or deuterium, such as ordinary or heavy water and certain hydroxides or deuteroxides. Other materials which are light enough to be good moderators otherwise, such as lithium or boron, have such large absorption cross sections as to preclude their use in reactors at all, except in apparatus deliberately intended to shut down the nuclear reaction.

The table below lists the practical moderating elements, together with typical properties for slowing down, scattering, and absorbing neutrons.

Element	Symbol	Thermal Absorption Cross Section $\sigma_{a\ th}$	Logarithmic Decrement of Neutron Energy ξ	Thermal Scattering Cross Section $\sigma_{s\ th}$
Hydrogen	$_1H^1$	0.32	1.000	20–80 *
Deuterium	$_1H^2(_1D^2)$	0.0000005	0.725	3.5
Beryllium	$_4Be^9$	0.009	0.209	6.9
Carbon	$_6C^{12}$	0.0045	0.158	4.8
Oxygen	$_8O^{16}$	0.0009	0.120	4.2

* Depending on the chemical binding forces in the particular molecule of which hydrogen is one component.

In this and the following tables all cross sections are expressed in barns, and are for thermal neutrons. For practical moderators it is necessary that these materials be used in forms having a relatively high atomic density, thus ruling out the gaseous materials. The possibly practical moderating materials are then primarily water (H_2O), heavy water (D_2O), graphite (C), beryllium metal (Be), beryllium oxide (BeO), beryllium carbide (Be_2C), and possibly some hydrocarbons and organic compounds, although there is a question of their stability under neutron irradiation.

For the reflectors of fast reactors, in which reflection of neutrons, without moderation, is required, it is necessary to have a low absorption cross section and a high scattering cross section for neutrons at those energies at which neutrons exist in large quantities in the reactor. A reflecting nucleus, heavy compared with the neutron, is required, instead of a light one (low logarithmic decrement of neutron energy) so that the neutrons will not lose appreciable energy in collisions. Since the neutron absorption cross sections are strong functions of neutron energy, being generally less at high energies than at thermal energies, larger quantities of materials which absorb thermal neutrons can generally be used in fast reactors. Noting from Equation 1-11-15 that the value of ξ, the logarithmic decrement, has decreased to less than 0.1 for sodium and all heavier nuclei, we might list the following elements which may appear in substantial quantities in the reflectors of fast reactors, depending of course on the absorption and scattering cross sections at the appropriate neutron energy levels.

Element	Symbol	Thermal Absorption Cross Section $\sigma_{a\ th}$	Thermal Scattering Cross Section $\sigma_{s\ th}$
Calcium	$_{20}$Ca	0.43	4.0
Iron	$_{26}$Fe	2.5	11.0
Nickel	$_{28}$Ni	4.4	18.0
Zirconium	$_{40}$Zi	0.4	8.0
Molybdenum	$_{42}$Mo	3.9	6.5
Tin	$_{50}$Sn	0.7	4.0
Lead	$_{82}$Pb	0.2	8.3
Bismuth	$_{83}$Bi	0.01	9

STRUCTURAL MATERIALS AND COOLANTS

Some of the common present structural materials, such as aluminum and magnesium for moderate temperatures and various steels and stainless steels for higher temperatures, are of interest also for the development of reactors. In addition some new materials are becoming available, such as zirconium, beryllium, and titanium for moderate temperatures. As refractory materials molybdenum, tantalum, and tungsten, and various ceramics like beryllium oxide, beryllium carbide, and graphite are of interest, for their possibilities for development. The nuclear process is not chemical, and hence does not require an oxidizing atmosphere for its existence. The absence of an oxidizing atmosphere makes possible the use of certain structural materials at temperatures higher than would be possible in an oxidizing atmosphere.

The high inherent temperature of the fission process, the lack of an oxidizing atmosphere, and the necessity to transfer large amounts of heat within small spaces for many applications result in the possibility of a different emphasis on the mechanism of heat transfer in nuclear reactors. Since there is no oxidizing atmosphere, the combination of liquid metals and high-temperature structural materials offers interesting possibilities for high heat transfer rates at high temperatures.

In some reactors one material may serve more than one purpose. For instance, water may act as both moderator and reactor coolant, or beryllium may act both as structural material and moderator. In many cases, structural and coolant materials may be used in engineering devices in ways the details of which are dictated by a detailed consideration of the neutron distribution.

The use of materials in a reactor is strongly influenced by the fact that all nuclear processes of interest in the reactor result in the generation of heat, not all of it being released at the point or time of fission. Heat is released everywhere in the immediate vicinity of the reactor core, making it necessary to cool all the structural materials of the reactor, including the reflector, continuously, even after shutdown of the reactor.

As has been stated previously, the amounts of many structural materials and coolants which can be used in a reactor are limited by their absorption of neutrons. Because of the decrease in absorption cross sections of most materials as the energy of the incident neutron increases, it is possible to use many structural and coolant materials in fast reactors which are not permissible in large quantities in thermal reactors. Likewise, in reactors in which the average neutron energy varies considerably from place to place in the reactor, more of the more heavily absorbing materials can be used in the regions of higher neutron energy. It is obvious that the materials used for both structure and coolant will depend on the operating temperature of the reactor. Based on the above considerations, the following elements are considered possible for reactor structural elements and coolants.

Possible structural materials for thermal reactors are beryllium, graphite, aluminum, and zirconium. Two ceramic materials for possible use as structural materials for thermal reactors are beryllium oxide or beryllium carbide. Possible coolants for thermal reactors are the gaseous elements, hydrogen, deuterium, helium, and oxygen. Also the following liquid metals are possible: sodium (in limited quantities because of its relatively high cross section), lead, bismuth, and lead-bismuth eutectic. The liquid compounds water and heavy water have been extensively used as moderators, and possibly some liquid hydrocarbons may have some use if radiation damage effects are not prohibitive. Possible structural materials for fast reactors are chromium, iron, nickel, and molybdenum. Cooling materials which may be used in reasonable amounts for fast reactors are sodium, potassium, sodium-potassium eutectic, tin, lead, bismuth, and lead-bismuth eutectic. It is to be noted that the coolants listed for fast reactors are all liquid metals.

5-2. Control of Reactor Power

As discussed under "Reactor Kinetics" in Chapter 3, changes in reactivity of the reactor due to various causes result in changes in reactor power unless measures are taken to counter their effects. Apparatus is installed on the reactor to control its behavior. The actual control of the supply of neutrons can theoretically be carried out by one of several means which change the configuration of the reactor, such as, for instance, moving a reflector to a new position more or less favorable to neutron conservation, or moving a source of neutrons, such as enriched fuel into or out of the high neutron flux region, or moving a strong absorber of neutrons into or out of the high flux region. The last of these, moving a strong neutron absorber, or poison, into or out of the high flux region, is the usual means of neutron control. In this control a use is found for the strong neutron poisons which, otherwise, have been so carefully excluded from the high flux region of the reactor. A common material for control rods, because of its very high absorption cross section, is boron. The following are some potential elements for deliberate nuclear poisoning of reactors.

Element	Symbol	$\sigma_{a\ th}$
Boron	B	740
Cadmium	Cd	2900
Lithium	Li	70
Hafnium	Hf	170

5-3. Shielding Materials

The materials used for shielding are very much dependent on the engineering application of the reactor. If the reactor is intended for a stationary power plant, the primary emphasis is on obtaining an unquestionable margin of safety for operating personnel with the least cost. In mobile applications, particularly aircraft, the emphasis on light weight and small space requirements will, in many cases, force the shield designer to design for limiting conditions, necessitating a much closer appraisal of the shielding properties of various possible combinations of materials for absorbing both neutrons and gamma rays.

For the stationary applications, relatively cheap bulk materials like concrete are used to provide absorption of both gamma rays and neutrons. Often iron is mixed with the concrete to give greater density for the absorption of gamma rays and for inelastic scattering of fast neutrons. Since thermal neutrons are easily absorbed by many materials which are normally present in most structural materials, it is necessary primarily to slow the fast neutrons down to thermal energy so that they can be absorbed. This is accomplished by any of the moderating materials, for instance, water or concrete (primarily because of its hydrogen content). Figure 4-4-1 of Chapter 4 shows the mass absorption coefficients for several elements of interest for shielding. It is to be noted that, of the more common materials, lead is very effective for shielding where limited space justifies its cost.

5-4. Radiation Damage to Reactor Materials

In Chapter 4 on shielding, it has been stated that various high-energy particles, if allowed to escape from the reactor, will result in damage to tissue in the bodies of operating personnel in the vicinity of the reactor. It was there stated that it was mostly gamma rays and neutrons which had sufficient penetrating power to escape from the reactor, and that these, in a powerful reactor, must be reduced from their intensity in the core of the reactor by factors like 10^{10} to protect personnel. Within the reactor, the full energy of fission, except for the relatively small leakage discussed above, must be transformed into thermal energy. A high-intensity stream of high-energy particles is continuously bombarding the materials of which the reactor is composed.

The cumulative effect of this high level of bombardment in the core of a high power reactor, over prolonged periods of time, can result in many changes in the physical properties of the materials of which the reactor is composed. For instance, the bombardment may result in a change in shape, an embrittlement, or a change in thermal conductivity or electrical resistivity, or hardness. The rate of corrosion of many materials is affected. Of course, some percentage of the reactor materials will be transmuted by the radiation to new chemical materials. It has been found that the basic fuel material, uranium, under radiation, goes to pieces, changing dimensions until it finally disintegrates.

Radiation effects on materials are dependent to some extent on factors which are independent of the radiation. For instance, the effects of radiation on uranium can be reduced by metallurgical treatment prior to radiation. Increased temperatures, either during or after radiation "anneal" out many of the effects of radiation on solid materials. In metals apparently many of the radiation damage effects which occur are annealed out continuously even at room temperature.

The mechanism by which the kinetic energy of a high-energy particle is transformed into "thermal" energy is pictured to be as follows. The motion of the high-energy particle causes it to collide with atoms of the material through which it is passing. In the collision the high-energy particle is slowed down, some of its energy being transferred to the atoms with which it collides, leaving them in a state of agitation. Each of these agitated atoms, in turn, transfers energy in the form of vibrational motion to its neighbors. Since the temperature of a material is measured by the energy of agitation of its atoms, it can be said that a region of high-temperature material is left in the track of the high-energy particle, and that this temperature lowers as the energy (or heat) is dissipated through a larger volume of material.

The picture presented above is more peaceful than one adequate to describe the havoc wreaked in the material affected by the higher energy particles or gamma rays. Actually these particles have sufficient energy that many atoms along the path are permanently displaced from their normal positions in the crystal structure and driven into new ones. Holes are left at the positions from which the atoms are driven, and extra, or "interstitial," atoms are left where they stop. All along the path electrons are detached from their orbits about atoms and scattered (the atoms are ionized). Owing to nuclear processes, some of the materials in the path of the high-energy particles are transmuted to new materials. These transmuted atoms can be considered as "impurity" atoms in the original material. Within atomic distances of the passage of a high-energy particle then, a region exists in which a permanent disruption of the lattice arrangement of atoms has occurred. This region is sometimes referred to as a *thermal spike*. These changes due to the passage of high-energy particles (vacancies, interstitials, impurity atoms, and exceedingly high local temperatures), under prolonged and intense exposure to high-energy particles, cause changes in certain of the macroscopic properties of solid materials. It is the purpose of this section to list some of these changes in properties and to discuss the microscopic mechanisms which have been postulated to "explain" them.

Radiation damage effects can be grouped into the two categories mentioned above, displacement of atoms and ionization. A large fraction of the energy of either charged or uncharged high-energy particles is ultimately dissipated in ionization, since even the uncharged particles set large numbers of charged atoms in motion, hence causing ionization by these secondary particles. In a good conductor the ionization effects disappear quickly except for heating of the material. In an insulating material the electrons liberated by ionization may be trapped in the lattice, resulting in more or less permanent changes in the substance. The displacement of a significant fraction of the atoms of a solid material from their lattice positions results in many changes in the properties of the material. Prior irradiation results in changes in both elastic and plastic properties. During irradiation the plastic properties (rate processes) may be changed.

The physical properties which have been most studied as a macroscopic measure of radiation damage are the electrical resistivity, thermal conductivity, and hardness. These quantities are measured primarily for two reasons. First, for many materials, the effects of radiation damage on these quantities are quite pronounced, and hence relatively easy to detect. Second, within the theoretical framework which has been established to explain these properties of solids under more ordinary conditions, some feeling can be established for some of the results to be expected from the irradiation of solids.

Let us form an elementary picture of a solid, as the physicist sees it. A solid, as indicated by many experiments of an indirect nature, is composed mostly of empty space. There are about 0.602×10^{24} (Avogadro's number) molecules in a gram-mole of any material. The atom, as has been stated before, consists of a nucleus surrounded by a "cloud" of electrons. The diameter of the atom (from Avogadro's number) is of the order of 10^{-8} cm, whereas the diameter of its nucleus (supposedly the "solid" part of the atom) is only of the order of 10^{-12} cm. These dimensions are much too small to "see" in an engineering sense. The knowledge of what happens inside the atom is therefore of a statistical, and not a detailed, nature. The nucleus of the atom is pictured as a small particle in a relatively empty space, held to an approximate location, about which it oscillates, by a system of forces which is so postulated as to correlate certain macroscopic experimental results. When the nucleus is in its equilibrium position relative to other nuclei, there is supposedly no net force on it. If these nuclei are forced to positions closer to one another than those for equilibrium, repulsive forces set in; for more distant positions the forces are attractive. If the nuclei are pulled apart by an ever-increasing force, a point is reached at which the attractive forces are less than the disrupting force, and the whole system becomes unstable. This may be pictured as in Figure 5-4-1.

An individual particle moving through a lattice arrangement of the atoms of a solid is repelled by those particles closest to it and attracted by those more distant. A given amount of energy transmitted to an individual particle will cause it to vibrate about its equilibrium position in the force field. If the energy becomes large enough it will cause the particle to escape the force field of its neighboring atoms, leaving a vacant space in the position from which it departs and creating an interstitial atom where it comes to rest in the lattice.

If an experiment is conducted in which a material is deformed by a shear stress, it is found that the stress necessary to cause a permanent

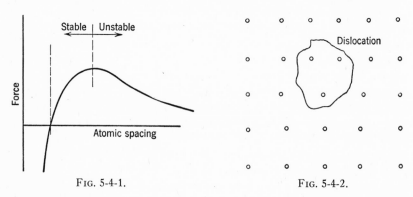

FIG. 5-4-1.   FIG. 5-4-2.

deformation is less than the force which would be expected, from theoretical considerations involving the forces between atoms, by a factor of the order of 1000. This is explained by postulating a dislocation, whose nature is such that the force on a whole plane of shearing atoms concentrates on just one of these atoms. This is like a local stress concentration, which causes a failure condition to propagate with relative ease through a body.

A dislocation is pictured as shown in Figure 5-4-2. Owing to asymmetry of the force field about it, the dislocation can be moved through the lattice with relative ease. Shear deformation can be discussed in terms of the probability that a dislocation will exist among a given number of atoms, and in terms of the mobility of the dislocation. As the number of dislocations increases beyond a certain point, interferences arise among them which inhibit their motion; further shearing deformations then require a larger stress. This corresponds to the macroscopic phenomenon of *strain hardening*. Eventually the phenomenon of strain hardening saturates, when supposedly the maximum density of stuck dislocations has been established. As is known from experience, strain hardening can be relieved by raising the temperature, corresponding to migration of the atoms of the stuck dislocations back to equilibrium positions in the lattice. This is called *annealing*. Also well known from experience is the fact that a hardened configuration can be accomplished in many materials by suddenly cooling the material from a high temperature, or *quenching*. This process freezes in the high-temperature configuration of atoms, which does not correspond to the low-temperature equilibrium lattice. This quenching may also be annealed by again raising the temperature.

Many effects of radiation damage are found to be analogous to the effects from more common metallurgical experience. Based on the similarity of effects, it is postulated that the effects on properties of solids of variations of the lattice arrangement of atoms depend only on the final locations of the atoms, and not on how the atoms got there. Thus the effect of interstitial atoms is expected to be the same whether they were caused by radiation damage or by shear deformation. The effects of impurity atoms are expected to be the same whether they were put into the lattice by a deliberate alloying procedure, or were created by transmutation of atoms by particle bombardment, or were left over as the aftermath of fission. Many of the effects of radiation damage can be annealed out, just as the effects of cold work or heat treatment in common metallurgical experience.

The theory of solids is still in a rather elementary state, with a multiplicity of effects which are not "understood." For instance, it is difficult to estimate theoretically the effects of radiation on the creep rate. It can be postulated that the lattice imperfections formed should act as focal points for stuck dislocations, and therefore should impede creep, or that the dislocations should move more readily because of the increased mobility of many atoms under radiation. Accurate experiments on creep under radiation are difficult to conduct, primarily because of difficulty in controlling the temperature under radiation conditions, and experiments on the radiation effects on creep are, at this time, contradictory. Many experiments under controlled conditions will be needed to enable the engineer to predict the limit performance of materials under radiation damage. It can be anticipated that some engineering limitations on radiation damage will be found from the malfunctioning of materials in actual service.

REFERENCES

A.E.C. Neutron Cross Section Advisory Group, *Neutron Cross Sections*, AECU-2040, Office of Technical Services, Department of Commerce, May 15, 1952.

Dienes, G. J., "Radiation Effects in Solids," *Annual Review of Nuclear Science*, Vol. II, 1953.

Liquid-Metals Handbook, Atomic Energy Commission, Department of the Navy, NAVEXOS P-733 (Rev.), U. S. Government Printing Office, Washington, D. C.

Seitz, F., *The Physics of Metals*, McGraw-Hill Book Co., New York, 1943.

Slater, J. C., "The Effects of Radiation on Materials," *Journal of Applied Physics*, Vol. 22, No. 3, March, 1951.

Sullivan, W. H., *Trilinear Chart of Nuclear Species*, John Wiley and Sons, New York, 1949.

CHAPTER 6

THERMAL STRESS

Power Removal from Reactors

Until the present time we have been talking about the problem that is specifically new for nuclear reactors, namely, the generation of power from the fission process. The next task is to remove the power generated by the fission process in the reactor. If we know the distribution of this power throughout the reactor, it is now our problem to remove it, consistent with certain limitations, some of which are nuclear (for instance, we cannot use heavy neutron absorbers for heat removal) and some of which are purely mechanical. The mechanical problems are connected primarily with heat transfer. (1) If we are dealing with large power densities there will generally be large temperature gradients and attendant large thermal stresses. We will try to find out to what extent we can mitigate the thermal stress problem and to what extent we must live within its confines. (2) If we are designing a thermal power plant, its thermal efficiency will depend largely on the top temperature available at the exit from the reactor. Hence we will want to know how much we can gain from pushing the creep resistance of high-temperature materials to their limits. (3) The removal of thermal energy will generally involve the circulation of a cooling fluid. The more power we remove from the reactor, the more power we must use in pumping the fluid. We will wish to determine limitations on power removal due to pumping power requirements. For this purpose it will be necessary to discuss some aspects of fluid flow and thermodynamics.

Heat transfer is conventionally studied in three categories: (1) radiation, (2) convection, and (3) conduction. Here radiation will be ignored on the assumption that engineering applications of the immediate future will be limited by materials considerations to temperatures at which radiation effects can be considered as corrections, of small magnitude, to the convection heat transfer. Heat transfer by convection will be studied to determine the limitations on power den-

159

sity due to the pressure losses which accompany it. Heat transfer by conduction will be studied in this chapter primarily in its relationship to the thermal stress problem.

6-1. Order of Magnitude of Thermal Stress

Most materials, when their temperature is raised, experience an expansion of their dimensions, unless they are in some manner constrained. This change in dimensions is usually expressed in dimensionless form as the change in length per unit original length. The usual expression for the relation between temperature and dimension change is

$$\epsilon = \alpha \, \Delta T \qquad \text{(6-1-1)}$$

in which ϵ is the change in length per unit length (called the strain), α is the linear coefficient of thermal expansion, and ΔT is the temperature difference measured above a reference temperature.

If an element is unconstrained, the above relation will define dimensional changes in the element. If it is constrained, stresses in the element will be set up so that each element in the material will have dimensions compatible with neighboring elements.

Stress also produces a strain which, in elastic materials, is proportional to the stress

$$\epsilon = \sigma/E \qquad \text{(6-1-2)}$$

where σ is the stress and E is called the modulus of elasticity, or Young's modulus. It has the dimensions of a stress.

Equation 6-1-2 is Hooke's law relating elastic stresses and strains. Also, it has been found experimentally that when stresses are applied a change in dimension normal to the applied stress occurs. This change is opposite in direction to the direction of the stress, and related to it by a factor μ, called *Poisson's ratio*. Therefore, we must write, owing to the stress in the x direction,

$$\epsilon_x = \sigma_x/E \qquad \text{(6-1-3)}$$

and owing to the stresses in the y and z directions

$$\epsilon_x = -\mu\sigma_y/E \qquad \text{(6-1-4)}$$

and

$$\epsilon_x = -\mu\sigma_z/E \qquad \text{(6-1-5)}$$

Adding together the effects of these stresses gives the total strain in the x direction:

$$\epsilon_x = \frac{1}{E} \{\sigma_x - \mu(\sigma_y + \sigma_z)\} \qquad \text{(6-1-6)}$$

Similarly, the strains in the y and z directions due to stresses are

$$\epsilon_y = \frac{1}{E}\{\sigma_y - \mu(\sigma_z + \sigma_x)\} \qquad (6\text{-}1\text{-}7)$$

and

$$\epsilon_z = \frac{1}{E}\{\sigma_z - \mu(\sigma_x + \sigma_y)\} \qquad (6\text{-}1\text{-}8)$$

Equations 6-1-6, 6-1-7, and 6-1-8 are called the generalized Hooke's law for elastic strains. The factor μ has values for different materials between zero and one-half. For most engineering materials it is about 0.3. For rubber it is close to one-half, the limiting value for an incompressible material. If both temperature differences and stresses exist we must add Equation 6-1-1 to Equation 6-1-6 to find the total strains in the x direction,

$$\epsilon_x = \frac{1}{E}\{\sigma_x - \mu(\sigma_y + \sigma_z)\} + \alpha\,\Delta T \qquad (6\text{-}1\text{-}9)$$

to Equation 6-1-7 to find the total strain in the y direction,

$$\epsilon_y = \frac{1}{E}\{\sigma_y - \mu(\sigma_z + \sigma_x)\} + \alpha\,\Delta T \qquad (6\text{-}1\text{-}10)$$

and to Equation 6-1-8 to find the total strain in the z direction,

$$\epsilon_z = \frac{1}{E}\{\sigma_z - \mu(\sigma_x + \sigma_y)\} + \alpha\,\Delta T \qquad (6\text{-}1\text{-}11)$$

Let us now consider the application of these equations to some simple, standard cases to find out how thermal stresses arise and to establish an order of magnitude of thermal stress.

The simplest case of thermal stress is a uniform straight rod constrained between two fixed walls as shown in Figure 6-1-1, so that as it is heated its length cannot change. Then the strain is

$$\epsilon_x = \frac{du}{dx} = \frac{\Delta l}{l} = 0 \qquad (6\text{-}1\text{-}12)$$

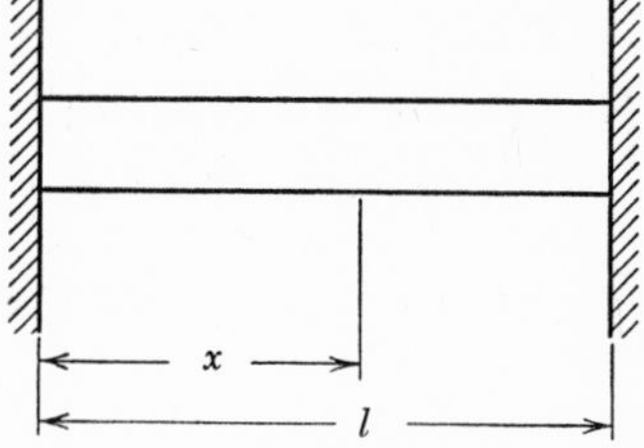

Fig. 6-1-1.

where u is the deformation (the total displacement of a point from its original position along the rod). Since there are no lateral constraints on the bar, $\sigma_y = \sigma_z = 0$. Hence, from Equation 6-1-9,

$$\sigma_x = -E\alpha\,\Delta T \qquad (6\text{-}1\text{-}13)$$

From Equations 6-1-10 and 6-1-11,

$$\epsilon_y = \epsilon_z = -\frac{\mu}{E}\sigma_x + \alpha\,\Delta T \qquad (6\text{-}1\text{-}14)$$

Combining Equations 6-1-13 and 6-1-14 gives

$$\epsilon_y = \epsilon_z = (1 + \mu)\alpha\,\Delta T \qquad (6\text{-}1\text{-}15)$$

The next case is a body constrained in the x and y directions and free to expand in the z direction. For this case, ϵ_x and $\epsilon_y = 0$ and $\sigma_z = 0$. Then for this two-dimensional stress case, from Equation 6-1-9,

$$\sigma_x - \mu\sigma_y = -E\alpha\,\Delta T \qquad (6\text{-}1\text{-}16)$$

From Equation 6-1-10,

$$\sigma_y - \mu\sigma_x = -E\alpha\,\Delta T \qquad (6\text{-}1\text{-}17)$$

or combining Equations 6-1-16 and 6-1-17 gives

$$\sigma_x = \sigma_y = -\frac{E\alpha\,\Delta T}{1 - \mu} \qquad (6\text{-}1\text{-}18)$$

From Equation 6-1-11,

$$\epsilon_z = -\frac{\mu}{E}(\sigma_x + \sigma_y) + \alpha\,\Delta T \qquad (6\text{-}1\text{-}19)$$

or combining Equations 6-1-18 and 6-1-19 gives

$$\epsilon_z = \frac{1 + \mu}{1 - \mu}\alpha\,\Delta T \qquad (6\text{-}1\text{-}20)$$

The third case is a body constrained in all three directions so that no strains are allowed. For the three-dimensional stress case, $\epsilon_x = \epsilon_y = \epsilon_z = 0$. Then, from Equations 6-1-9, 6-1-10, and 6-1-11 the stresses are the same in all three directions, and are given by

$$\sigma_x = \sigma_y = \sigma_z = -\frac{E\alpha\,\Delta T}{1 - 2\mu} \qquad (6\text{-}1\text{-}21)$$

For an incompressible medium ($\mu = 0.5$), Equation 6-1-21 would give an infinite stress.

The stresses in each of the three examples have the same form. In general, there will exist in a heated material some maximum stress

$$\sigma_{\max} = n\,\frac{E\alpha\,\Delta T}{1 + a\mu} \qquad (6\text{-}1\text{-}22)$$

where n has a value depending on the amount of constraint

$$0 \leq n \leq 1$$

and a depends on whether the constraints exist in one, two, or three coordinate directions.

Constraints	a
1	0
2	1
3	2

There are cases involving irregular shapes of structural members in which the value of n is greater than unity. These cases can be handled either by more elaborate calculations or in many cases by standard considerations of stress concentration factors. In general it can be stated that the order of magnitude of thermal stress is given by

$$K = \frac{E\alpha \, \Delta T}{1 - a\mu} \tag{6-1-23}$$

where ΔT is considered as the maximum temperature difference existing between any two points in the material. In general, if K is small compared with the allowable stress for the material, the thermal stress problem can be ignored. If it is not, a detailed calculation is necessary to determine the value of n, which depends on geometrical considerations.

Some representative values for modulus of elasticity, coefficient of thermal expansion, and their product are given below for materials of interest for reactors.

	Modulus of Elasticity E in lb/in.^{2}	Coefficient of Thermal Expansion α in in./in. °F	$E\alpha$ lb/in.^{2} °F
Steel	30×10^6	7×10^{-6}	210
Stainless steel	25×10^6	11×10^{-6}	275
Aluminum	10×10^6	15×10^{-6}	150
Graphite	1×10^6	1×10^{-6}	1
Alumina	50×10^6	5×10^{-6}	250

For the same temperature difference it would seem that the thermal stress in alumina is 250 times that in graphite. To know the value for an appropriate temperature difference, ΔT, it is necessary to find some information concerning the temperature distribution through the body under consideration. The determination of the temperature distribution will involve a study of the conduction of heat through the material.

The study of the problem of conduction of heat led Fourier to the equation of heat conduction which bears his name and to the Fourier series method of its solution. The Fourier equation for heat conduction is written

$$q = -kA \frac{\Delta T}{\Delta x} \qquad (6\text{-}1\text{-}24)$$

where q is the heat energy per unit time transferred across a slab of material having a cross section normal to the direction of flow of heat, A, and a temperature difference, ΔT, between two faces separated by a small distance, Δx. The coefficient k is the thermal conductivity of the material of which the slab is composed, and for dimension consistency must have the dimension

$$\frac{\text{(energy)}}{\text{(time)(temperature)(length)}}$$

If Δx is allowed to approach the limit zero, the remaining expression gives the heat transferred per unit time across a surface of area, A:

$$q = -kA \frac{\partial T}{\partial x} \qquad (6\text{-}1\text{-}25)$$

The negative sign indicates that heat flows from higher to lower temperatures. Equation 6-1-25 can be used to derive the standard differential equation for temperature distribution in the interior of a solid body, in which the conductivity k is a function of space and in which an energy source, whose strength, S, varies with location, is distributed throughout the solid. This equation states that the heat generated by an internal source in an element must either be conducted away or accounted for by a rise in the temperature of the element. For the x direction, this is given by

$$AS = \frac{\partial q}{\partial x} + A C_p \gamma \frac{\partial T}{\partial t} \qquad (6\text{-}1\text{-}26)$$

where C_p is the specific heat of the material through which heat is flowing and γ is its density:

$$C_p \sim \frac{\text{(energy)}}{\text{(weight)(temperature)}}$$

$$\gamma \sim \frac{\text{(weight)}}{\text{(length)}^3}$$

Substituting the value of q from Equation 6-1-25 into Equation 6-1-26 gives

$$\frac{\partial}{\partial x}\left(k\frac{\partial T}{\partial x}\right) + S = C_p\gamma\frac{\partial T}{\partial t} \qquad (6\text{-}1\text{-}27)$$

By symmetry, if we have heat flowing also in the y and z directions,

$$\frac{\partial}{\partial x}\left(k\frac{\partial T}{\partial x}\right) + \frac{\partial}{\partial y}\left(k\frac{\partial T}{\partial y}\right) + \frac{\partial}{\partial z}\left(k\frac{\partial T}{\partial z}\right) + S = C_p\gamma\frac{\partial T}{\partial t} \qquad (6\text{-}1\text{-}28)$$

or, in customary notation,

$$\nabla\cdot(k\,\nabla T) + S = C_p\gamma\frac{\partial T}{\partial t} \qquad (6\text{-}1\text{-}29)$$

Equation 6-1-29 is the equation for the temperature distribution in a solid body with a distributed heat source. If the conductivity is constant, Equation 6-1-29 becomes

$$\nabla^2 T + \frac{S}{k} = \frac{C_p\gamma}{k}\frac{\partial T}{\partial t} \qquad (6\text{-}1\text{-}30)$$

The dimensional coefficient

$$\frac{k}{C_p\gamma} \quad \frac{(\text{length})^2}{(\text{time})}$$

is called the thermal diffusivity. Being a function only of the physical properties of the heat-transfer material, it can be found tabulated for many engineering materials.

For purposes of calculating the thermal stress we are generally, although not always, interested in the steady-state equation, where $\partial T/\partial t = 0$. For this case Equation 6-1-29 becomes

$$\nabla\cdot(k\,\nabla T) + S = 0 \qquad (6\text{-}1\text{-}31)$$

This equation must be solved for any specific case to determine the temperature pattern.

Let us look at Equation 6-1-31 for an order of magnitude of temperature difference. For this purpose, it is convenient to convert the equation to dimensionless terms. The operator ∇ has the dimensions of an inverse length. Let this length be represented by L. Let us define a dimensionless temperature $T/\Delta T$ where ΔT is the maximum difference of temperature existing in the body, and a dimensionless conductivity k/k_0 where k_0 is the conductivity at some reference position in the body. Then Equation 6-1-31 becomes

$$\frac{1}{L^2}k_0\,\Delta T\,L\nabla\cdot\left(\frac{k}{k_0}L\nabla\frac{T}{\Delta T}\right) + S = 0 \qquad (6\text{-}1\text{-}32)$$

To make Equation 6-1-32 fully dimensionless, the variables k and T can be replaced by a dimensionless variable β^2 defined as

$$\beta^2 = -L\nabla \cdot \left(\frac{k}{k_0} L\nabla \frac{T}{\Delta T}\right) \qquad (6\text{-}1\text{-}33)$$

Substituting Equation 6-1-33 into Equation 6-1-32 gives

$$\frac{SL^2}{k_0 \Delta T} - \beta^2 = 0 \qquad (6\text{-}1\text{-}34)$$

Since every term in Equation 6-1-34 is constant except for S and β^2, then β^2 must have the same dependence on spatial variables as S, so that the ratio S/β^2 is a constant. Equation 6-1-34 can be solved for the temperature difference, ΔT, giving

$$\Delta T = SL^2/\beta^2 k_0 \qquad (6\text{-}1\text{-}35)$$

Without a detailed solution to the problem of the temperature distribution we do not, of course, know a numerical value for β^2. We can expect, however, that the temperature difference will depend directly on the source strength, S, and the square of a dimension of the body, L, and inversely on the thermal conductivity, k.

We previously have developed an order of magnitude expression for maximum thermal stress in terms of maximum temperature difference. Substituting Equation 6-1-35 into Equation 6-1-22 gives a new order of magnitude expression for thermal stress as a function of S and β^2

$$\sigma_{max} = n \frac{E\alpha SL^2}{(1 - a\mu)\beta^2 k_0} \qquad (6\text{-}1\text{-}36)$$

The maximum stress depends on the source strength, on geometrical factors, L^2, n, a, β^2, and on physical properties of the materials used, μ and $E\alpha/k$. The factor μ varies very little among most structural materials. The values of $E\alpha/k$ are given for the same materials which were considered before.

	Thermal Conductivity k in Btu/hr °F ft	$E\alpha/k$ lb-ft hr/in.^{2} Btu
Steel	15	14
Stainless steel	8	34
Aluminum	125	1.2
Graphite	100	0.01
Alumina	2	125

It can be seen that for the same source strength and general size and configuration, the stress in alumina would be expected to be about

12,500 times that in graphite. For a low stress with a given source strength (power density) it is therefore important to have a low modulus of elasticity, E, a low coefficient of thermal expansion, α, relatively small dimensions, L, of heated pieces of the body, high thermal conductivity, k, and to the limit within which this can be controlled, a low value of Poisson's ratio, μ. Sources of heat, as represented by the term S, exist in varying intensities throughout the reactor. The primary source of heat is, of course, the fission process. As has been implied elsewhere, because of the long distances traveled by some radiations from the fission process, heat is generated in regions, such as reflectors and shielding, which are relatively remote from the fission source. Heat is generated in all structural materials used in the reactor by these radiations.

We are interested in knowing how the mechanical sufficiency of a piece of apparatus depends on the thermal stress which is calculated by the above general considerations. It is evident that the required strength of the material is somehow dependent on σ_{max}. For a really brittle material σ_{max} could not be allowed to exceed the tensile strength of the material without rupture. For a very ductile material, and only a few cycles of heating and cooling, plastic flow of the material will prevent σ_{max} from exceeding the failure stress, even for very large calculated values of elastic stress. This is explained by saying that thermal stresses are "displacement stresses," and any plastic flow which occurs will "relieve" the stress. For large numbers of repeated cycles over the yield stress, the alternating direction of the plastic flow will eventually result in a "fatigue" failure, very much like the failure of a turbine blade due to mechanical vibrations. The criterion here must be that the alternating heating and cooling will not result in cyclic plastic flow. A good rule which can be shown to hold for this case limits the calculated elastic stress for cyclic operation to less than the sum of the yield strengths in tension and compression. For ductile materials, where the tensile and compressive strength are about equal, this means that the calculated elastic stress must not exceed twice the yield strength.

We have seen here that certain factors which determine thermal stress are to some extent under the control of the designer, both properties of materials and design dimensions. Also under the control of the designer are the arrangements of mechanical components subject to thermal deformations which can be used to limit the thermal stresses. It will be shown that a criterion for all thermal stresses to be zero for a body unconstrained at the edges is that the distribution of temperature in a rectangular coordinate system should be a linear function of the coordinates. As an example of this principle, consider the two methods of mounting a cold bearing in a hot shell shown in Figure 6-1-2. In method 1 thermal stresses will be determined entirely by the difference in temperature between inside and outside of

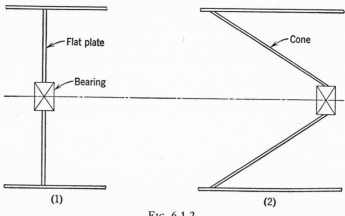

Fig. 6-1-2.

the flat plate. In method 2, if it is possible to design the cone so that the axial distribution of temperatures is linear, there will be no thermal stresses, as will be demonstrated later.

As was discussed in Chapter 5, the properties of many structural materials for reactors are susceptible to change caused by radiation damage. The strength, modulus of elasticity, and thermal conductivity of many materials are all affected by radiation. These properties also are changed for many materials by exposure to high temperatures. These changes must be taken into account in the prediction of thermal stresses.

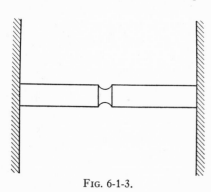

Fig. 6-1-3.

Some mention of stress concentrations should be made. It is obvious that if a bar with a notch is placed between two fixed walls as shown in Figure 6-1-3, and heated, the maximum stress will be much greater than that anticipated for a uniform bar:

$$\sigma_{max} >>> E\alpha\,\Delta T$$

In general, large changes in cross section should be avoided in members conducting large quantities of heat. Sudden changes in thickness such as might be created by welding parts of different thickness should also be avoided.

The above considerations are sufficient solution to many engineering problems. If the order of magnitude of the thermal stress is sufficiently low there is no need for an elaborate calculation so far as an engineer is concerned. An ingenious design to eliminate thermal stress is preferable to an ingenious calculation of an inferior design. However, there are some problems of thermal stress which cannot be so easily handled, but in which the thermal stress itself sets a design limit on a configuration. In such a case it is necessary to make a detailed calculation to find this limit.

THERMAL STRESS CALCULATIONS

The calculation of thermal stress, like the order of magnitude calculation which has just been made, can be arbitrarily divided into two parts. First it is necessary to calculate the temperature distribution in a body under consideration. Next it is necessary to calculate the stress which exists due to the temperature distribution. For the purpose of the calculation it will be assumed that the strains in the body are elastic.

6-2. Temperature Distribution

In order to illustrate the principles to be developed, a heat-transfer model will be used. This same model will then be used to calculate the thermal stress which results. This model may be thought of as an idealized tube representing a center tube in a tube bundle in a simplified reactor.

This model is shown in Figure 6-2-1. A cooling fluid flows through a tube in whose walls heat is being generated. The heat which is generated within the walls must be carried to the inner surface by conduction, and carried away from the surface by convection. All variables are considered to be uniform in the tangential and axial directions, varying only with radius. This assumption is satisfactory for a long tube, except near the ends. It is also assumed that no heat flows across the outer boundary of the tube. This assumption corresponds either to a thermally insulated boundary or to a bundle of tubes where the temperature distribution is the same for all the tubes. The thermal conductivity is assumed constant throughout the tube material. Many other models could have been taken. For instance, the heat could be generated within the fluid, the tube in this case being merely a container or possibly, in addition, also a moderator. Our purpose at the moment is to demonstrate the origin and magnitude of thermal stress, and the causes of high temperature in solid materials. Later this same model will be used to discuss convective heat transfer and its

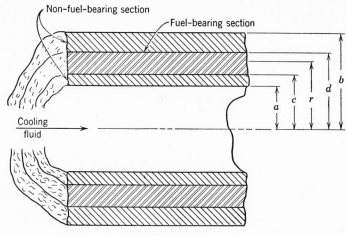

Fig. 6-2-1.

accompanying pressure losses. For these purposes the tubular model, having heat generation within its walls, is sufficient.

For the tubular model, Equation 6-1-30 becomes

$$\frac{1}{r}\frac{\partial}{\partial r}\left(r\frac{\partial T}{\partial r}\right) + \frac{S}{k} = \frac{C_p\gamma}{k}\frac{\partial T}{\partial t} \tag{6-2-1}$$

since in this case

$$\nabla^2 T = \frac{1}{r}\frac{\partial}{\partial r}\left(r\frac{\partial T}{\partial r}\right) \tag{6-2-2}$$

Steady-state conditions are assumed, giving

$$\frac{1}{r}\frac{d}{dr}\left(r\frac{dT}{dr}\right) + \frac{S}{k} = 0 \tag{6-2-3}$$

Equation 6-2-3 is to be integrated subject to two boundary conditions. The first states that there is no heat flow across the outer boundary, or

$$\frac{dT}{dr}\bigg]_{r=b} = 0 \tag{6-2-4}$$

Since, owing to the source term, S, heat is being generated within the tube material, the temperature of the tube will rise indefinitely unless the heat is carried away at the inner boundary. When the heat carried away by the cooling fluid is the same as that generated within the tube for a given interval of time, the temperature of the tube wall will stabilize. The second condition states that the temperature at some point in the material will be fixed by the capacity of the convective heat-transfer system. This can be stated so:

$$T]_{r=b} = T_b \tag{6-2-5}$$

Integrating Equation 6-2-3 once, we have

$$r\frac{dT}{dr} + \frac{1}{k}\int_a^r Sr_1\,dr_1 + C_1 = 0 \tag{6-2-6}$$

From Equation 6-2-4,

$$C_1 = -\frac{1}{k}\int_a^b Sr_1\,dr_1 \tag{6-2-7}$$

Substituting this value for C_1 gives

$$r\frac{dT}{dr} + \frac{1}{k}\int_b^r Sr_1\,dr_1 = 0 \tag{6-2-8}$$

Integrating Equation 6-2-8, we obtain

$$T + \frac{1}{k}\int_a^r \frac{dr_1}{r_1}\int_b^{r_1} Sr_2\,dr_2 + C_2 = 0 \tag{6-2-9}$$

From Equation 6-2-5,

$$T_b + \frac{1}{k}\int_a^b \frac{dr_1}{r_1}\int_b^{r_1} Sr_2\,dr_2 + C_2 = 0 \tag{6-2-10}$$

Subtracting Equation 6-2-10 from Equation 6-2-9 gives

$$T - T_b + \frac{1}{k}\int_b^r \frac{dr_1}{r_1}\int_b^{r_1} Sr_2\,dr_2 = 0 \tag{6-2-11}$$

The maximum temperature difference existing in the tube wall is

$$T_b - T_a = \frac{1}{k}\int_b^a \frac{dr_1}{r_1}\int_b^{r_1} Sr_2\,dr_2 \tag{6-2-12}$$

We now have an expression for temperature variation as a function of the heat source variable, S. In our model we have assumed that the strength of the heat source may vary only with radius. It is convenient to define this variation in dimensionless terms as a variation from a reference value, S_0, and to relate S to the average power density, $\overline{S}$, as a reference. A dimensionless radius and a dimensionless source are defined as

$$\xi = r/b \qquad\qquad (6\text{-}2\text{-}13)$$

$$\gamma = S/S_0 \qquad\qquad (6\text{-}2\text{-}14)$$

where S_0 is the power density at some reference point. Equation 6-2-11 becomes

$$T - T_b + \frac{b^2 S_0}{k} \int_1^{\xi} \frac{d\xi_1}{\xi_1} \int_0^{\xi_1} \gamma \xi_2 \, d\xi_2 = 0 \qquad\qquad (6\text{-}2\text{-}15)$$

Equation 6-2-12 becomes

$$T_a - T_b + \frac{b^2 S_0}{k} \int_1^{a/b} \frac{d\xi_1}{\xi_1} \int_0^{\xi_1} \gamma \xi_2 \, d\xi_2 = 0 \qquad\qquad (6\text{-}2\text{-}16)$$

The average power density, $\overline{S}$, for the space occupied by the tube can be related to the reference value, S_0, by the following integral:

$$\overline{S} = -2S_0 \int_1^{a/b} \gamma \xi_1 \, d\xi_1 \qquad\qquad (6\text{-}2\text{-}17)$$

Eliminating S_0 between Equations 6-2-16 and 6-2-17 gives

$$T_a - T_b = \frac{b^2 \overline{S}}{2k} \frac{\displaystyle\int_1^{a/b} \frac{d\xi_1}{\xi_1} \int_1^{\xi_1} \gamma \xi_2 \, d\xi_2}{\displaystyle\int_1^{a/b} \gamma \xi_1 \, d\xi_1} \qquad\qquad (6\text{-}2\text{-}18)$$

In general where properties of materials and the distributions of heat sources varied at random throughout the materials of interest, it would be necessary to perform the integration of Equation 6-2-18 numerically. Let us consider here a case for which the integration can be done analytically. The double integral in Equation 6-2-18 can be integrated by parts to give

$$\int_1^{a/b} \frac{d\xi_1}{\xi_1} \int_1^{\xi_1} \gamma \xi_2 \, d\xi_2 = \left[\log \xi \int_1^{\xi} \gamma \xi_1 \, d\xi_1 \right]_1^{a/b} - \int_1^{a/b} (\log \xi_1) \gamma \xi_1 \, d\xi_1$$

$$= \log \frac{a}{b} \int_1^{a/b} \gamma \xi_1 \, d\xi_1 - \int_1^{a/b} (\log \xi_1) \gamma \xi_1 \, d\xi_1 \qquad\qquad (6\text{-}2\text{-}19)$$

Substituting into Equation 6-2-18, we obtain

$$T_a - T_b = \frac{b^2 \overline{S}}{2k} \left[\log \frac{a}{b} - \frac{\displaystyle\int_1^{a/b} (\log \xi_1)\gamma \xi_1 \, d\xi_1}{\displaystyle\int_1^{a/b} \gamma \xi_1 \, d\xi_1} \right] \qquad (6\text{-}2\text{-}20)$$

For the purpose of illustration let us assume that the source strength S does not vary within the fuel-bearing region from $r = c$ to $r = d$,

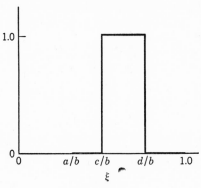

FIG. 6-2-2.

but is zero outside the fuel-bearing region. Then for our case γ has the form of a step function, as shown in Figure 6-2-2. For this case

$$\int_1^{a/b} \gamma \xi_1 \, d\xi_1 = \int_{d/b}^{c/b} \xi_1 \, d\xi_1 = -\frac{d^2 - c^2}{2b^2} \qquad (6\text{-}2\text{-}21)$$

and

$$\int_1^{a/b} (\log \xi_1)\gamma \xi_1 \, d\xi_1 = \int_{d/b}^{c/b} (\log \xi_1)\xi_1 \, d\xi_1 \qquad (6\text{-}2\text{-}22)$$

Integrating by parts, we have

$$\int_{d/b}^{c/b} (\log \xi_1)\xi_1 \, d\xi_1 = \left[(\log \xi)\frac{\xi^2}{2} \right]_{d/b}^{c/b} - \frac{1}{2}\int_{d/b}^{c/b} \xi_1 \, d\xi_1$$

$$= \frac{1}{4}\left[\left(\frac{c}{b}\right)^2 \log \left(\frac{c}{b}\right)^2 - \left(\frac{d}{b}\right)^2 \log \left(\frac{d}{b}\right)^2 + \frac{d^2 - c^2}{b^2} \right]$$

$$(6\text{-}2\text{-}23)$$

Hence Equation 6-2-20 becomes, after simplification,

$$T_b - T_a = \frac{b^2 \overline{S}}{4k}\left[d^2 \frac{\log (d/c)^2}{d^2 - c^2} - 1 + \log (c/a)^2 \right] \qquad (6\text{-}2\text{-}24)$$

Since it was found in the last section that the thermal stress depended for its order of magnitude on ΔT, which here is $(T_b - T_a)$, we would like to find from Equation 6-2-24 the conditions under which, for a given average power density, $\overline{S}$, we will have the minimum temperature difference. We can see first that we wish to have a large thermal conductivity, k, and a small tube diameter, b. Looking at the quantity inside the brackets, we see that it becomes zero for $(c/a) = (d/c) = 1$. Hence, we want the thinnest layer of fuel-bearing material from which we can abstract the required amount of heat, and the thinnest cladding layer we can stand between the fuel and the cooling fluid. The limiting thickness for the fuel layer is of course set by the amount of fuel required.

The highest temperature difference would exist when the fuel was spread throughout the tube material. Then

$$T_b - T_a = \frac{b^2 \overline{S}}{4k} \left[\frac{(b/a)^2 \log (b/a)^2}{(b/a)^2 - 1} - 1 \right] \qquad (6\text{-}2\text{-}25)$$

For this case it is desirable to have (b/a) as close to one as possible. Approximately

$$T_b - T_a \simeq \frac{bt\overline{S}}{2k} \qquad (6\text{-}2\text{-}26)$$

where t is the thickness of the tube wall.

6-3. Thermal Stress in Power-Producing Elements

It is the purpose of this section to demonstrate the application of the theory of elasticity to the detailed investigation of the distribution of thermal stress.

The distribution of stresses in any elastic body must satisfy three conditions: (1) equilibrium; (2) compatibility; and (3) Hooke's law. Condition 1 states that the summation of forces on any isolated element of the body must be equal to zero. Condition 2 states that the strains in the body must add up over the whole body to fit the deformations imposed on the body. Condition 3 requires the stresses and strains in the body to be linearly interdependent. In general, these three conditions will result in a linear system of equations which must be solved simultaneously. For certain classes of problems, like the bending of beams, assumptions can be made which enable us to satisfy each of these conditions separately, and great simplifications result. In many of these problems we merely solve an equation for equilibrium for a statically determinate system, and we are hardly aware even of the existence of other conditions.

For demonstration purposes we will write down the three conditions on the elastic stresses for the heated tube which we discussed in Section 6-2, and will use these conditions to find the distribution of thermal stress. All variables are considered as uniform axially and tangentially, the only variation being with radius. This assumption means that we have what is called *plane strain*, in which cross sections of the tube remain plane during deformation (axial strain is independent of radius). The equations we write will fit these idealizations.

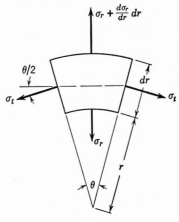

FIG. 6-3-1.

Let us isolate from the tube a section of solid material and find what is necessary to satisfy the equilibrium of forces on it. The stresses are shown in Figure 6-3-1. We adopt here the conventions that a positive sign with a stress designates a tension; a negative sign designates compression. σ_t is tangential stress, and σ_r is radial stress. From the diagram

$$\left(\sigma_r + \frac{d\sigma_r}{dr}\,dr\right)(r + dr)\theta - \sigma_r r\theta - 2\sigma_t\,dr \sin\frac{\theta}{2} = 0 \qquad (6\text{-}3\text{-}1)$$

Simplifying Equation 6-3-1 and neglecting second-order terms, we have

$$\frac{d(r\sigma_r)}{dr} - \sigma_t = 0 \qquad (6\text{-}3\text{-}2)$$

Equation 6-3-2 is the equilibrium condition on the stresses in the tube. The radial strain, ϵ_r, is related to the radial deformation, u, by

$$\epsilon_r = \frac{\partial u}{\partial r} \qquad (6\text{-}3\text{-}3)$$

The tangential strain, ϵ_t, is related to the radial deformation by

$$\epsilon_t = u/r \qquad (6\text{-}3\text{-}4)$$

The axial strain, ϵ_z, is a constant since all quantities are by definition uniform in the z direction. Equations 6-3-3 and 6-3-4 can be combined to eliminate u, giving

$$\frac{d}{dr}(r\epsilon_t) = \epsilon_r \qquad (6\text{-}3\text{-}5)$$

Equation 6-3-5 is called the *compatibility condition* for the strains. Hooke's law gives three equations relating stresses and strains (Equations 6-3-6, 6-3-7, 6-3-8):

$$\epsilon_r = \frac{1}{E}\{\sigma_r - \mu(\sigma_t + \sigma_z) + E\alpha(T - T_0)\} \qquad (6\text{-}3\text{-}6)$$

where T_0 is a reference temperature whose significance will be considered later. The tangential strain is

$$\epsilon_t = \frac{1}{E}\{\sigma_t - \mu(\sigma_z + \sigma_r) + E\alpha(T - T_0)\} \qquad (6\text{-}3\text{-}7)$$

Axial strain, which is constant, is

$$\epsilon_z = \frac{1}{E}\{\sigma_z - \mu(\sigma_r + \sigma_t) + E\alpha(T - T_0)\} = C \qquad (6\text{-}3\text{-}8)$$

Equations 6-3-5, 6-3-6, 6-3-7, and 6-3-8 will now be combined to eliminate the strains. Solving Equation 6-3-8 for σ_z gives

$$\sigma_z = \mu(\sigma_r + \sigma_t) - E\alpha(T - T_0) + \epsilon_z E \qquad (6\text{-}3\text{-}9)$$

Substituting Equation 6-3-9 into Equations 6-3-6 and 6-3-7 gives

$$\epsilon_r = \frac{1}{E}[(1 - \mu^2)\sigma_r - \mu(1 + \mu)\sigma_t + (1 + \mu)E\alpha(T - T_0)] - \epsilon_z\mu$$

and $$\qquad\qquad\qquad\qquad\qquad\qquad\qquad\qquad\qquad\qquad (6\text{-}3\text{-}10)$$

$$\epsilon_t = \frac{1}{E}[(1 - \mu^2)\sigma_t - \mu(1 + \mu)\sigma_r + (1 + \mu)E\alpha(T - T_0)] - \epsilon_z\mu$$

$$\qquad\qquad\qquad\qquad\qquad\qquad\qquad\qquad\qquad\qquad (6\text{-}3\text{-}11)$$

Substituting Equations 6-3-10 and 6-3-11 into Equation 6-3-5 gives the compatibility condition in terms of stresses instead of strains:

$$\frac{d}{dr}\left\{\frac{r}{E}[(1 - \mu^2)\sigma_t - \mu(1 + \mu)\sigma_r + (1 + \mu)E\alpha(T - T_0)]\right\}$$

$$= \frac{1}{E}[(1 - \mu^2)\sigma_r - \mu(1 + \mu)\sigma_t + (1 + \mu)E\alpha(T - T_0)] \quad (6\text{-}3\text{-}12)$$

Equations 6-3-2 and 6-3-12 are two equations in two variables, σ_t and σ_r. It is desired to eliminate σ_t to obtain an equation for σ_r. It will be assumed that the modulus of elasticity, E, is constant throughout the stressed material. The result of the combination of Equations 6-3-2 and 6-3-12, after simplification, is

$$\frac{d}{dr}\left(r^3 \frac{d\sigma_r}{dr}\right) + \frac{E\alpha r^2}{1-\mu}\frac{dT}{dr} = 0 \qquad (6\text{-}3\text{-}13)$$

We substitute into Equation 6-3-13 the value of $\dfrac{dT}{dr}$ from Equation 6-2-8, which gives

$$\frac{d}{dr}\left(r^3 \frac{d\sigma_r}{dr}\right) = \frac{E\alpha}{k(1-\mu)}\,r\int_b^r Sr_1\,dr_1 \qquad (6\text{-}3\text{-}14)$$

Equation 6-3-14 is a differential equation for the radial, thermal, stress in terms of properties of the tube and the distributed heat source, S. It is to be integrated twice subject to appropriate boundary conditions. These conditions will depend on the radial stresses imposed on the boundaries of the heated tube. Let us include two arbitrary constants in the integration of Equation 6-3-14 for later adjustment. Integrating Equation 6-3-14 once, including an arbitrary constant which depends on the slope of the stress curve at $r = b$, gives

$$\frac{d\sigma_r}{dr} = \frac{E\alpha}{k(1-\mu)}\frac{1}{r^3}\left[\int_b^r r_1\,dr_1\int_b^{r_1} Sr_2\,dr_2 + 2A\right] \qquad (6\text{-}3\text{-}15)$$

Integrating again, including a second constant which depends on the magnitude of the stress at $r = b$, gives

$$\sigma_r = \frac{E\alpha}{k(1-\mu)}\left[\int_b^r \frac{dr_1}{r_1^3}\int_b^{r_1} r_2\,dr_2\int_b^{r_2} Sr_3\,dr_3 + A\left(\frac{1}{b^2}-\frac{1}{r^2}\right)+B\right]$$

$$(6\text{-}3\text{-}16)$$

From Equation 6-3-2 the tangential stress is

$$\sigma_t = r\frac{d\sigma_r}{dr} + \sigma_r \qquad (6\text{-}3\text{-}17)$$

Substituting Equations 6-3-15 and 6-3-16 into Equation 6-3-17 gives

$$\sigma_t = \frac{E\alpha}{k(1-\mu)}\left[\frac{1}{r^2}\int_b^r r_1\,dr_1\int_b^{r_1} Sr_2\,dr_2 + \int_b^r \frac{dr_1}{r_1^3}\int_b^{r_1} r_2\,dr_2\int_b^{r_2} Sr_3\,dr_3\right.$$

$$\left. + A\left(\frac{1}{b^2}+\frac{1}{r^2}\right)+B\right] \qquad (6\text{-}3\text{-}18)$$

Substituting Equations 6-3-16 and 6-3-18 into Equation 6-3-9 gives

$$\sigma_z = \frac{E\alpha\mu}{k(1-\mu)}\left[\frac{1}{r^2}\int_b^r r_1\,dr_1\int_b^{r_1} Sr_2\,dr_2 + 2\int_b^r \frac{dr_1}{r_1^{\,3}}\int_b^{r_1} r_2\,dr_2\int_b^{r_2} Sr_3\,dr_3\right.$$

$$\left. + \frac{2A}{b^2} + 2B\right] - E\{\alpha(T-T_0) - \epsilon_z\} \quad (6\text{-}3\text{-}19)$$

From Equation 6-2-11,

$$T - T_b = -\frac{1}{k}\int_b^r \frac{dr_1}{r_1}\int_b^{r_1} Sr_2\,dr_2 \quad (6\text{-}3\text{-}20)$$

Hence the axial stress is

$$\sigma_z = \frac{E\alpha\mu}{k(1-\mu)}\left[\frac{1}{r^2}\int_b^r r_1\,dr_1\int_b^{r_1} Sr_2\,dr_2 + 2\int_b^r \frac{dr_1}{r_1^{\,3}}\int_b^{r_1} r_2\,dr_2\int_b^{r_2} Sr_3\,dr_3\right.$$

$$\left. + \frac{(1-\mu)}{\mu}\int_b^r \frac{dr_1}{r_1}\int_b^{r_1} Sr_2\,dr_2 + \frac{2A}{b^2} + 2B\right]$$

$$- E\{\alpha(T_b - T_0) - \epsilon_z\} \quad (6\text{-}3\text{-}21)$$

We now have equations for the three stresses in the tube in terms of the internal heat source and the geometry of the tube system. These can be simplified for purposes of analysis by using the previous dimensionless variables,

$$\xi = r/b$$

$$\gamma = S/S_0$$

and the definition of average power density from Equation 6-2-17,

$$\bar{S} = -2S_0\int_1^{a/b} \gamma\xi_1\,d\xi_1$$

Now Equation 6-3-16 becomes

$$\sigma_r = -\frac{E\alpha\bar{S}b^2}{2k(1-\mu)\displaystyle\int_1^{a/b}\gamma\xi_1\,d\xi_1}\left[F_1(\xi) + A'\left(1 - \frac{1}{\xi^2}\right) + B'\right] \quad (6\text{-}3\text{-}22)$$

where

$$F_1(\xi) = \int_1^\xi \frac{d\xi_1}{\xi_1^{\,3}}\int_1^{\xi_1} \xi_2\,d\xi_2\int_1^{\xi_2} \gamma\xi_3\,d\xi_3 \quad (6\text{-}3\text{-}23)$$

Equation 6-3-18 becomes

$$\sigma_t = -\frac{E\alpha\overline{S}b^2}{2k(1-\mu)\displaystyle\int_1^{a/b}\gamma\xi_1\,d\xi_1}\left[F_1(\xi) + F_2(\xi) + A'\left(1 + \frac{1}{\xi^2}\right) + B'\right]$$

$$(6\text{-}3\text{-}24)$$

where

$$F_2(\xi) = \frac{1}{\xi^2}\int_1^{\xi}\xi_1\,d\xi_1\int_1^{\xi_1}\gamma\xi_2\,d\xi_2 \qquad (6\text{-}3\text{-}25)$$

Equation 6-3-21 becomes

$$\sigma_z = -\frac{E\alpha\overline{S}b^2\mu}{2k(1-\mu)\displaystyle\int_1^{a/b}\gamma\xi_1\,d\xi_1}$$

$$[2F_1(\xi) + F_2(\xi) + F_3(\xi) + 2A' + 2B' + C'] \qquad (6\text{-}3\text{-}26)$$

where

$$F_3(\xi) = \frac{1-\mu}{\mu}\int_1^{\xi}\frac{d\xi_1}{\xi_1}\int_1^{\xi_1}\gamma\xi_2\,d\xi_2 \qquad (6\text{-}3\text{-}27)$$

and

$$\frac{E\alpha\overline{S}b^2\mu}{2k(1-\mu)\displaystyle\int_1^{a/b}\gamma\xi_1\,d\xi_1}C' = E\{\alpha(T_b - T_0) - \epsilon_z\} \qquad (6\text{-}3\text{-}28)$$

It is to be noted that the constant C' is dependent on the reference temperature, T_0, and on the constant (by assumption) axial strain, σ_z. Hence, for a given value of C', assigning a value to the axial strain amounts to assigning a value also to the reference temperature. Equations 6-3-22, 6-3-23, and 6-3-24 give the distributions of the stresses in the heated tube. Let us now assign boundary conditions for determination of the arbitrary constants A', B', and C' in these equations. A useful set of conditions for many problems results from the assumption that no external, or surface, forces are exerted on the heated tube. These conditions are satisfied by writing three equations. The first equation states that there is no radial stress on the inner boundary of the tube, at $r = a(\xi = a/b)$, or

$$\sigma_{ra} = 0 \qquad (6\text{-}3\text{-}29)$$

The second equation states that there is no radial stress on the outer boundary of the tube, at $r = b(\xi = 1)$, or

$$\sigma_{rb} = 0 \qquad (6\text{-}3\text{-}30)$$

The third equation states that the total force exerted over a cross section normal to the axis is zero, or

$$2\pi b^2 \int_{a/b}^{1} \sigma_z \xi_1 \, d\xi_1 = 0 \tag{6-3-31}$$

Applying the condition from Equation 6-3-30 to Equation 6-3-22 requires that

$$B' = 0 \tag{6-3-32}$$

Applying the condition from Equation 6-3-29 to Equation 6-3-22 requires that

$$A' = \frac{a^2}{b^2 - a^2} F_1 \left(\frac{a}{b} \right) \tag{6-3-33}$$

Applying the condition from Equation 6-3-31 to Equation 6-3-26 requires that

$$C' = -2A' - 2 \frac{b^2}{b^2 - a^2} \int_{a/b}^{1} [2F_1(\xi) + F_2(\xi) + F_3(\xi)] \xi \, d\xi \tag{6-3-34}$$

Equations 6-3-22, 6-3-24, and 6-3-26, along with the qualifying Equations 6-3-32, 6-3-33, and 6-3-34, give a complete description of the stresses in the heated tube under the boundary conditions specified. These equations can be simplified for our present purposes by partial integrations.* First

$$F_2(\xi) = \frac{1}{\xi^2} \int_{1}^{\xi} \xi_1 \, d\xi_1 \int_{1}^{\xi_1} \gamma \xi_2 \, d\xi_2 = \frac{1}{2} \int_{1}^{\xi} \gamma \xi_1 \, d\xi_1 - \frac{1}{2\xi^2} \int_{1}^{\xi} \gamma \xi_1^3 \, d\xi_1$$

$$\tag{6-3-35}$$

Next

$$F_3(\xi) \frac{\mu}{1 - \mu} = \int_{1}^{\xi} \frac{d\xi_1}{\xi_1} \int_{1}^{\xi_1} \gamma \xi_2 \, d\xi_2 = \log \xi \int_{1}^{\xi} \gamma \xi_1 \, d\xi_1 - \int_{1}^{\xi} \gamma \xi_1 \log \xi_1 \, d\xi_1$$

$$\tag{6-3-36}$$

Similarly

$$F_1(\xi) = \frac{1}{2} \log \xi \int_{1}^{\xi} \gamma \xi_1 \, d\xi_1 - \frac{1}{2} \int_{1}^{\xi} \gamma \xi_1 \log \xi_1 \, d\xi_1$$

$$+ \frac{1}{4\xi^2} \int_{1}^{\xi} \gamma \xi_1^3 \, d\xi_1 - \frac{1}{4} \int_{1}^{\xi} \gamma \xi_1 \, d\xi_1 \tag{6-3-37}$$

* Let $v = \int_{1}^{\xi} \xi_1 \, d\xi_1$, $u = \int_{1}^{\xi} \gamma \xi_1 \, d\xi_1$, then $\int_{1}^{\xi} u \, dv = [uv]_1^{\xi} - \int_{1}^{\xi} v \, du$.

We are interested in knowing the maximum stress which occurs in the heated tube. The radial stresses at the inner and outer surfaces of the tube are, by assumption, zero. The radial stresses in the tube are everywhere considerably lower than the maximum stress in the tube. It can be shown that for the boundary conditions used here the maximum axial stress is less than the maximum tangential stress. The maximum tangential stress is found at the inner surface of the tube, at $\xi = a/b$. From Equations 6-3-24 and 6-3-33 this stress is

$$\sigma_{ta} = $$

$$- \frac{E\alpha\bar{S}b^2}{2k(1-\mu)\int_1^{a/b} \gamma\xi_1 \, d\xi_1} \left[F_1\left(\frac{a}{b}\right)\left(\frac{2b^2}{b^2 - a^2}\right) + F_2\left(\frac{a}{b}\right) \right] \quad (6\text{-}3\text{-}38)$$

Let us evaluate this stress for the case of the step distribution of power, used previously, and represented in Figure 6-2-2. For this case, from Equation 6-2-21,

$$\int_1^{a/b} \gamma\xi_1 \, d\xi_1 = \int_{d/b}^{c/b} \xi_1 \, d\xi_1 = -\frac{d^2 - c^2}{2b^2} \quad (6\text{-}3\text{-}39)$$

and, similarly,

$$\int_1^{a/b} \gamma\xi_1{}^3 \, d\xi_1 = \int_{d/b}^{c/b} \xi_1{}^3 \, d\xi_1 = -\frac{d^4 - b^4}{4b^4} \quad (6\text{-}3\text{-}40)$$

From Equation 6-2-23,

$$\int_1^{a/b} \gamma\xi_1 \log \xi_1 \, d\xi_1 = \frac{1}{4}\left[\left(\frac{c}{b}\right)^2 \log\left(\frac{c}{b}\right)^2 - \left(\frac{d}{b}\right)^2 \log\left(\frac{d}{b}\right)^2 + \frac{d^2 - c^2}{b^2} \right]$$

$$(6\text{-}3\text{-}41)$$

Substituting Equations 6-3-39, 6-3-40, and 6-3-41 into Equation 6-3-37, and simplifying, gives

$$F_1\left(\frac{a}{b}\right) = \frac{1}{4}\left(\frac{d^2 - c^2}{2b^2}\right)\left[\log\left(\frac{c}{a}\right)^2 + \frac{d^2}{d^2 - c^2}\log\left(\frac{d}{c}\right)^2 - \frac{d^2 + c^2}{2a^2} \right]$$

$$(6\text{-}3\text{-}42)$$

From Equation 6-3-35,

$$F_2\left(\frac{a}{b}\right) = \frac{1}{4}\left(\frac{d^2 - c^2}{2b^2}\right)\left[-2 + 2\frac{d^2 + c^2}{2a^2} \right] \quad (6\text{-}3\text{-}43)$$

Substituting Equations 6-3-39, 6-3-42, and 6-3-43 into Equation 6-3-38, and simplifying, gives for the tangential stress at the inner surface of the tube

$$\sigma_{ta} = \frac{E\alpha \bar{S} b^2}{4k(1-\mu)(b^2-a^2)}\left[b^2\left\{\frac{d^2}{d^2-c^2}\log\left(\frac{d}{c}\right)^2 - 1 + \log\left(\frac{c}{a}\right)^2\right\}\right.$$
$$\left. + \frac{d^2+c^2-2a^2}{2}\right] \quad (6\text{-}3\text{-}44)$$

Let us look briefly at Equation 6-3-44 for the significance of some of its terms. The ratio $(b^2 - a^2)/b^2$ is a measure of the fractional solidity of the tube. We can write $(d^2 - c^2) = (d + c)(d - c)$, and

$$\frac{d^2+c^2-2a^2}{2} = \frac{(d+c)(d-c)}{2} + (c+a)(c-a)$$

The quantity $(d - c)$ is the thickness of the fuel-bearing layer, whereas $(c - a)$ is the thickness of the cladding layer. Let us take the limit of the quantity in brackets in Equation 6-3-44 as these thicknesses approach zero, or as c and d both approach a. This limit is zero. For the case in which heat is generated throughout the tube wall, $d = b$ and $c = a$. For this case the quantity in the brackets has the value

$$\frac{b^4}{b^2-a^2}\log\left(\frac{b}{a}\right)^2 - \frac{b^2-a^2}{2} - b^2$$

By comparison with Equation 6-2-24 for the two limiting cases of very thin walls ($b \approx a$) and very thin walls ($b \gg a$), it can be shown that the maximum stress in the heated tube is always between fixed limits. These limits are

$$\frac{2}{3}\frac{E\alpha(T_b - T_a)}{1-\mu} \leqq \sigma_{\max} \leqq \frac{E\alpha T_b - T_a}{1-\mu}$$

It is apparent that significant decreases in the maximum value of the thermal stress in a heated tube can be accomplished only by reducing the temperature difference across the tube, if the physical characteristics of the material are fixed. For a low value of the stress with a given average power density, it is, therefore, important to have:

1. Low modulus of elasticity, E.
2. Low coefficient of thermal expansion, α.
3. Thin tube.
4. Thin fuel layer and cladding.
5. High thermal conductivity, k.
6. Low value of Poisson's ratio, μ.

This illustration is a typical problem in the thermal stress analysis of reactor systems. Other arrangements and geometries may be analyzed in exactly parallel steps to those illustrated above. Particular care must be taken in determining appropriate boundary conditions. For most cases involving variable parameters, such as modulus of elasticity and thermal conductivity, the integrations of equations must be done numerically.

6-4. Temperature Variations Which Do Not Cause Thermal Stress

It is of interest to know under what circumstances temperature distributions can exist in a body without causing thermal stresses. For this purpose let us consider some equations for the thermal stress in a rectangular coordinate system. The equations needed are: (1) Hooke's law, (2) the compatibility conditions, and (3) the heat-conduction equation. Since it is desired to find the circumstances in which the thermal stress is zero, let us assume all stresses to be zero and find the conditions on the temperature distribution which must be satisfied.

Hooke's law is expressed in the general case by six equations. They are:

$$\epsilon_x = \frac{1}{E}\{\sigma_x - \mu(\sigma_y + \sigma_z)\} + \alpha T$$

$$\epsilon_y = \frac{1}{E}\{\sigma_y - \mu(\sigma_z + \sigma_x)\} + \alpha T$$

$$\epsilon_z = \frac{1}{E}\{\sigma_z - \mu(\sigma_x + \sigma_y)\} + \alpha T$$

$$\gamma_{yz} = \frac{2(1 + \mu)\tau_{yz}}{E}$$

$$\gamma_{zx} = \frac{2(1 + \mu)\tau_{zx}}{E}$$

$$\gamma_{xy} = \frac{2(1 + \mu)\tau_{xy}}{E} \tag{6-4-1}$$

where τ is shear stress and γ is shear strain on a plane designated by the subscripts. Where all stresses are zero, the Equations 6-4-1 reduce to

$$\epsilon_x = \epsilon_y = \epsilon_z = \alpha T$$

$$\gamma_{yz} = \gamma_{zx} = \gamma_{xy} = 0 \tag{6-4-2}$$

The six general conditions for compatibility of stresses and strains are:

$$\frac{\partial^2 \epsilon_x}{\partial y^2} + \frac{\partial^2 \epsilon_y}{\partial x^2} = \frac{\partial^2 \gamma_{xy}}{\partial x\, \partial y}$$

$$\frac{\partial^2 \epsilon_y}{\partial z^2} + \frac{\partial^2 \epsilon_z}{\partial y^2} = \frac{\partial^2 \gamma_{yz}}{\partial y\, \partial z}$$

$$\frac{\partial^2 \epsilon_z}{\partial x^2} + \frac{\partial^2 \epsilon_x}{\partial z^2} = \frac{\partial^2 \gamma_{zx}}{\partial z\, \partial x}$$

$$2\frac{\partial^2 \epsilon_x}{\partial y\, \partial z} = \frac{\partial}{\partial x}\left(-\frac{\partial \gamma_{yz}}{\partial x} + \frac{\partial \gamma_{xz}}{\partial y} + \frac{\partial \gamma_{xy}}{\partial z} \right)$$

$$2\frac{\partial^2 \epsilon_y}{\partial z\, \partial x} = \frac{\partial}{\partial y}\left(-\frac{\partial \gamma_{zx}}{\partial y} + \frac{\partial \gamma_{xy}}{\partial z} + \frac{\partial \gamma_{yz}}{\partial x} \right)$$

$$2\frac{\partial^2 \epsilon_z}{\partial x\, \partial y} = \frac{\partial}{\partial z}\left(-\frac{\partial \gamma_{xy}}{\partial z} + \frac{\partial \gamma_{yz}}{\partial x} + \frac{\partial \gamma_{zx}}{\partial y} \right) \qquad (6\text{-}4\text{-}3)$$

Substituting the values of the strains from Equation 6-4-2, assuming that the coefficient of thermal expansion, α, is constant, gives

$$\frac{\partial^2 T}{\partial y^2} + \frac{\partial^2 T}{\partial x^2} = \frac{\partial^2 T}{\partial z^2} + \frac{\partial^2 T}{\partial y^2} = \frac{\partial^2 T}{\partial x^2} + \frac{\partial^2 T}{\partial z^2} = 0$$

$$\frac{\partial^2 T}{\partial y\, \partial z} = \frac{\partial^2 T}{\partial z\, \partial x} = \frac{\partial^2 T}{\partial x\, \partial y} = 0 \qquad (6\text{-}4\text{-}4)$$

Adding the first three of Equations 6-4-4 gives

$$\frac{\partial^2 T}{\partial x^2} + \frac{\partial^2 T}{\partial y^2} + \frac{\partial^2 T}{\partial z^2} = 0 \qquad (6\text{-}4\text{-}5)$$

Equation 6-4-5, which is Laplace's equation, must then be satisfied by any temperature distribution which does not cause thermal stress. The steady-state heat conduction equation, assuming that thermal conductivity, k, is constant, is

$$\frac{\partial^2 T}{\partial x^2} + \frac{\partial^2 T}{\partial y^2} + \frac{\partial^2 T}{\partial z^2} + \frac{S}{k} = 0 \qquad (6\text{-}4\text{-}6)$$

Equations 6-4-5 and 6-4-6 are mutually incompatible unless

$$S = 0 \qquad (6\text{-}4\text{-}7)$$

Thus any body having a distributed heat source will have thermal stress. Combining Equation 6-4-5 with the first three of Equations 6-4-4 gives

$$\frac{\partial^2 T}{\partial x^2} = \frac{\partial^2 T}{\partial y^2} = \frac{\partial^2 T}{\partial z^2} = 0$$

$$\frac{\partial^2 T}{\partial y\, \partial z} = \frac{\partial^2 T}{\partial z\, \partial x} = \frac{\partial^2 T}{\partial x\, \partial y} = 0 \qquad (6\text{-}4\text{-}8)$$

Only equations which satisfy all of Equations 6-4-8 give temperatures for steady-state distribution which cause no thermal stress. By usual procedures for the solution of partial differential equations it can be seen that the most general solution to Equations 6-4-8 has the general form

$$T = A + Bx + Cy + Dz \qquad (6\text{-}4\text{-}9)$$

where A, B, C, and D are arbitrary constants. It should be pointed out also that, to have no internal stresses in the body, the boundary stresses must also be zero. Equation 6-4-9 states that only temperature distributions which are linear functions of the coordinates, in a rectangular coordinate system, cause no thermal stress. It is to be noted that Equation 6-4-9 is a solution also to Equation 6-4-5, as it is required to be.

REFERENCES

Peterson, R. E. *Stress Concentration Design Factors*, John Wiley & Sons, Inc., New York, 1953.

Timoshenko, S., *Theory of Elasticity*, McGraw-Hill Book Co., New York, 1934 (Introduction and Chapters VI and VII).

Timoshenko, S., *Strength of Materials, Part I*, D. Van Nostrand Co., New York, 1941 (Chapters I and II).

CHAPTER 7

POWER EXTRACTION FROM REACTORS

In Chapter 2 we discussed the nuclear characteristics of a reactor operating under steady-state conditions and generating thermal power at a uniform rate. In this chapter we shall discuss the engineering principles involved in extracting energy from reactors. A fluid (gas or liquid) is assumed as the means of removing the heat energy generated within the reactor. This fluid flows through the reactor in passages arranged to provide heat extraction distributed throughout the reactor. This fluid, or a second fluid, is the working fluid in the power plant associated with the reactor.

The objectives are to design the heat-extraction system to remove a maximum of energy from a reactor without local overheating, and to do this with a minimum expenditure of energy for pumping the fluid. These objectives can be expressed in terms of the power density and the efficiency of heat transfer, which vary with the geometry of the heat-transfer apparatus and the physical properties of working fluids. It will be necessary first to discuss briefly the flow of fluids and heat transfer to flowing fluids.

The problem of heat transfer to viscous fluids will be divided into two main parts, the first involving the pressure losses in the fluid, the second involving the transfer of heat to the flowing fluid. The pressure lost and the amount of heat transferred will be shown to be related.

7-1. Pressure Losses in Viscous Flow

For the flow of viscous fluids through tubes it is customary to write an expression for the pressure loss per unit length of tube, due to friction, of the form

$$\frac{dp}{dx} = -\frac{4f\gamma}{D}\frac{w^2}{2g} \tag{7-1-1}$$

where dp is the pressure loss in distance, dx, D is the hydraulic diameter of the tube, $D = 4A/S = 4m$, A is the cross section of the tube, S is the wetted perimeter, m is the hydraulic radius, w is the average velocity of flow in the tube, g is the acceleration of gravity, f is the friction factor, and γ is the weight density of fluid. It is to be noted that the hydraulic radius, m, for a circular tube is one-half the actual radius. We will be primarily concerned with establishing values for the factor, f, which are adequate for engineering purposes. Authors define f sometimes based on diameter, sometimes on radius, and sometimes on hydraulic radius. Definitions of f by different authors, therefore, differ by factors of two or four, and the reader must often be exceedingly wary to infer from the context which definition is being used.

There is another source of pressure loss of practical importance besides wall friction of passages, which is due to entrance and exit conditions, or to sudden contractions or expansions in the passage. These losses are expressed analogously to Equation 7-1-1 by the expression

$$\Delta p = -\beta(w^2/2g)$$

where β depends on the conditions of the expansion or contraction.

A great deal of work has been done to establish appropriate values for the friction factor, f, for various geometries and fluid properties. It has been found that f depends greatly on whether the fluid flow is laminar or turbulent. In laminar flow the fluid can be considered as moving in layers with relatively little mixing of adjacent layers. Turbulent flow is accompanied by an agitation of the fluid by eddies which thoroughly mix the fluid. For the laminar flow an analytical solution for the friction factor can be found, whereas the turbulent flow must be handled experimentally, with some help from dimensional analysis.

LAMINAR FLOW OF A VISCOUS FLUID

The analytical solution for steady flow of a laminar fluid and the corresponding friction factor can be found in the references. For a circular tube, the velocity profile is parabolic with radius, the highest velocity being at the center of the tube. The friction factor for this case is found by equating the force on the fluid due to the pressure drop to that due to the shearing force at the outside wall. It is

$$f = \frac{16}{wD\rho/\mu} \tag{7-1-2}$$

where ρ = mass density = γ/g,
   μ = viscosity of the fluid at the wall.

In Equation 7-1-2 the dimensionless ratio

$$wD\rho/\mu = (Re) \qquad (7\text{-}1\text{-}3)$$

is called the Reynolds number. This number is found to be an important criterion for the characteristics of the flow of viscous fluids. It will appear many times in the following sections. With this definition, Equation 7-1-2 becomes

$$f = 16/(Re) \qquad (7\text{-}1\text{-}4)$$

The Reynolds number is a criterion for the flow of fluids where the viscous forces become of significance compared to the inertia forces in the fluid.

It is necessary to make the Reynolds number dimensionless, using data from experimental compilations. To fit the definition of viscosity, μ is assigned the units

$$\frac{(force)(time)}{(length)^2}$$

The most commonly quoted unit for viscosity is the poise, which has the dimension

$$\frac{dyne\ sec}{cm^2}$$

or the centipoise which is one one-hundredth of a poise. The *kinematic viscosity* is defined μ/ρ and has the dimensions of diffusivity or

$$\frac{(length)^2}{(time)}$$

The dimensions used in this ratio should be consistent with the requirement that the Reynolds number be dimensionless.

TURBULENT FLOW OF A VISCOUS FLUID

It has been found experimentally that if the velocity of a fluid stream is increased indefinitely a point is reached above which the flow is no longer laminar, but breaks up into vortices which cause violent agitation of the stream. A criterion for the onset of this turbulent motion has been found to be the Reynolds number. Below a Reynolds number of about 1000, laminar flow exists. Above this value, there is a transition range in which the flow may be either laminar or turbulent, depending on disturbances in the stream. However, under most engineering conditions turbulent flow will exist if the Reynolds number is above 2000.

It has been found by experimental methods that a layer of laminar flow still exists, at high Reynolds numbers, next to the passage wall. This boundary layer has been shown to have a thickness of the order of $D/\sqrt{\text{Re}}$. It is thought to consist of two portions. Next to the wall is a layer truly laminar. A transition or buffer layer separates this layer from the turbulent region. When it is remembered that for turbulent flow the Reynolds number is generally greater than 2000 it can be seen that the boundary layer is generally small compared to the characteristic dimension, D.

It is desirable to express the pressure drop due to friction in turbulent flow by Equation 7-1-1. No analytical solution for f has been

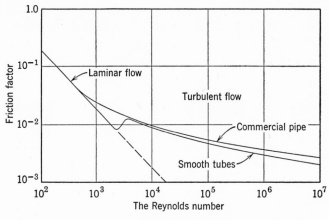

FIG. 7-1-1.

found for the turbulent case. Experimentally, it is found that f is inversely proportional no longer to the first power of the Reynolds number, but to a much smaller power. Roughness of surfaces acts to increase the value of f. A typical curve for f is shown in Figure 7-1-1 as a function of the Reynolds number.

A satisfactory empirical formula for the friction factor for long smooth tubes, for Reynolds numbers between 5000 and 200,000, is

$$f = \frac{0.046}{(\text{Re})^{0.2}} \tag{7-1-5}$$

Equation 7-1-1, with appropriate data for the value of the friction factor from Equation 7-1-2 or Figure 7-1-1, provides information to permit the calculation of friction pressure losses in the passages of reactor cooling systems, once the physical properties of the fluid and the geometry are established.

FLUID FLOW IN PASSAGES

An analysis will now be made of the flow of fluid in passages. This analysis has as its objective formulae for the calculation of pressure losses and heat transfer in stream tubes. A stream tube is defined as a passage through each section of which the same total weight flow passes. The cross section of the tube may change. The tube may have real walls or may be defined as a filament in a larger fluid flow. Steady flow will be assumed as appropriate to the reactor heat-extraction problem.

The conditions of flow in a stream tube are defined by equations expressing three principles: (1) conservation of momentum; (2) conservation of mass; and (3) conservation of energy, and the necessary relations between fluid properties. Equations for these conditions can be written for the fluid element, pictured in Figure 7-1-2.

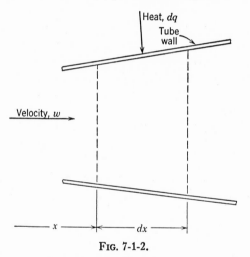

Fig. 7-1-2.

We will consider first the conservation of momentum. The equation for the conservation of momentum requires that the summation of forces over a fluid element be zero. These forces are due to acceleration of the element, pressure differences across the element, and viscous friction forces along the wall of the element. The momentum equation for the tubular element is

$$A \, dx \, \frac{\gamma}{g} \frac{dw}{dt} + \left(p + \frac{\partial p}{\partial x} dx \right) A - pA - \frac{\partial F}{\partial x} dx = 0 \qquad (7\text{-}1\text{-}6)$$

where dF is the force due to friction on the walls. For steady flow

$$\frac{dw}{dt} = g \frac{d}{dx} \left(\frac{w^2}{2g} \right) \qquad (7\text{-}1\text{-}7)$$

Substituting in Equation 7-1-6 gives

$$\frac{d}{dx}\left(\frac{w^2}{2g}\right) + \frac{1}{\gamma}\frac{dp}{dx} - \frac{1}{\gamma A}\frac{dF}{dx} = 0 \qquad (7\text{-}1\text{-}8)$$

Equation 7-1-8 is the expression for the conservation of momentum. If we use the expression for the pressure loss due to friction from Equation 7-1-1, Equation 7-1-8 becomes

$$\frac{d}{dx}\left(\frac{w^2}{2g}\right) + \frac{1}{\gamma}\frac{dp}{dx} + \frac{4f}{D}\left(\frac{w^2}{2g}\right) = 0 \qquad (7\text{-}1\text{-}9)$$

This is the momentum equation in the form in which we will find it useful. Equation 7-1-9 is essentially the Bernoulli equation. The friction factor, f, has been discussed previously.

The equation of continuity of mass states that fluid is neither created nor destroyed inside the confines of the element. The flow per unit time through the tube is $\gamma w A$. Its conservation requires that

$$\frac{\partial}{\partial x}(\gamma w A)\,dx = A\frac{\partial \gamma}{\partial t}\,dx \qquad (7\text{-}1\text{-}10)$$

Or for steady-state conditions,

$$\gamma w A = Gg = \text{constant} \qquad (7\text{-}1\text{-}11)$$

where G is the mass flow per unit time. This equation can be combined with the momentum equation to provide a more convenient expression for pressure drop. Equation 7-1-9 can be rewritten as

$$dp + \frac{\gamma w}{g}\left(dw + \frac{2fl}{D}w\,d\xi\right) = 0 \qquad (7\text{-}1\text{-}12)$$

where $\xi = x/l$. Substituting Equation 7-1-11 into Equation 7-1-12 gives

$$dp + \frac{G}{A}\left(dw + \frac{2fl}{D}w\,d\xi\right) = 0 \qquad (7\text{-}1\text{-}13)$$

This can be integrated from the beginning of the passage to any point x, to give the pressure drop to point x,

$$p_0 - p = G\left[\int_0^\xi \frac{dw}{A} + \int_0^\xi \frac{2fl}{AD}w\,d\xi\right] \qquad (7\text{-}1\text{-}14)$$

For a passage having a constant cross section, Equation 7-1-14 becomes

$$p_0 - p = \frac{G}{A}\left[w - w_0 + \frac{2l}{D}\int_0^\xi fw\,d\xi\right] \qquad (7\text{-}1\text{-}15)$$

Equation 7-1-5 shows that the friction factor in the turbulent region is dependent on the Reynolds number (or therefore on the velocity) only to the one-fifth power. For many purposes, then, the friction factor can be considered constant, and Equation 7-1-15 becomes

$$p_0 - p = \frac{G}{A}\left[w - w_0 + \frac{2fl}{D}\int_0^{\xi} w\, d\xi \right] \qquad (7\text{-}1\text{-}16)$$

Equation 7-1-14 defines the pressure drop in terms of the variables, mass flow, velocity, area, hydraulic diameter, friction factor, and length. Area and hydraulic diameter are related by the proportions of the cross sections of the passage. Since velocity and friction factor both vary in general with the fluid temperature, a solution of Equation 7-1-14 will be possible only after the equation for conservation of energy is developed and the fluid temperature determined from considerations of the mechanism of heat transfer.

We are ready to discuss the principle of conservation of energy. The thermodynamic equation for the conservation of energy for the moving fluid to which external heat is added and from which external work is extracted is given by

$$dq - dw = dh + dk + de \qquad (7\text{-}1\text{-}17)$$

where dq is the external heat added per unit weight of fluid, dw is the external work done by fluid, dh is the change in enthalpy per unit weight of fluid, dk is the change in kinetic energy, and de is the change in potential energy. Equation 7-1-17 applies to an element of fluid moving down the passage. If, for our tubular system, no external work is done by the fluid, and changes in potential energy are negligible, then Equation 7-1-17 becomes

$$dq = dh + dk \qquad (7\text{-}1\text{-}18)$$

The kinetic energy is

$$k = w^2/2g \qquad (7\text{-}1\text{-}19)$$

where w is velocity of fluid and g is acceleration of gravity. Equation 7-1-18 is hence

$$dq = dh + d\left(\frac{w^2}{2g}\right) \qquad (7\text{-}1\text{-}20)$$

It should be noted that combining Equations 7-1-9 and 7-1-20 to eliminate $d(w^2/2g)$ gives the expression

$$dq = du - p\, d\left(\frac{1}{\gamma}\right) - \frac{4f}{D}\left(\frac{w^2}{2g}\right) \qquad (7\text{-}1\text{-}21)$$

in which the internal energy, u, is related to the enthalpy, h, by $h = u + p/\gamma$. This is the usual statement of the first law of thermodynamics except for the last term. This last term is made necessary by the irreversibility involved in the viscous friction. The usual statement of the first law applies only to reversible processes and hence is not applicable to a great many problems in engineering, such as this one.

We must now define the characteristics of the working fluid. For perfect gases the enthalpy is a function only of temperature, being independent of pressure. For ideal incompressible liquids, also, since pressure obviously can have no effect, enthalpy is also a function only of temperature. Actually many engineering fluids can be treated approximately on the basis that enthalpy is a function only of temperature (within certain pressure ranges). This can be expressed as

$$dh = c_p\, dT \qquad\qquad (7\text{-}1\text{-}22)$$

where c_p is the specific heat at constant pressure, which generally varies with temperature. The obvious engineering case which cannot easily be handled by Equation 7-1-22 is evaporation or condensation in which, although the temperature remains constant, there is a large change in the enthalpy (called *latent heat*). Here the specific heat in Equation 7-1-22 would be required to be infinite to give a finite change in enthalpy, since dT is zero. The boiling phenomenon involves a change of state. Let us consider here only cases for which Equation 7-1-22 is applicable. Then Equation 7-1-20 becomes

$$dq = c_p\, dT + d\left(\frac{w^2}{2g}\right) \qquad\qquad (7\text{-}1\text{-}23)$$

It is customary to combine the two terms on the right to give an expression for Equation 7-1-23:

$$dq = c_p\, dT_t \qquad\qquad (7\text{-}1\text{-}24)$$

where

$$T_t = T + \frac{1}{c_p}\left(\frac{w^2}{2g}\right) \qquad\qquad (7\text{-}1\text{-}25)$$

The quantity T_t is called the total temperature of the fluid. This is the temperature which would exist in the fluid if the kinetic energy were changed adiabatically to internal energy (if the fluid were completely stopped adiabatically). For large velocities in the fluid (close to the velocity of sound), the second term in Equation 7-1-25 becomes of importance. Equation 7-1-24 is a much simplified form of the expression for the conservation of energy, applicable only to fluids for which the enthalpy is essentially independent of pressure (not necessarily to constant pressure processes—like boiling).

Equation 7-1-24 gives an expression for the heat added to a flowing fluid in terms of the temperature rise of the fluid. In order to find the temperature distribution in the fluid, for use in the solution of Equation 7-1-14, we will now develop another expression for the heat added to the fluid stream. For this purpose we will consider the factors which determine the heat transfer through the boundary layer, in terms of the temperature difference across the boundary layer. It will be found that this temperature difference, between the passage wall and the flowing gas, is related for many cases to the pressure loss in the fluid.

7-2. Heat Transfer to Flowing Fluids

The quantity of heat transferred per unit time across an interface between a solid and a flowing fluid is expressed by Newton's law of cooling. This equation is written

$$Q = hA'(T_w - T_t) \qquad (7\text{-}2\text{-}1)$$

where Q is the heat flowing per unit time, A' is the heat-transfer area, T_w is the temperature of the wall at the interface, T_t is the average total temperature of the fluid, and h is the heat-transfer coefficient. This equation looks like the Fourier equation for the conduction of heat in a solid, except that for lack of detailed information concerning gradients in the fluid boundary, the coefficient, h, has replaced $k/\Delta x$ and $(T_w - T_t)$ has replaced ΔT. The linear form of the equation has been preserved by inventing h, which in general is far from being either constant or independent of temperature. For dimensional consistency, h must have the dimension

$$h \sim \frac{\text{(energy)}}{\text{(length)}^2 \text{(time)}\text{(temperature)}}$$

h has been found to have a very complicated dependence on a combination of geometrical and physical parameters.

A considerable discussion can be found in heat-transfer publications concerning what temperature should be taken as representative of the heat-transfer fluid when selecting coefficients. It is found that, owing to conductivity of the fluid, the temperature which actually exists in the fluid boundary layer at the wall, where the fluid has been stopped adiabatically, is not T_t, but may be either higher or lower, depending on the properties of the fluid (Prandtl number). The difference is small enough to be insignificant considering the state of knowledge of heat transfer.

Equation 7-2-1 gave an expression for the heat transferred per unit time across an area A'. This area is given by the product of the wetted perimeter of the heat-transfer passage, S, and the length of element, dx. Since we have previously defined a hydraulic diameter, D, as four times the ratio of the cross section, A, of the fluid flow passage to the wetted perimeter, Equation 7-2-1 can be written

$$Q = \frac{4hA}{D} (T_w - T_t) \, dx \qquad (7\text{-}2\text{-}2)$$

The heat absorbed in the element per unit weight of cooling fluid is

$$dq = \frac{Q}{\gamma w A} = \frac{4h}{\gamma w D} (T_w - T_t) \, dx \qquad (7\text{-}2\text{-}3)$$

Many empirical and semi-empirical formulae can be found for the heat-transfer coefficient, based on the physical characteristics of the fluid, the configuration of the heat-transfer passage, and the velocity of flow. These formulae are based on analyses of test data. For h, as for f, it is necessary first to prescribe whether the fluid flow is laminar or turbulent.

No attempt will be made here to provide an exhaustive list of heat-transfer coefficients pertinent to specific heat-transfer configurations and coolants. A designer must use considerable caution to make sure that the experimental data which he uses are pertinent to his needs. However, certain fairly general statements can be made about heat-transfer coefficients. The most general of these statements is that the heat-transfer coefficient is very sensitive to the Prandtl number:

$$(\text{Pr}) = \frac{c_p \mu}{k}$$

where c_p is the specific heat at constant pressure of the coolant, μ is the viscosity of the coolant, and k is the thermal conductivity of the coolant. The Prandtl number is the ratio of the molecular diffusivity of momentum, μ/ρ, to the thermal diffusivity, $k/c_p\rho$. It is therefore a measure of the ratio of the heat carried across the boundary layer by eddy convection to that carried by thermal conduction. For liquid metals, then, which have a very high thermal conductivity, the Prandtl number is low (of order 1/100), whereas for oils, which have a low thermal conductivity, the Prandtl number is high. The Prandtl number for gases is about unity; for water it is somewhat above this, depending on the temperature. For oils the Prandtl number is of the order of 100.

For fluids having a Prandtl number corresponding to gases or higher, the dimensionless equation which has been found experimentally to give a good fit for turbulent flow in tubes is

$$(Nu) = 0.023(Re)^{0.8}(Pr)^{0.4} \qquad (7\text{-}2\text{-}4)$$

where the Nusselt number is

$$(Nu) = hD/k$$

It is often advantageous to express this in terms of the Stanton number, St, which is defined as

$$(St) = \frac{h}{\gamma w c_p} = \frac{Ah}{G g c_p}$$

Equation 7-2-4 then becomes

$$(St) = \frac{0.023}{(Re)^{0.2}(Pr)^{0.6}} \qquad (7\text{-}2\text{-}5)$$

The reasons for using the Stanton number instead of the Nusselt number for many cases are: (1) since the Reynolds number occurs only to the one-fifth power, the results in this form are relatively independent of the Reynolds number; (2) the mass flow, G, is a constant for steady flow and is easy to measure; and (3) the conductivity which is hard to measure for many materials, or unknown, appears only in the Prandtl number for which fairly good values are known for many materials.

For liquid metals, Lyon gives the expression for tubes

$$(Nu) = 7 + 0.025 \, (Re \, Pr)^{0.8} \qquad (7\text{-}2\text{-}6)$$

The constant factor, 7, accounts for the effect of the high conductivity on the heat-transfer coefficient at low Reynolds numbers. For laminar flow of liquids in tubes the empirical equation

$$(Nu) = 1.62 \left(Re \, Pr \, \frac{D}{L} \right)^{1/3} \left(\frac{\mu}{\mu_s} \right)^{0.14} \qquad (7\text{-}2\text{-}7)$$

which gives good correlation with experiments for values of $\left(Re \, Pr \, \dfrac{D}{L} \right)$ greater than about 10. In Equation 7-2-7 D is the tube diameter, L is the tube length (heated portion), μ is the viscosity of fluid in the turbulent core, and μ_s is the viscosity of the fluid at the surface of the tube. The viscosity correction is due to the warpage of the profile from a parabolic one due to the variation of viscosity with temperature, as shown in Figure 7-2-1. The viscosity of gases generally rises with increasing temperature whereas that of liquids decreases with rising temperature.

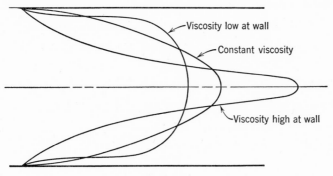

Fig. 7-2-1.

BOILING HEAT TRANSFER

The discussion of heat-transfer coefficients, above, pertained to fluids which are not changing state. A special topic in heat-transfer coefficients is boiling liquids, since here large amounts of heat are transferred across the interface between a solid and a boiling liquid with relatively little dependence on the velocity of the fluid along the interface.

Experimental determinations have been made of heat-transfer coefficients which are appropriate to various situations in boiling heat transfer. A typical plot * of the results of experiments is shown in Figure 7-2-2 for water boiling at one atmosphere and at 100 psi gage under natural convection circulation past a submerged chromel wire. Here h is defined by the equation

$$Q = hA' \, \Delta T \qquad (7\text{-}2\text{-}8)$$

where Q is the heat transferred per unit time, h is the heat-transfer coefficient, A' is the heated surface area, and ΔT is the difference between the temperature of the wall and the saturation temperature of the liquid. For appraisal of the potentialities of boiling heat transfer, part of the curve for $h \, \Delta T$ is sketched in dashed lines, in Figure 7-2-2.

* E. A. Farber and R. L. Scorah, "Heat Transfer to Water Boiling under Pressure," *Transactions*, ASME, May, 1948, p. 369.

One example, in common experience, of the boiling phenomenon represented by the plot is the dancing of a drop on the top of a hot stove. If the temperature of the stove surface is slightly above the boiling point of the water, the water drop will flatten out on the stove and evaporate quietly but quickly. If the temperature of the surface is considerably over the boiling temperature, a film of vapor is formed between the drop and the surface. Heat transfer into the drop in the

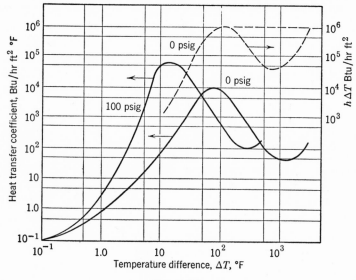

Fig. 7-2-2.

latter case occurs only through this film, and the drop may evaporate more slowly than on the cooler surface, though its motion on the hot surface is agitated.

As the temperature of a surface, submerged in a liquid, is increased above the boiling point, the heat-transfer coefficient increases considerably as shown in the plot. In this region heat transfer to the liquid occurs by a process called nucleate boiling, in which small bubbles are formed immediately at the surface, diffusing from there into the surrounding fluid, where they are recondensed. The shape and size of bubbles formed and the rate of formation (hence the heat-transfer coefficient) are dependent on the properties of the fluid and the condition of the surface—particularly as these affect surface tension and surface wetting. An oil on the surface will considerably retard the heat transfer. It is seen from the plot that the heat-transfer coefficients are markedly improved by pressurizing the system.

As the temperature of the surface is raised, a limit is reached where the heat passing through the surface can no longer be accommodated by the nucleate boiling process. Here the liquid breaks away from the surface, forming a film of vapor between liquid and surface. Since the amount of heat passing through the surface requires a larger temperature difference between liquid and surface after the breakaway, the surface temperature for equilibrium with a given heat input suddenly rises to a new value as indicated by the horizontal dashed line in the plot. This new temperature is in general so high as to result in failure of the heat-transfer apparatus by melting, unless the heat input is reduced as a consequence of the formation of the vapor film.

Before this phenomenon had been recognized experimentally there had been some boiler failures, due mostly to local hot spots in boiler tubes where film boiling occurred. One of the deterrents to pushing boiling heat transfer to its limit is fear of this instability, particularly at hot spots. Also there is always fear that one tube, which for some reason gets more heat, will generate more steam than its neighbor; thus its flow will be impeded, it will become hotter still, and eventually will pass over into film boiling and, hence, failure. An additional difficulty in reactors is the change in density, since the cooling fluid may also be serving as a moderator or absorber of neutrons.

The promise in nucleate boiling is sufficiently great, due to high potential heat-transfer coefficients, to cause considerable interest, particularly under conditions of forced circulation.

HEAT-TRANSFER ANALOGIES

Correlations have been established between heat-transfer and friction coefficients, which are called *heat-transfer analogies*. An example of an analogy can be seen by examining Equations 7-1-5 and 7-2-5. Taking the ratio of these two equations gives

$$\frac{(St)}{f/2} = \frac{1}{(Pr)^{0.6}} \tag{7-2-9}$$

For cases to which these equations are appropriate, Equation 7-2-9 establishes a very convenient correlation between h and f, which is independent of the Reynolds number. For gases and low-conductivity liquids Equation 7-2-9 represents experimental data quite well. For a Prandtl number close to unity, we can write approximately

$$\frac{(St)}{f/2} = 1 \tag{7-2-10}$$

This is the Reynolds analogy, which is good for gases. The worst departures from Equation 7-2-9 occur for heat transfer to liquid metals at low Reynolds numbers, and for heat transfer in laminar flow (see Equations 7-2-6 and 7-2-7). For a more general representation of the heat-transfer analogy we must write *

$$\frac{(St)}{f/2} = \lambda \qquad (7\text{-}2\text{-}11)$$

where λ is a function of both the Reynolds number and the Prandtl number, to be determined experimentally. Equation 7-2-11 will be used later in our calculations of temperature distribution and of convective heat-transfer efficiency.

We now have two equations for dq, Equations 7-2-3 and 7-1-24. Eliminating dq between them gives

$$\frac{dT_t}{T_w - T_t} = \frac{4h}{\gamma w D c_p} dx \qquad (7\text{-}2\text{-}12)$$

From Equation 7-2-12 we have an expression for temperature distribution in a heated passage. It can be rearranged by use of Equation 7-2-11 for the ratio of Stanton number to friction factor, giving

$$\frac{dT_t}{T_w - T_t} = 2\lambda f \frac{dx}{D} \qquad (7\text{-}2\text{-}13)$$

For those cases in which λ and f can be assigned values for the given conditions of flow, Equation 7-2-13 can be integrated to give the temperature distribution in the fluid. The wall temperature must be specified along the length of the passage. This temperature, of course, can be specified for an actual case only by solving the entire problem of heat transfer through the fissionable material in the reactor. However, it is useful to solve Equation 7-2-13 for several assumed temperature distributions.

Several cases of temperature distribution have been considered in connection with reactor work, among them (1) constant power output per unit length of passage, (2) constant wall temperature, and (3) a sine distribution of power along the heat-transfer passage. The first of these, constant power distribution, requires (assuming h constant in Equation 7-2-3)

$$T_w - T_t = \Delta T = \text{constant} \qquad (7\text{-}2\text{-}14)$$

* R. C. Martinelli, "Heat Transfer to Molten Metals," *Transactions of the American Society of Mechanical Engineers*, November, 1947.

This represents a desirable situation from the point of view of heat transfer and is approximately achieved in certain reflected reactors where the fuel density and thermal flux are nearly constant over the core. For this case Equation 7-2-13 can be integrated analytically (assuming λ, f, and D constant) to give

$$\frac{T_t - T_{t0}}{T_w - T_t} = 2\lambda f \frac{x}{D} \qquad (7\text{-}2\text{-}15)$$

where x is the distance along the heated passage, and T_{t0} is the total temperature at inlet to the passage. For the total length of passage

$$\frac{T_{t1} - T_{t0}}{T_{w1} - T_{t1}} = 2\lambda f \frac{l}{D} \qquad (7\text{-}2\text{-}16)$$

where T_{t1} is the total temperature at outlet from the passage, and T_{w1} is the wall temperature at the outlet. Equation 7-2-15 can be arranged to give

$$\frac{T_{t1}}{T_{t0}} - 1 = \left(\frac{T_{w1}}{T_{t0}} - 1\right) \frac{2\lambda f \dfrac{l}{D}}{1 + 2\lambda f \dfrac{l}{D}} \qquad (7\text{-}2\text{-}17)$$

The second assumed condition, constant wall temperature, requires that $T_w = T_{w1} = $ constant. This represents a condition which would be advantageous, if attainable, in that every part of the reactor would be operating at the maximum temperature set by materials considerations. It is unattainable in practice and is of interest only in representing a limiting situation. For this case Equation 7-2-12 integrates to

$$\log \frac{T_{w1} - T_t}{T_{w1} - T_{t0}} = -2\lambda f \frac{x}{D} \qquad (7\text{-}2\text{-}18)$$

or, with some rearranging, for the whole length of passage

$$\frac{T_{t1}}{T_{t0}} - 1 = \left(\frac{T_{w1}}{T_{t0}} - 1\right)(1 - e^{-2\lambda f(l/D)}) \qquad (7\text{-}2\text{-}19)$$

The third assumed condition is defined by

$$T_w - T_t = C \sin \frac{\pi x}{l} \qquad (7\text{-}2\text{-}20)$$

where C is a constant depending on the maximum power density in the reactor. This does not represent a favorable situation from the point of view of heat transfer or nuclear considerations since the ends of the reactor passage do not contribute any power. However, this situation does exist in bare reactors if nothing is done to alleviate it. For this case Equation 7-2-13 integrates to

$$T_t - T_{t0} = \frac{2\lambda fC}{\pi} \frac{l}{D}\left(1 - \cos\frac{\pi x}{l}\right) \tag{7-2-21}$$

The temperature at the end of the tube is given by

$$\frac{T_{t1}}{T_{t0}} - 1 = \frac{4\lambda fC}{\pi T_{t0}} \frac{l}{D} \tag{7-2-22}$$

The end temperature, T_{t1}, is not the highest temperature in the tube. It can be found that the maximum temperature occurs somewhere in the last quarter of the tube and is given by

$$T_{w\ max} - T_{t0} = C\left[\sin\frac{\pi x_0}{l} + \frac{2\lambda f}{\pi} \frac{l}{D}\left(1 - \cos\frac{\pi x_0}{l}\right)\right] = CK \tag{7-2-23}$$

where x_0 is defined by the equation

$$\cot\frac{\pi x_0}{l} = -\frac{2\lambda f}{\pi} \frac{l}{D}$$

Using the value for C from Equation 7-2-23, we can write the temperature of the fluid at the end of the tube in terms of the maximum wall temperature as follows:

$$\frac{T_{t1}}{T_{t0}} - 1 = \left(\frac{T_{w\ max}}{T_{t0}} - 1\right)\frac{4\lambda fK}{\pi} \frac{l}{D} \tag{7-2-24}$$

Equations 7-2-17, 7-2-19, and 7-2-24 give the relationship among reactor inlet temperature, T_{t0}, outlet temperature, T_{t1}, and maximum reactor wall temperature, T_{w1} or $T_{w\ max}$, in terms of λ, f, and l/D for the three cases of temperature distribution considered here. When λ and f could not be considered constant, a more detailed treatment would be required. In general we can assume that the relationship of temperatures will always be of the form of these equations and write

$$\frac{T_{t1}}{T_{t0}} - 1 = 2\left(\frac{T_{w\ max}}{T_{t0}} - 1\right)\alpha\lambda f \frac{l}{D} \tag{7-2-25}$$

where α is a particular function of λ, f, and l/D, depending on the temperature distribution.

7-3. Power Density and Pumping Efficiency

We are now in a position to write expressions for the power density (power per unit volume) and the pumping efficiency (pumping power as a fraction of power extracted). These are two overall criteria which measure the desirability of a given cooling system for a power reactor. Expressions for these criteria will be written in terms of the variables and parameters derived above describing the cooling fluid.

The average steady-state power density generated in a reactor can be written

$$\delta = \frac{FGgC_pT_{t0}}{lA}\left(\frac{T_{t1}}{T_{t0}} - 1\right) \tag{7-3-1}$$

where F is the free flow ratio (ratio of flow area for coolant through reactor to cross section of reactor normal to direction of flow). Substituting the value for the quantity in parenthesis from Equation 7-2-25 gives

$$\delta = \frac{2FGgC_pT_{t0}\alpha\lambda f}{DA}\left(\frac{T_{w\ max}}{T_{t0}} - 1\right) \tag{7-3-2}$$

A high-power density is desirable to reduce the inventory of the fissionable material required for a given amount of power, reduce the cost of shielding, and for other reasons. It can be seen that power density is increased by choosing a fluid having a large specific heat, c_p, and a large value of the heat conductivity parameter, λ. The geometry of the reactor and cooling passages should be arranged to use a low hydraulic diameter, D, and to produce a favorable distribution of energy along the passages, as measured by the parameter α. The temperature difference, $T_{w\ max} - T_0$, should be as great as possible. This last requirement is incompatible with the requirement for good pumping efficiency, which will now be discussed.

The pumping power can be determined from Equation 7-1-13, which gives the pressure drop in a cooling passage due to friction and to acceleration of the fluid. Additional losses due to sudden expansions or contractions can be added. These are usually expressed, as was stated at the beginning of the chapter, analogously to Equation 7-1-1. The pressure drop due to acceleration of the fluid can be recovered in diffusers and is not properly chargeable to pumping loss for the passage. An appropriate pumping work term can be derived by writing the expression for these losses for a tube element. A constant area cooling passage is assumed. Equation 7-1-13 then becomes

$$dp = -(1 + \beta)\frac{2fl}{D}\frac{G}{A}w\,d\xi \tag{7-3-3}$$

The factor β represents the increase in losses due to end effects. The pumping power required per unit volume of reactor is

$$d\eta = -\frac{dp\,Fw}{l} \tag{7-3-4}$$

where F is again the free flow ratio. These two equations can be combined and integrated over the tube length to give the average pumping power per unit volume:

$$\eta = 2(1+\beta)\frac{FfG}{DA}\int_0^1 w^2\,d\xi \tag{7-3-5}$$

The efficiency of pumping is defined as one minus the ratio of pumping power to heat energy transferred:

$$\epsilon = 1 - \frac{\eta}{\delta} \tag{7-3-6}$$

Substituting Equations 7-3-2 and 7-3-5 gives

$$\epsilon = 1 - \frac{(1+\beta)\displaystyle\int_0^1 w^2\,d\xi}{gc_pT_{t0}\alpha\lambda\left(\dfrac{T_{w\,\max}}{T_{t0}}-1\right)} \tag{7-3-7}$$

For a high pumping efficiency, the fluid velocities should be small. This, of course, is opposite to the requirement on velocity for high-power density. The remaining parameters, temperature difference, $(T_{w\,\max} - T_0)$, specific heat, c_p, temperature distribution factor, α, and heat conductivity parameter, λ, should be large, as is also desirable for good power density. Since λ is an inverse function of the Prandtl number, the Prandtl number should be as small as possible.

Both Equations 7-1-16 and 7-3-7 contain the velocity term, w, under the integral sign. The velocity in the heat-transfer passage is to be found from the continuity condition, Equation 7-1-11, which states that $\gamma wA = Gg$ (a constant). For an incompressible fluid in a constant section passage this condition requires that the velocity be also constant, and the integrations can be performed immediately. For compressible fluids it is necessary to have an "equation of state" relating the density, γ, to the temperature, T. For instance in a perfect gas

$$P/\gamma = RT$$

where R is the gas constant. It is usual to make some simplifying assumptions appropriate to a particular problem at hand (such as that the pressure, where it appears under an integral sign, is relatively constant) to decrease the complexity of these interrelationships. Specific solutions of equations like Equation 7-3-7 for gases are found in several references.*

The problem of analyzing the extraction of heat from reactors is extremely complex in detail and can be solved only by assuming tremendous simplification or by building a fund of experimental data. The parameters and concepts described are useful as an overall check and evaluation of detailed calculations and experiment.

REFERENCES

Jakob, Max, *Heat Transfer*, John Wiley and Sons, New York, 1949.

Lyon, R. N., Editor, *Liquid-Metals Handbook*, NAVEXOS P-733 (Rev.), Atomic Energy Commission and Department of the Navy, June, 1952.

McAdams, W. H., *Heat Transmission*, McGraw-Hill Book Co., New York, 1942.

Prandtl-Tietjens, *Applied Hydro- and Aeromechanics*, McGraw-Hill Book Co., New York, 1934.

* B. L. Hicks, D. J. Montgomery, and R. H. Wasserman, "On the One-Dimensional Theory of Steady Compressible Fluid Flow in Ducts with Friction and Heat Addition," *Journal of Applied Physics*, October, 1947, p. 891.

J. N. Nielsen, *Compressibility Effects on Heat Transfer and Pressure Drop in Smooth Cylindrical Tubes*, National Advisory Committee for Aeronautics, NACA–ARR, No. L4C16, October, 1944.

A. H. Shapiro and W. R. Hawthorne, "The Mechanics and Thermodynamics of One Dimensional Gas Flow," *Journal of Applied Mechanics*, December, 1947, pp. A-317 to A-351.

A. S. Thompson, "Flow of Heated Gases," *Journal of Applied Mechanics*, March, 1950, pp. 91–98.

CHAPTER 8

THERMAL POWER CYCLES

In Chapter 7 we were concerned with the problem of extracting heat from reactors. In this chapter some engineering considerations for using this source of heat as a part of a useful power plant will be discussed. No attempt will be made to treat thoroughly the subject of thermal power cycles. Instead, attention will be focused on some aspects of thermal power cycles which require special attention in connection with the application of a nuclear reactor to the generation of thermal power.

8-1. Idealized Four-Component Power Cycle

The simplest cycle which can be considered for the generation of mechanical power consists of four components: (1) a compressor, or pump, in which the pressure level of the working fluid is raised above ambient; (2) a heater (the reactor) in which the fluid is heated to some top temperature; (3) a turbine by which shaft work is done; and (4) a heat exchanger which cools the fluid again to ambient temperature for entrance to the compressor. This system is considered because it is the simplest thermodynamic system capable of producing an appreciable excess of mechanical work and is fundamental to more complicated systems, because some general conclusions can be drawn concerning the interdependence of various quantities of interest in the preliminary analysis of power plants, and because some actual power plants in common use have cycles which correspond quite closely to this arrangement.

The most efficient idealized power cycle of this type is the Carnot cycle, which consists of isentropic compression and expansion processes and constant temperature processes for adding heat and rejecting it. The Carnot cycle is shown on a temperature-entropy diagram in Figure 8-1-1. Absolute temperatures are used throughout this chapter.

As will be shown later, areas on a temperature-entropy diagram represent work done and heat added and rejected in reversible processes. The whole cross-hatched area in Figure 8-1-1 represents the heat added, Q_1, and the doubly cross-hatched area represents the work done by the cycle, W. The ratio of these two areas, W/Q_1, represents the cycle efficiency, or, from the diagram, the Carnot efficiency is given by

$$E = \frac{\tau - 1}{\tau} \qquad \text{(8-1-1)}$$

where $\tau = T_2/T_1$. It is obvious that, for the maximum efficiency of any cycle operating between a top temperature T_2 and an ambient

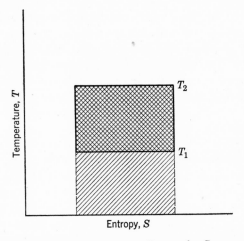

FIG. 8-1-1.   Temperature-entropy diagram for Carnot cycle.

temperature T_1, the area between T_2 and T_1 should be as completely filled as possible, and that the Carnot efficiency, then, represents the maximum attainable efficiency.

Real power cycles cannot achieve the Carnot efficiency for two main reasons. First, they do not have infinite sources and sinks for thermal energy, and hence cannot achieve the addition and rejection of heat at constant temperature. Second, they cannot achieve isentropic (reversible) expansions and compressions or frictionless heat exchanges. The closest approach to the Carnot cycle, in actual power plant practice, is obtained by liquid-vapor systems (like steam or mercury) whose constant temperature phase changes, by the use of large apparatus, can be made to approach the effect of infinite sources and sinks for heat. A representative T-S diagram for a liquid-vapor system is shown schematically in Figure 8-1-2. The superheat and reheat, which cause the main departure from the Carnot cycle, are necessary because of turbine efficiency problems and turbine blade erosion problems which usually arise if too much moisture is allowed in the vapor.

The simple gas turbine cycle, if it could be made reversible, would consist of constant pressure heat additions and rejections, and isentropic expansions and compressions. The T-S diagram for the simple gas turbine cycle is shown schematically in Figure 8-1-3. It will be shown later that, if the gas turbine cycle is designed for the maximum work output per unit weight of fluid per unit time, the efficiency is

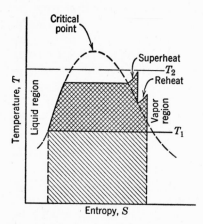

Fig. 8-1-2.   Temperature-entropy diagram for liquid-vapor cycle.

$$E = \frac{\tau^{\frac{1}{2}} - 1}{\tau^{\frac{1}{2}}} \qquad (8\text{-}1\text{-}2)$$

This is considerably lower than the efficiency of the Carnot cycle, particularly for low-temperature ratios. The ratio of the efficiency of the Carnot cycle to that of the idealized gas turbine cycle is $(\tau^{\frac{1}{2}} + 1)/\tau^{\frac{1}{2}}$, which is two when $\tau = 1$ and approaches unity as τ approaches infinity.

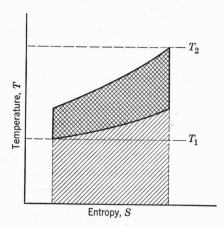

Fig. 8-1-3.   Temperature-entropy diagram for idealized gas turbine.

If additional components, regenerators, intercoolers, reheaters, etc., are added to the gas turbine, its idealized cycle can be made to approach more closely the Carnot efficiency. We can conclude that the liquid-vapor cycle would be preferred for efficiency reasons, in the absence of other overriding requirements or limitations such as light weight or small space, unavailability of cooling water, etc.

The importance of a high temperature of the working fluid in achieving good efficiency and a high output of mechanical work per pound of working fluid is evident from the above cycle discussion. Both of these objectives are highly desirable in a nuclear power plant to reduce the cost and size of the reactor for a selected output. It was pointed out in Chapter 7, however, that a high power density in a reactor demands a large difference between the maximum working fluid temperature and the maximum temperature of the reactor itself. Also there are definite ceilings on the working temperatures of all present structural materials. Thus the actual top temperature for the thermal cycle will be a compromise value chosen to obtain the best overall performance of the operating power plant.

There are two obvious choices in the selection of a working fluid for a nuclear power plant. The simplest choice is to use a single working fluid which acts both as the heat-transfer medium for the reactor and as the working fluid for the power plant. This arrangement has two main advantages. A minimum of apparatus is required. The maximum temperature in the cooling fluid is also the top temperature in the cycle. However, there are several disadvantages. The working fluid must have properties compatible both with the nuclear requirements of the reactor and with the usual power plant requirements. The working fluid may become radioactive and contaminate the entire plant, thus increasing the cost of plant maintenance and also of shielding requirements. If a liquid-vapor reactor coolant and working fluid is used, the problem of boiling heat transfer, as discussed in Chapter 7, must be given special attention during both design and operation.

The use of two fluids, one of which extracts heat from the reactor and transmits this heat through an exchange to the power plant working fluid, overcomes all the disadvantages listed above. However, this system has some disadvantages of its own. The top temperature of the thermodynamic cycle is reduced because of the drop in temperature through the intermediate heat exchanger. The pumping power requirement is greater because of the addition of the additional heat-transfer apparatus. Both these factors tend to reduce the output available from a given size of reactor. The added complexity of equipment also is a disadvantage.

It would seem that a firm choice of reactor power system for a particular application requires extensive development experience and analysis to reveal the magnitude of the engineering problems connected with each working fluid and type of system.

8-2. Cycle Efficiency

The purpose of this section is to demonstrate, in a general way, the dependence of the power output and thermal efficiency of a power plant on the cycle temperatures and component efficiencies. In order to do this it is necessary to show the analytical conditions for the existence of a cycle, to develop expressions for the performance of the components of the power cycle, and to find the dependence of cycle efficiency and work on these expressions and on cycle temperature.

The analytical expressions which describe a thermodynamic cycle relate the physical states of the working fluid to a limited number of thermodynamic variables which can be independently controlled by the designer. A cycle exists when these physical states repeat periodically.

This discussion of thermodynamic cycles is not meant to be complete from a mechanical engineer's viewpoint. It is meant to present a method for the preliminary analysis of thermodynamic cycles. The examples presented here are simple and are used for purposes of illustration.

This discussion is meant further to demonstrate a technique for analyzing more complicated and varied cycles to which it is readily adapted. It is particularly hoped that the specific statement of requirements for the existence of a thermodynamic cycle will afford some measure of protection against the susceptibility to design thermodynamic perpetual motion machines, for nuclear power. Most actual cycles, with varying specific heats as a function of temperature and more complicated interrelationships of variables than those demonstrated here, will require numerical, rather than analytical, solutions. These solutions will generally require trial-and-error procedures to arrive at a cycle which has the required performance. For some thermodynamic fluids of use in power plants accurate charts are available for the interrelationships of thermodynamic variables. Where such charts are available they should, of course, be used for the analysis of any final design of power cycle. The method of preliminary design presented here enables us to find quite rapidly many general characteristics of a new type of power cycle, often a tedious task using charts. It is also useful for investigation of power cycles based on new power media for which there is only a small amount of information available.

A DEFINITION OF A THERMODYNAMIC CYCLE

It is assumed that the physical states of the working fluid are completely determined by the assignment of values to two thermodynamic variables, here temperature and entropy. A plot of a typical cycle is then as shown in Figure 8-2-1, relating the fluid temperature, T, to the entropy, S.

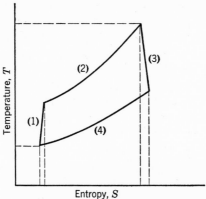

FIG. 8-2-1. (1) Compression; (2) heating; (3) expansion; (4) rejection.

If the cycle is to operate continuously, the plot of $S = S(T)$, as shown in Figure 8-2-1, must be a closed figure. This can be expressed analytically by stating that the requirements for the existence of a thermodynamic cycle are

$$\oint dT = 0 \tag{8-2-1}$$

and

$$\oint \frac{dS(T)}{dT} dT = 0 \tag{8-2-2}$$

where the symbol $\oint$ implies integration around the complete cycle.

To use Equations 8-2-1 and 8-2-2 it is necessary to establish the relationship $S = S(T)$. It will be found that this involves the friction losses in the components, which will be used to define a component efficiency, as well as characteristics of the working fluid and the way it is used in the power plant. The cycle efficiency and power output will then be expressed in terms of the component efficiencies and the temperature ratios across the components.

Equation 8-2-1 can be expressed for a four-component system

$$\sum_{m=1}^{4} (T_m - T_{m-1}) = 0 \qquad (8\text{-}2\text{-}3)$$

where T_m is the temperature at the end of the mth component, and where the symbol Σ represents a summation of terms. Equation 8-2-3 can be rewritten by changing the indices

$$\sum_{m=1}^{4} T_m = \sum_{m=0}^{3} T_m \qquad (8\text{-}2\text{-}4)$$

Canceling identical terms, Equation 8-2-4 becomes

$$T_4/T_0 = 1 \qquad (8\text{-}2\text{-}5)$$

Since the temperature ratio in Equation 8-2-5 can be represented,

$$\frac{T_4}{T_0} = \prod_{m=1}^{4} \tau_m$$

where $\tau_m = T_m/T_{m-1}$, and where the symbol Π represents a product of terms

$$\prod_{m=1}^{4} \tau_m = 1 \qquad (8\text{-}2\text{-}6)$$

Equation 8-2-6 takes the place of Equation 8-2-1 for the discrete processes of the four-component cycle. For the same discrete processes Equation 8-2-2 becomes

$$\sum_{m=1}^{4} (S_m - S_{m-1}) = 0 \qquad (8\text{-}2\text{-}7)$$

In order to express Equation 8-2-7 in terms of the cycle temperatures it is necessary to find thermodynamic expressions relating the changes in entropy in a given component to the temperatures in the component. This will require expressions for the work done by and the heat added to the fluid in the component, including the effects of friction.

COMPONENT PERFORMANCE

For any thermodynamic process we can write an incremental expression for the conservation of energy

$$dq - dw = dh + dk + de \qquad (8\text{-}2\text{-}8)$$

where dq is the heat added to unit weight of fluid, dw is the external work done by the fluid, dh is the change in enthalpy of the fluid, dk is the change in kinetic energy of the fluid, and de is the change in potential energy. The conservation of momentum requires that

$$-dw = dk + de + \frac{1}{\gamma} dp + df \tag{8-2-9}$$

where γ is the weight density of the fluid, p is the pressure in the fluid, and df is the frictional energy dissipated per unit weight of fluid. Since enthalpy is, by definition,

$$dh = du + \frac{1}{\gamma} dp + pd \left(\frac{1}{\gamma} \right) \tag{8-2-10}$$

where du is the change in internal energy of the fluid, Equation 8-2-8 can be written

$$dq - dw = du + pd \left(\frac{1}{\gamma} \right) + \frac{1}{\gamma} dp + dk + de \tag{8-2-11}$$

Subtracting Equation 8-2-9 from Equation 8-2-11 gives

$$dq + df = du + pd \left(\frac{1}{\gamma} \right) \tag{8-2-12}$$

By definition the change in entropy, ds, is given by

$$ds = \frac{du + pd(1/\gamma)}{T} \tag{8-2-13}$$

Combining Equations 8-2-12 and 8-2-13 gives

$$ds = \frac{dq + df}{T} \tag{8-2-14}$$

In Equation 8-2-14 it is necessary to express the frictional loss, df, in terms of the known changes in the cycle and then to express these known energy changes in terms of temperatures in the cycle.

The mechanical efficiency of a process is defined as the ratio of the energy output from the process, E_o, to the energy input, E_{in},

$$\mu = -E_o/E_{in} \tag{8-2-15}$$

For instance, in a compressor, shaft work is the input and an enthalpy change in the gas is the output. In a turbine the converse is true; the enthalpy change in the gas going through the turbine is the input, and shaft work is the output. For a given process—adding or subtracting heat or doing work—the values of energy input and energy output must differ by the amount of the frictional losses, so that

$$E_o + E_{in} + E_f = 0 \qquad (8\text{-}2\text{-}16)$$

Equations 8-2-15 and 8-2-16 can be combined to eliminate either E_{in} or E_o in solving for E_f. For the process where the input is from an external source (compressor or reactor), eliminating E_o, we have

$$E_f = -(1 - \mu)E_{in} \qquad (8\text{-}2\text{-}17)$$

For the process in which the output is external (turbine or heat sink), eliminating E_{in}, we have

$$E_f = -(1 - \mu^{-1})E_o \qquad (8\text{-}2\text{-}18)$$

Now df can be defined for a process involving work (compressor or turbine)

$$df_1 = -(1 - \mu_1^{\pm 1})\, dw \qquad (8\text{-}2\text{-}19)$$

where the positive sign in the exponent indicates compression, the negative expansion. For a process involving heat (reactor or heat sink),

$$df_2 = (1 - \mu_2^{\pm 1})\, dq \qquad (8\text{-}2\text{-}20)$$

where the positive sign in the exponent indicates heat added to the cycle (reactor), the negative sign heat taken from the cycle. The efficiency, μ, used in Equation 8-2-19, corresponds to what is sometimes called by gas turbine designers *small stage efficiency*. It is the limit of the efficiency for a stage as the number of stages to perform a given compression or expansion approaches infinity. For a process involving both heat and work simultaneously we can write *

$$df = -(1 - \mu_1^{\pm 1})\, dw + (1 - \mu_2^{\pm 1})\, dq \qquad (8\text{-}2\text{-}21)$$

Substituting Equation 8-2-21 into Equation 8-2-14 gives

$$ds = \frac{-(1 - \mu_1^{\pm 1})\, dw + (2 - \mu_2^{\pm 1})\, dq}{T} \qquad (8\text{-}2\text{-}22)$$

According to our original assumption concerning our power media—that $S = S(T)$—the changes, dw and dq, must be expressible as functions of temperature,

$$dw = -\psi_1(T)\, dT \qquad (8\text{-}2\text{-}23)$$

---

* Another term could be added for the friction losses due to changes in velocity, for instance, in diffusers or nozzles.

where the negative sign implies that positive work done by the fluid is accompanied by a decrease in the temperature, and

$$dq = \psi_2(T) \, dT \qquad (8\text{-}2\text{-}24)$$

Substituting Equations 8-2-23 and 8-2-24 into Equation 8-2-22, we have

$$ds = \frac{(1 - \mu_1{}^{\pm 1})\psi_1(T) + (2 - \mu_2{}^{\pm 1})\psi_2(T)}{T} \, dT \qquad (8\text{-}2\text{-}25)$$

If the processes are considered to extend only over small enough intervals that ψ_1 and ψ_2 are essentially constant, we can write

$$dw = -C_1 \, dT \qquad (8\text{-}2\text{-}26)$$

and

$$dq = C_2 \, dT \qquad (8\text{-}2\text{-}27)$$

and

$$ds = \frac{(1 - \mu_1{}^{\pm 1})C_1 + (2 - \mu_2{}^{\pm 1})C_2}{T} \, dT \qquad (8\text{-}2\text{-}28)$$

where C_1 and C_2 are the appropriate specific heats for the thermodynamic process. Let us now integrate Equations 8-2-26, 8-2-27, and 8-2-28 over a component in which work is done and heat is added. For the mth process the work done is

$$\Delta w_m = -C_{1m}T_{m-1}(\tau_m - 1) + \delta_{1m} \qquad (8\text{-}2\text{-}29)$$

where δ_{1m} represents the sum of the discontinuous changes in the function Δw_m due to work done isothermally, for instance, in isothermal compression. The heat added is

$$\Delta q_m = C_{2m}T_{m-1}(\tau_m - 1) + \delta_{2m} \qquad (8\text{-}2\text{-}30)$$

where δ_{2m} represents the sum of the discontinuous changes in the function Δq_m due to latent heat, for instance, in boiling or condensing. The entropy change in the mth process is, from Equation 8-2-28,

$$s_m - s_{m-1} = \Delta s_m = \ln(\tau_m{}^{K_{1m}}) + K_{2m} \qquad (8\text{-}2\text{-}31)$$

where

$$K_{1m} = (1 - \mu_{1m}{}^{\pm 1})C_{1m} + (2 - \mu_{2m}{}^{\pm 1})C_{2m} \qquad (8\text{-}2\text{-}32)$$

and

$$K_{2m} = -(1 - \mu_{1m}{}^{\pm 1})\frac{\delta_{1m}}{T_{1m}} + (2 - \mu_{2m}{}^{\pm 1})\frac{\delta_{2m}}{T_{2m}} \qquad (8\text{-}2\text{-}33)$$

The temperatures T_{1m} and T_{2m} represent the temperatures at which the isothermal changes in work and heat occur. Substituting Equation 8-2-31 into Equation 8-2-7 gives

$$\sum_{m=1}^{4} [\ln (\tau_m{}^{K_{1m}}) + K_{2m}] = 0 \qquad (8\text{-}2\text{-}34)$$

Using the properties of logarithms, we have

$$\prod_{m=1}^{4} (\tau_m{}^{K_{1m}}) = \prod_{m=1}^{4} (e^{K_{2m}}) \qquad (8\text{-}2\text{-}35)$$

Equations 8-2-6 and 8-2-35 are the conditions for the existence of a thermodynamic cycle, in terms of the component temperature ratios and performance characteristics. Satisfaction of these conditions is a guarantee that all thermodynamic variables will undergo a cyclic variation. From Equation 8-2-8, then, for any cycle so defined

$$\oint \frac{dq}{dT} dT = \oint \frac{dw}{dT} dT \qquad (8\text{-}2\text{-}36)$$

This is a statement that the net heat added during one complete cycle is equal to the net work done during the cycle. From Equation 8-2-14,

$$\oint \frac{dq}{dT} dT = \oint T \frac{ds}{dT} dT - \oint \frac{df}{dT} dT \qquad (8\text{-}2\text{-}37)$$

Equation 8-2-37 states that the area on the temperature-entropy diagram enclosed by the cycle represents the net heat added *plus the frictional losses*.

Let us consider now the same four-component cycle previously used, consisting of (1) a compression, (2) heat addition, (3) an expansion, and (4) heat rejection. Let these processes be designated by the subscripts, c for compressor, r for reactor, t for turbine, and h for heat exchanger. Then the work done by the compressor is

$$\Delta w_c = -c_{1c} T_1 (\tau_c - 1) + \delta_{1c} \qquad (8\text{-}2\text{-}38)$$

For the reactor the heat added is

$$\Delta q_r = c_{2r} T_1 \tau_c (\tau_r - 1) + \delta_{2r} \qquad (8\text{-}2\text{-}39)$$

The work done by the turbine is

$$\Delta w_t = -c_{1t} T_1 \tau_c \tau_r (\tau_t - 1) + \delta_{1t} \qquad (8\text{-}2\text{-}40)$$

The heat rejected by the heat exchanger is

$$\Delta q_h = c_{2h} T_1 \tau_c \tau_r \tau_t (\tau_h - 1) + \delta_{2h} \qquad (8\text{-}2\text{-}41)$$

The heat which must be added to the cycle from the burning of nuclear fuel is given by Equation 8-2-39 as

$$Q_1 = c_{2r}T_1\tau_c(\tau_r - 1) + \delta_{2r} \qquad (8\text{-}2\text{-}42)$$

The net work done by the cycle is given by the sum of Equations 8-2-38 and 8-2-40 as

$$W = T_1[-c_{1t}\tau_c\tau_r(\tau_t - 1) - c_{1c}(\tau_c - 1)] + \delta_{1t} + \delta_{1c} \qquad (8\text{-}2\text{-}43)$$

Let us define the overall temperature ratio of the cycle, τ, as the ratio of the highest temperature in the cycle, after heating, to the lowest temperature in the cycle, at inlet to the compressor. Then the value of τ is defined by

$$\tau = \tau_c\tau_r \qquad (8\text{-}2\text{-}44)$$

Substituting this value of τ into Equations 8-2-42 and 8-2-43 to eliminate τ_r gives

$$Q_1 = c_{2r}T_1(\tau - \tau_c) + \delta_{2r} \qquad (8\text{-}2\text{-}45)$$

and

$$W = T_1[-c_{1t}\tau(\tau_t - 1) - c_{1c}(\tau_c - 1)] + \delta_{1t} + \delta_{1c} \qquad (8\text{-}2\text{-}46)$$

The efficiency of the cycle is, by definition, $E = W/Q$. From Equations 8-2-44 and 8-2-45, then, we have

$$E = \frac{-c_{1t}\tau(\tau_t - 1) - c_{1c}(\tau_c - 1) + (\delta_{1t} - \delta_{1c})/T_1}{c_{2r}(\tau - \tau_c) + \delta_{2r}/T_1} \qquad (8\text{-}2\text{-}47)$$

Equations 8-2-45, 8-2-46, and 8-2-47 are subject to the conditions stated by Equations 8-2-6 and 8-2-35, or

$$\tau\tau_t\tau_h = 1 \qquad (8\text{-}2\text{-}48)$$

and

$$\tau_c^{K_{1c}-K_{1r}}\tau_r^{K_{1r}}\tau_t^{K_{1t}}\tau_h^{K_{1h}} = e^{-(K_{2c}+K_{2r}+K_{2t}+K_{2h})} \qquad (8\text{-}2\text{-}49)$$

and the condition that the net heat added to the cycle must be equal to the net work done, or

$$-c_{1t}\tau(\tau_t - 1) - c_{1c}(\tau_c - 1) - \frac{\delta_{1t} - \delta_{1c}}{T_1}$$

$$= c_{2r}(\tau - \tau_c) + c_{2h}(1 - \tau\tau_t) + \frac{\delta_{2r} + \delta_{2h}}{T_1} \qquad (8\text{-}2\text{-}50)$$

In addition to the conditions stated by Equations 8-2-48 and 8-2-49, one other condition on some component temperature ratio is generally needed to make the performance equations determinate, since it is desired eventually to express the performance in terms of one variable only, namely, the overall cycle temperature ratio, τ. This added condition may be provided in some cases by optimizing the cycle for efficiency or power output. In other cases it is pretty much determined by some physical or mechanical limitation on the power cycle, such as a maximum practical pressure ratio for mechanical or thermodynamic reasons.

8-3. Effects of Component Efficiencies on the Performance of Idealized Cycles

Let us now consider as examples the two cycles previously discussed, the Carnot cycle and the gas turbine cycle, to find a rough measure of the effects of component efficiency as well as cycle temperature on the overall cycle efficiency.

GAS TURBINE CYCLE

Let us design a simple gas turbine cycle in which the temperature ratio in the compressor is adjusted to give the maximum amount of work per pound of air circulating through the engine. In the simple gas turbine cycle there are no processes which involve latent heat. Therefore, all quantities which involve processes at constant temperature, δ and K_2, are zero. Equation 8-2-46 becomes

$$W = T_1[-c_{1t}\tau(\tau_t - 1) - c_{1c}(\tau_c - 1)] \tag{8-3-1}$$

Equation 8-2-47 becomes

$$E = \frac{-c_{1t}\tau(\tau_t - 1) - c_{1c}(\tau_c - 1)}{c_{2r}(\tau - \tau_c)} \tag{8-3-2}$$

The condition stated by Equation 8-2-48 stays in its present form,

$$\tau\tau_t\tau_h = 1 \tag{8-3-3}$$

The condition stated by Equation 8-2-49 becomes

$$\tau_c{}^{K_{1c}-K_{1r}}\tau^{K_{1r}}\tau_t{}^{K_{1t}}\tau_h{}^{K_{1h}} = 1 \tag{8-3-4}$$

Equation 8-2-50 gives no information which is necessary for our present purpose. Eliminating τ_h from Equations 8-3-3 and 8-3-4 and solving for τ_t gives

$$\tau_t = \frac{\tau^v}{\tau_c{}^u} \tag{8-3-5}$$

where

$$u = \frac{K_{1r} - K_{1c}}{K_{1h} - K_{1t}} \qquad (8\text{-}3\text{-}6)$$

and

$$v = \frac{K_{1r} - K_{1h}}{K_{1h} - K_{1t}} \qquad (8\text{-}3\text{-}7)$$

Substituting Equation 8-3-5 into Equation 8-3-1 gives for the work in the cycle

$$W = T_1 \left[-c_{1t}\tau \left(\frac{\tau^v}{\tau_c{}^u} - 1 \right) - c_{1c}(\tau_c - 1) \right] \qquad (8\text{-}3\text{-}8)$$

The maximum work from the cycle, for a given temperature ratio τ, occurs when $dW/d\tau_c = 0$, or when

$$\tau_c = \alpha\tau^{(1+v)/(1+u)} \qquad (8\text{-}3\text{-}9)$$

where

$$\alpha = \left[u \frac{c_{1t}}{c_{1c}} \right]^{1/(1+u)} \qquad (8\text{-}3\text{-}10)$$

Substituting Equations 8-3-5 and 8-3-9 into Equation 8-3-2 gives, for the cycle efficiency,

$$E = \frac{-c_{1t}\tau \left(1 - \dfrac{1}{\alpha^u \tau^{(u+v)/(1+u)}} \right) - c_1 \left(\alpha\tau^{(1+v)/(1+u)} - 1 \right)}{c_{2r}(\tau - \alpha\tau^{(1+v)/(1+u)})} \qquad (8\text{-}3\text{-}11)$$

For the simple gas turbine cycle, all specific heats, both c_1 and c_2, are specific heats at constant pressure. If, for convenience, we take the specific heat to be constant throughout the cycle, and take all component efficiencies to be the same, then we have $c_{1c} = c_{1r} = c_{1t} = c_p$, $\mu_c = \mu_r = \mu_t = \mu_h = \mu$, and

$$K_{1c} = c_p(1 - \mu)$$

$$K_{1r} = c_p(2 - \mu)$$

$$K_{1t} = c_p \left(1 - \frac{1}{\mu} \right)$$

$$K_{1h} = c_p \left(2 - \frac{1}{\mu} \right)$$

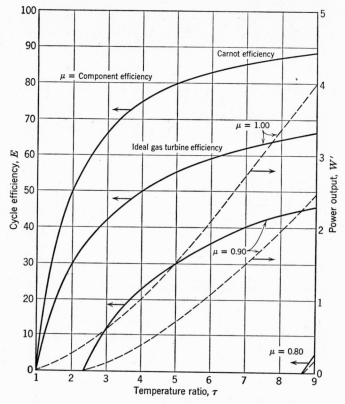

FIG. 8-3-1.   Thermodynamic performance of simple gas cycle.

From Equations 8-3-6 and 8-3-7, $u = 1$ and $v = \dfrac{1}{\mu} - \mu$. With these values, Equation 8-3-9 becomes

$$\tau_c = \tau^a \qquad\qquad (8\text{-}3\text{-}12)$$

where

$$a = \frac{1}{2}\left[1 + \frac{1}{\mu} - \mu\right]$$

Equation 8-3-5 becomes

$$\tau_t = \frac{1}{\tau^{1-a}} \qquad\qquad (8\text{-}3\text{-}13)$$

From Equation 8-3-8 the cycle work is

$$W = c_p T_1[(\tau^{1/2} - 1)^2 - 2(\tau^a - \tau^{1/2})] \qquad\qquad (8\text{-}3\text{-}14)$$

The efficiency, from Equation 8-3-11, is

$$E = \frac{(\tau^{\frac{1}{2}} - 1)^2 - 2(\tau^a - \tau^{\frac{1}{2}})}{\tau - \tau^a} \qquad (8\text{-}3\text{-}15)$$

If component efficiency is 100 percent, $a = \frac{1}{2}$. The efficiency then becomes, as in Equation 8-1-2,

$$E = \frac{\tau^{\frac{1}{2}} - 1}{\tau^{\frac{1}{2}}} \qquad (8\text{-}3\text{-}16)$$

A plot of both cycle efficiency and work output is shown for this case in Figure 8-3-1, where $W' = W/c_p T_1$. It can be seen that the effect of component efficiencies less than 100 percent is to reduce drastically both the cycle efficiency and the work output.

CARNOT CYCLE

Let us now consider the effect of reduced component efficiency and of actual fluid characteristics on the idealized Carnot cycle. To make the cycle definite, let us assume a liquid-vapor system with the following processes and characteristics. First, the power fluid is compressed to a high pressure in the liquid state. The energy used for this compression is relatively small in its effect on the cycle, and will therefore be neglected in this example. Next let the fluid be heated to its saturation temperature, then evaporated at constant temperature and pressure. This condition is closely approached in many actual liquid-vapor cycles. Next let the fluid be expanded through a turbine having an efficiency, μ_t. Finally let the fluid be condensed at constant temperature and pressure to its original condition. From this point on, the cycle repeats. Let the overall temperature ratio be, as before, τ. This cycle fits the Carnot diagram, except for the heating of the liquid to its saturation temperature and except for departures of the turbine efficiency from 100 percent. No superheating of the vapor is considered in this discussion.

For the cycle considered above, $\tau_c = \tau_h = 1$ and $c_{2r} = 0$. From Equation 8-2-48 $\tau = 1/\tau_t$. Since there are no entropy changes in the compression process, and since there are no additions of heat in the compression or expansion, $K_{1c} = K_{2c} = K_{2t} = 0$. Since all the heat rejected from the cycle is rejected at constant temperature, $K_{1h} = 0$. Therefore Equation 8-2-49 becomes

$$\tau^{K_{1r}} \tau_t^{K_{1t}} = e^{-(K_{2r} + K_{2h})} \qquad (8\text{-}3\text{-}17)$$

where $K_{1r} = c_{pr}(2 - \mu_r)$

$$K_{1t} = c_{pt}\left(1 - \frac{1}{\mu_t}\right)$$

$$K_{2r} = 2\frac{\delta_{2r}}{T_r}$$

$$K_{2h} = 2\frac{\delta_{2h}}{T_h}$$

Then, since $\tau_t = 1/\tau$ and $\tau = T_2/T_1$, Equation 8-3-17 becomes, on taking logarithms of both sides,

$$\frac{T_1}{2}\left\{-c_{pr}(2 - \mu_r) + c_{pt}\left(1 - \frac{1}{\mu_t}\right)\right\}\ln \tau = \delta_{2h} + \frac{1}{\tau}\delta_{2r} \quad (8\text{-}3\text{-}18)$$

Equation 8-2-50 becomes

$$c_{pt}T_1(\tau - 1) = \delta_{2r} + \delta_{2h} + c_{pr}T_1(\tau - 1) \quad (8\text{-}3\text{-}19)$$

The work done by the cycle, from Equation 8-2-46, is

$$W = c_{pt}T_1(\tau - 1) \quad (8\text{-}3\text{-}20)$$

The efficiency, from Equation 8-2-47, is

$$E = \frac{c_{pt}T_1(\tau - 1)}{\delta_{2r} + c_{pr}T_1(\tau - 1)} \quad (8\text{-}3\text{-}21)$$

Eliminating δ_{2h} between Equations 8-3-18 and 8-3-19 gives

$$\delta_{2r} = T_1\tau(c_{pt} - c_{pr}) + T_1\frac{c_{pr}(2 - \mu_r) + c_{pt}(1/\mu_t - 1)}{2}\frac{\tau}{\tau - 1}\ln \tau$$

$$(8\text{-}3\text{-}22)$$

Substituting this value of δ_{2r} into Equation 8-3-21 gives, for the cycle efficiency,

$$E = \frac{\tau - 1}{\tau}\frac{1}{1 + \dfrac{(1/\mu_t - 1) + c_{pr}/c_{pt}(2 - \mu_r)}{2}\dfrac{\ln \tau}{\tau - 1} - \dfrac{c_{pr}}{c_{pt}}\dfrac{1}{\tau}} \quad (8\text{-}3\text{-}23)$$

It can be seen that, when the turbine efficiency is equal to 100 percent and when the specific heat of the liquid, c_{pr}, is negligible, Equation 8-3-23 becomes the same as Equation 8-1-1 for the Carnot efficiency, $E = (\tau - 1)/\tau$. For all other cases the efficiency will be less than that for the Carnot cycle.

An actual liquid-vapor cycle will vary from the idealized cycle discussed here. Particularly, in a design in which space is very limited, as it is in a reactor core, the pressure losses in the boiling process cannot be neglected. In general it will be desirable, if not necessary, to superheat the vapor in order to limit the carryover of liquid outside the reactor, or boiling heat exchanger. This discussion is intended to show that simple liquid-vapor systems tend to be more efficient than simple gas turbine systems, using the same overall temperature ratios, and that, in addition, the liquid-vapor system is less susceptible to loss in performance because of losses in component efficiency than the gas turbine system. This effect can be pictured by realizing that, in a gas turbine, the net power output is a rather small difference between two large quantities, the power available from the turbine and that used to drive the compressor. Any deterioration in the efficiency of any component causes this small difference to disappear at a rapid rate. In the liquid-vapor system, by contrast, the power required for compression is a relatively small part of the total power output from the turbine. The gas turbine cycle can be made more efficient by the addition of more components. Furthermore, it is easier to achieve a high temperature in present gas turbines than in present liquid-vapor turbines. The gas turbine has certain special attributes, such as small size and low weight, and its independence from a water supply for cooling purposes, which cause it to be useful under special circumstances.

REFERENCES

Epstein, Paul S., *Textbook of Thermodynamics*, John Wiley and Sons, New York, 1937.

Eshbach, O. A., *Handbook of Engineering Fundamentals*, John Wiley and Sons, New York, 1952, Section 7.

Godsey, F. W., Jr., and Lloyd A. Young, *Gas Turbines for Aircraft*, McGraw-Hill Book Co., New York, 1949.

Hawkins, George A., *Thermodynamics*, John Wiley and Sons, New York, 1951.

Keenan, Joseph H., *Thermodynamics*, John Wiley and Sons, New York, 1941.

Stodola, A., and Louis C. Lowenstein, *Steam and Gas Turbines*, P. Smith, New York, 1945.

INDEX